KU-998-459

THE TONGUE-TIED CANARY

Also by Nicolas Bentley

★

BALLET HOO
(*revised from top to toe*)

SECOND THOUGHTS

THE TIME OF MY LIFE

The Tongue-Tied Canary

★

NICOLAS BENTLEY

THE THRILLER BOOK CLUB
121 CHARING CROSS ROAD
LONDON, W.C.2

THIS EDITION 1950

Set and printed in Great Britain by Tonbridge Printers, Ltd., Peach Hall Works, Tonbridge in Times ten on eleven point

★

MY DEDICATION

is to the author of
that other incomparable thriller,
The Law Relating to Money Lenders
and Unconscionable Bargains.

CHAPTER

1

THE DIFFICULTY WITH A STORY LIKE THIS IS TO KNOW WHERE TO begin. It really has no beginning, because what happened, so far as it concerned me, was only a very tiny incident in a very large picture; so large that it shows things happening as far away as Munich, and as long ago as 1923. That part of the picture shows a crook in a cheap mackintosh crouching in the gutter, and there are bullets whizzing down the street: it shows a dead cat taking one look at the crook, and then getting up and moving away.

Well, when I began to think about my part in the business, to see whether it would be worth giving an account of, it seemed such a shapeless and inconclusive sort of story that I was in two minds about going ahead: and they both won. I went ahead; and the whole thing still looks just as shapeless and inconclusive as it did when it happened. Whether it'll seem more so than if you were to take some particular slice of your own life, and lift it out of the context of a wider experience—well, that'll depend on the sort of imagination you've got—whether you use it as a stimulant or as a refuge.

Personally, I'm all for leading a neat and well-ordered existence; or I should be if there were any chance of it. The only person I know of who did manage to live that way was Diogenes. And re-reading all this in typescript, I'm not sure the time I spent writing it wouldn't have been better spent just sitting in a barrel. However, that's for you to judge.

The part of the picture where I come into this story shows a field in Kent. This field has a wide dip in it, where a Dornier crashed and blew up in 1940; now the place is covered over with grass. At the time I'm speaking of, I was walking through the field across this dip with Evelyn Herrick; we were near Pyke's Gate. Suddenly a hare got up from nowhere and streaked off towards the pit in front of us. I didn't wait to see what Herrick was going to do, though the hare should have belonged to him by rights; it was more on his side of the field than mine; anyway, I fired. It was a pretty good shot, though I say it, considering the distance. The hare's momentum sent it spinning over and over in a series of cart wheels, then suddenly it disappeared over the edge of the pit. Herrick hadn't even had time to get his gun up.

'That was a damn good shot,' he said, and we started trotting off towards the place where the hare had gone over. I yelled across the hedge for Bruce—that's the keeper's dog—who was barking like mad, and racing round trying to find some way to get into the field. He got through eventually, and rushed on in front of us.

Round the top of the pit there was a stake-and-wire fence, or there had been a long time ago; but the weather, and the cattle it was supposed to keep from falling into the pit, had made it just about safe for the birds to sit on, if they were careful of their deportment. Bruce bounded about, barking in that silly impotent way that dogs do bark when they're faced with the fact they can't get something they want.

We stood and looked down on the dead trees and scrub and overgrowth which filled the pit. The sides were pretty steep, and in some places they shelved right away and left just a ledge of turf hanging over at the top. At the bottom there was a pond of dark stagnant water, with great rotting branches sticking out of it like the skeleton of a Viking's ship.

We walked round for a while, peering down into the scrub and bushes; but there wasn't a hope in hell of finding anything in all that tangle of stuff; and the light was beginning to go, too, so I called Bruce off. He's a good dog—which means I dislike him less than most dogs. At any rate, he is mildly obedient.

I looked at my watch, and as it was getting on for tea time, we turned back towards the house. The Pit Field was on a piece of rising ground, and you could follow the line of the tree tops all the way up the lane towards the village. Over the trees you could just see the roof and the ugly Elizabethan chimneys of my uncle's house, and the farm buildings that lay alongside it.

As we walked back Herrick asked me if I'd ever tried shooting with a pistol.

'Puts your eye clean out for a twelve bore,' he said.

I reminded him of the course I'd had to go through during the war, which had included the whole bag of tricks, 'use of small arms,' and everything else; meaning everything from ju jitsu to the technique of silent assassination. And a lot of other little things, like the Morse code; and the handling of various explosives; and astral navigation; and the chemical re-agents for detecting sympathetic inks—all these things we took on the side.

But that was only part of the game. The psychological side of it was more difficult. Not everyone who's been brought up as a nice little gentleman always has the right instincts for the part. But if you have got them, they're not easy to overcome. We had to learn to be able to lie and bluff and cheat without turning a hair. The most fantastic tests were devised. In the oral tests you felt like a third degree victim, and in the practical test, like Jekyll to begin with and then like Hyde. In either case, you felt a swine, and it was only when you could do what had to be done without showing your feelings that they knew you were all right; and then they passed you, if you were unlucky.

And when they had passed you, the idea was that you were fit for parachuting into occupied territory. I made four drops and got away with them. Then one day, when I was on leave, I slipped off the kerb somewhere and broke an ankle. This ruled me out, of course, from making any more drops; so I was taken off and pushed behind a desk to try and work out other ways of getting our men into the enemy's camp.

I was either so brilliant at this, or such a failure—they never bothered to explain which—that presently they switched me over to working out ways of preventing the enemy doing the same thing to us. It was a lot more difficult, of course, for him to land over here than for us to infiltrate his territory. For one thing, being a fairly small island, we had a much shorter coast line to insulate. The Germans were vulnerable from the North Cape to Biarritz; and they had to contend, as well, with the whole network of waterways round the Dutch and Norwegian coasts. If they got any advantage out of being tied in a lover's knot with de Valera, this was probably cancelled out by our contacts with the resistance all over Europe.

Herrick had been my chief in this job. Who the real head of the whole outfit was, I hadn't the faintest idea; all I knew was that it wasn't Herrick. Over our particular department he himself exercised a sort of remote control, and he exercised it brilliantly. We never used to see a great deal of him, but when you did see him, you were astonished at the way he seemed to know every detail of the cases you were working on. Some were incredibly complicated; masses of people became involved; investigations went on for months, sometimes for years; and vast files were accumulated; but not the smallest point seemed to escape Herrick, and he never forgot anything. It wasn't just a matter of having a good memory and prodigious powers of concentration. He had a mind as sharp as a bacon slicer and about as quick.

Of course, he knew the Germans pretty well; he had lived in Germany for about six years. But any German who got over here while Herrick was at P Branch, was lucky if he lived six days; unless it was part of the game to let him pick up a lot of carefully cooked information and take it home with him.

Occasionally I used to be allowed out into the field to do a bit of snooping myself. Now and then, but not more often, things did flare up and become fairly exciting. I got shot at once by a Belgian acrobat in a hotel at Newcastle. As a matter of fact, he'd have done better to have jumped on me from the chandelier, because the only thing that suffered was a matron in the Red Cross who had her cockade blown off.

Usually it was a pretty dreary occupation, snooping, and without any sensational results. Still, it made a nice change from telling alien clerks and D.P.s turned cook-generals how to winkle out the information we were after. We did have other means, of course, of finding out what we wanted to know; and very ingenious some of these means were. But respect for the

Officials Secrets Act soon came to be as much a habit with me as the bodily functions, and it's a habit I've never lost.

The results of my efforts at this sort of thing were never very spectacular. I did manage once to do a job which I believe eventually led to something very much bigger. Anyway, Herrick seemed fairly pleased about it, I think. It was never easy to tell what he really felt about anything. A lot of his success lay in the fact that he looked like a member of the Devonshire Club—the kind other members are liable to sit on if they've forgotten their glasses; only I should think he was not much over fifty.

Although my Uncle Arthur was at least ten years older, he and Herrick had been friends for years, and now and again Herrick came down to stay with the old boy at Hawthorns for a week-end. Every so often I used to come down too, and when I came down there was usually someone else there to keep me company because Uncle Arthur couldn't get about very easily.

I hadn't met Herrick there since just after the end of the war; both of us were still in the trapping and scalping industry then. When I met him there on this second occasion, we had both got back to more civilized occupations. I was scribbling for my living again, and Herrick, as far as I knew, was back in his pre-war job; something to do with importing hides or hiding imports; I never knew quite what it was.

On this particular evening Uncle Arthur had settled down after dinner to lick himself at a game of patience, and Herrick and I were sitting in the window seat drinking our coffee, and listening to something on the radio which sounded like de Falla. Presently, what with the warmth of the room, and a second go of Armagnac, I began to feel a bit sleepy. I said to Herrick: 'What about a quick rush round the garden before bed?'

It was a dark night but the sky was clear; it had grown chilly, and you could tell there was nothing left of autumn. We stood at the far end of the lawn, where the garden seems to merge more by accident than by design into the fringes of a copse; and we listened to the nocturnal sounds. A roosting pheasant stirred in the trees and muttered something I couldn't catch; there were the faint unaccountable twitchings and rustlings you hear in a wood at night; and far away somebody was trying to start up an obstinate car. I could just make out Herrick standing a little way off in the darkness; when he drew on his cigar a faint gleam showed up round the lower part of his face. It grew colder after a while, and I shivered and made an appropriate noise. We started back towards the house, but after a few steps Herrick stopped.

'Before we go in . . .' he said—I was leading the way back—'I was asking myself a rather difficult question when I came down here.'

'D'you get any answer?' I said.

'Yes, I did get an answer,' he said. He always spoke rather slowly, and whatever was on his mind at the moment seemed to slow him up more than usual. 'I was debating with myself whether to ask you what you'd feel about doing some sort of . . . research for the old firm.'

At this distance in time I don't remember feeling anything except rather surprised by the idea. But knowing me, I think there must have been some faint feelings of excitement deep down in my sluggish being. I stood still, and Herrick came up beside me in the dark.

'I thought the whole Branch had packed up?' I said.

'Well—not exactly. It doesn't do a quarter of what it used to do, naturally. But it still has certain functions; certain jobs have to be done from time to time.'

'And what's the one you want me to do?' I said.

But he wasn't going to fall for anything as bald as that. I might have known that his way would be to sound every joint and every limb before giving away even a sniff of the problem. He may have been pretty sharp, but when it suited him he could show a downy side which would make the breast feathers of a dove seem like concrete. Now that I came to think of it, there must have been all sorts of moments during the week-end, conversations, incidents of behaviour, tests of my dexterity or my reactions to certain situations, which might have seemed trivial enough to anyone else, but which had all been helping him to make up his mind whether I should be a good or a bad risk. God knows, I'm not much of an animal lover, but I suddenly felt a wave of fellow-feeling with all the guinea pigs I'd ever known.

'Well, to begin with, how are you placed about your work?' Herrick said. 'Presumably, you're more or less your own master, as regards time?'

'Well—to some extent,' I said. As long as I turned out my bread-and-butter column every week, and got a few other regular bits and pieces through on time, I wasn't under an obligation to anyone, thank God.

'If, for instance, you decided you might like to have a look at this . . . assignment'—I noticed he carefully chose a word that wouldn't give anything away—'it's one that might take you a matter of weeks, or it might be months.'

'I see. Tell me one thing, though,' I said. 'Why should you have picked on me rather than Campion, say; or Sykes, or Bosanquet?'

'Well . . . I had a sort of hunch you might be the right man for the job. Besides, you're rather less tied, aren't you, than they are? Not that that's the main reason, I admit. I thought, as a matter of fact, that what you did over that man Van Lieven showed you to be rather wasted sitting behind a desk.'

'That's what I thought,' I said. He couldn't have seen me smiling, but he must have guessed.

'This is a case that looks as if it might be rather the same in some ways; needs the same sort of persistence and the same sort of ingenuity. That was a very good piece of work, that Van Lieven business.'

I was delighted he should have thought so. 'My cheek,' I said, 'would shame the damask rose.'

'Maybe it would,' he said. 'But there was quite a good chance, you know, of your losing your skin over that thing.'

'Not mine,' I said, 'it fits too well.'

'Well, I'm glad to hear it; because in this case I should think the chances are even higher.' There was nothing facetious in the way he spoke this time.

We were near the house now, standing in a square-flagged space, where rose trees were growing in beds the shape of bananas. The light from the library window shone out on the beds, and you could see a late forlorn rose dangling here and there; through the window you could see Uncle Arthur swearing to himself over his cards. We ran our shoes over the scraper, and then we went indoors.

Before we went up we looked in to the library and said good night to the old boy. When we got upstairs Herrick stopped outside his door, and he said, 'Sleep on the idea, will you? See how you feel in the morning.' He opened the book he was carrying and fluttered its pages, as if he felt the need to fidget; then he said, 'I do warn you though—a very great deal may depend on the success of this thing.'

'And even more, presumably, if it fails?'

He looked at me for a moment; then he took out his watch, and began to wind it up.

'I didn't mean that,' he said. 'What I meant was, the question of failure doesn't enter into it.' He spoke quite quietly. 'This is something a good deal bigger than the kind of individual cases we were dealing with in the war. It'll be a pretty tricky business, bound to be; and it might easily turn out to be quite a nasty one. Would you mind that?'

'Can't think of anything I should dislike more,' I said.

He smiled, and we said good night.

CHAPTER

2

IF I HAD EVER BEEN THE SORT OF CHILD WHO IS SICK AT PARTIES, not through over-eating, but from nerves, I suppose the idea of a proposition like Herrick's would have kept me awake all night. As it was, I slept perfectly well. After I'd gone into my room I sat on my bed, smoking and thinking the thing over. I didn't really need to think it over: my mind had been more or less made up even before we had got back to the house.

There were several reasons why the proposition interested me. For one thing, I was beginning to feel a bit stagnant; it was about six months since I'd been out of London, except for an occasional week-end. And for another, I was badly bogged down in the story I was working on. Maybe these two things were inter-acting on each other; anyway, I was beginning to feel I needed something to jerk me out of the rut I was getting into.

Then, of course, there was the Boy Scout element; rather over-developed in me, I sometimes feel. But the basic impulse was the hunter's, of course. During the war, I admit frankly, the thrill of the chase had given me a perfectly good satisfaction of its own. If you were successful—that is, if you bagged some poor little squit with steel-plated nerves and a wife and family sitting at home in the Fatherland, and whose original sin was believing blindly in the justice of Germany's cause—well, then your sense of triumph or self-satisfaction was quite considerable.

Stripping my motives to the edge of indecency, I suppose it was those honeyed phrases Herrick had used about my persistence and ingenuity and courage which had really tipped the balance, and I knew it.

Anyway, I knew what my answer was before we had said

good night; only it struck me Herrick might have rather more confidence in his 'hunch' if I gave the impression of having thought the whole thing over. Not that a 'hunch' really had anything to do with it, of course. Herrick wasn't a man who acted on hunches. I knew there must have been good and solid reasons for his picking on me, and I couldn't see any except those he had given me. I was more or less a free agent; hadn't any attachments, in the family sense; I'd had quite a bit of experience in this kind of racket, at both ends of the job; and there seemed to be some sort of similarity between the case he had in mind and the business I'd handled for him about Van Lieven. Besides, Herrick knew that once I got my nose to the ground, it'd be likely stick there. Maybe he'd heard about that framed text I've got hanging over my bed, one that says: *Mountie, git your man!*

Breakfast was early at Hawthorns on Monday mornings because there was usually somebody there who had to get back to London. I had put away a grape fruit and some eggs and bacon before Herrick showed up. It was only a quarter-past eight then. He was coming up with me in my car, and by half-past we were ready to start.

So we said good-bye to Uncle Arthur and took off. He stood there on the loggia, looking the spit of Hogarth, in a sort of turban and a dressing-gown, and he waved us away with a handful of toast and marmalade.

It was a crisp, bright morning, the sort to be bowling along in a phaeton, not a Ford. We drove up the lane and through St. Vitus village—it looked very spruce and cosy in the early sunlight—and on towards Rudleigh.

For the first mile or two neither of us said very much. I was trying to work out a conversational gambit to introduce last night's topic; I didn't want to seem too eager, though the more I thought of it, the more my hunting instincts warmed to the idea. Then Herrick saved me any more trouble.

'I take it your decision is favourable?' he said. Sometimes he sounded faintly pompous; this was one of the times. He caught my eye in the mirror, and saw me wondering how he'd guessed.

'You've got a keen, abstracted look in your eye,' he said. 'Better get rid of it. Makes you too conspicuous.'

'Don't worry,' I said. 'I shall soon revert to type.' I wasn't aware of having a keen, abstracted look; still, to please him, I lapsed into looking like a doughnut.

'You do understand, then, the kind of thing you may be in for?' he said.

'What, for instance?'

'That you may have to take some rather unpleasant risks; and that if you do, you'll have to take them absolutely on your own initiative. If you get yourself into any sort of trouble, no one will be able to lift a finger. I shan't. I don't exist. Nor does the Branch, officially; it still only exists *sub rosa.*'

I knew that well enough. And of course there'd be risks, I knew that too. But I didn't imagine them likely to be worse than one or two bowel-watering moments I'd had when I was trying to contact the *maquis.*

The drive up took us about an hour and a half, and in that time Herrick gave me an outline of the job, and filled in a few details as well. There weren't a great many. My assignment, roughly speaking, was to fill in those that were missing.

First of all, though, I wanted to get his position straight; how he still came to be tied up with P Branch. Really, he said, it was a sort of hangover from the nineteen-fourteen war. He'd started that in the gunners; then some anonymous donor had presented him with a basinful of shrapnel, and the brilliant prospects he'd had as a battery sergeant went west; so after that they had had to fall back on using his brains. One thing had apparently led to another, and finally he seemed to have ended up more or less in the position he was in when I'd come into the Branch in 1940. In between wars his job had looked like a business man's from the outside; but I gathered, more from what he left out than what he said, that his under-cover work had gone on just the same.

He went on then about the process of de-Nazification, the idea of letting the Germans do their own de-lousing. On the whole, he said, it seemed to have worked pretty well. That, and the various trials of war criminals, had probably routed out most of the better-known or more suspicious cases. But what the process had also done, and what was obviously even more important for the future, was that it had shown how deep you'd got to go to get the roots up.

'Of course, directly after the war, for many months afterwards, in fact, any insects who managed to get away lay pretty low. They're still lying low, too; and are likely to, of course, as long as there's any form of occupying force over there. And the longer they're allowed to lie, the more dangerous they're likely to become.'

'Why d'you think that?' I said.

'Giving them exactly what they want, that's why. It's giving 'em time.'

'For what?'

'*Der Tag*, *Deutschland uber Alles*, whatever you like to call it. A chance to make plans which'll come into action the very second Allied forces get out of Germany, believe me.'

'You mean you think they'll really want to have another crack,' I said, 'after a beating like they had this time?'

'Who d'you mean by "they"? The ones I mean are the lot who form that hard core of homicidal lunacy that runs through the German nation as a whole. You often hear people speak as if it were something that only comes out in the Prussians. These are a kind of creature you'll find in every part of Germany: what was Goering? A Bavarian. So was Himmler. Streicher came from Saxony, and Goebbels came from the Rhineland: all of them lunatics, all had the same form of dementia. What is a lunatic, after all? A man who's lost his sense of balance, sense of proportion, that's all. To these people the idea of *Deutschland uber Alles* seems perfectly sensible; inevitable, in fact. In the end it becomes, to them, the most important thing in the whole world. Doesn't matter what happens to them or anyone else as long as the idea's realized. And they're absolutely sincere about it; which, of course, is the greatest danger of all.'

He said a lot more than that, of course; sounds a bit over-simplified as I've put it, but that was the gist of what he said. Presently he lit a cigarette for me and passed it over, and we drove on for a bit without saying much. Then Herrick said, as if it weren't *apropos* of anything:

'How soon d'you think you could start?'

'I've started,' I said.

'Good! Well now, you'd better take very careful note of all this because nothing must be put on paper at all. There mustn't be any shred or particle of evidence that could show whom you're working for. Nothing whatever.'

I wondered if ten easy lessons would do all that Pelmanism claimed, and I nodded as Herrick looked at me in the mirror. If I got myself caught, it would be my own funeral—only the bit in my will about 'cremation' probably wouldn't be observed.

I was to go back on the Branch salary list as long as the job lasted; and, of course, it was to take preference over whatever else I might have on hand. At the same time, I'd got to keep up an appearance of doing my ordinary work as usual; just how this act of schizophrenia was to be got over was something I should have to figure out later on.

I should have all the necessary details of the case sent to me, and I was to memorize these and then burn them. I should also be given a telephone number which I was to use if I needed to get hold of Herrick; but I was only to get hold of him if it was a case of dire emergency. He would call me, though, from time to time, so that I could report progress.

I suppose if you have romantic ideas about intelligence work—and most people seem to have pretty highly-coloured notions of what goes on—Herrick and I just talking like this as we drove up to London, must seem very prosaic. Still, that's the way a lot of the dirty work gets done. I don't mean there isn't sometimes plenty of excitement; that's usually at a later stage though. But many a web's been spun—I've helped to spin a few myself—in some innocent-looking little tea shop or during a walk in the Park.

'I'll tell you what's happened so far,' Herrick said. 'Sometime during the early part of the war—might even have been before it started—a fellow called Bruno Rankel—we don't know what he calls himself now—came here from Stuttgart. How he got here we don't know either, except that it was illegally.'

'No records, you mean?'

'No, none. But from the information that started us off on the whole thing we do know that somehow or other he managed to stay here right through the war——'

'We didn't get a line on him at all?'

'Not a thing.'

'What was he doing, then?'

'Nothing. His job here didn't begin till the war had ended.'

'Oh? And what is his job?'

'Organizer for the Hitler Youth.'

In Peter Cheyney this would obviously have been the cue for a long, low whistle. It sounded pretty fantastic; but no more so than some things the Branch had unearthed during the war.

'Shows they're taking no chances,' Herrick said. 'They knew they'd need an outside base. Remember the great comb-out there was about eighteen months ago in the British and American zones? He couldn't have been missed, not if he'd been operating there then.'

I liked it so far. 'Go on,' I said.

'Well, we know that up till a few weeks ago Rankel was in fairly regular communication with Germany.'

'How did we find that out?'

'Because some of his own messages—messages he'd sent from this country—were dug out by our people in Dusseldorf. Then, apparently, some ass over there went and put a foot wrong, and the rabbit got scared.'

'And communication stopped?'

'Stopped completely.'

'It was all coded, I suppose?'

'It was, but we'd just broken it. That was the maddening part. But, of course, it left Rankel in mid-air.'

'And he's still floating, you mean?'

'Still floating. But'—he dropped on the word, and I waited—'it's given us the one chance we've been wanting. Until—or unless—they can somehow re-establish a code—a new code, of course—he's going to be pretty helpless.'

'Ah—and I'm to be the bung that stops him getting it?'

'No?—that's just what you're not to be. We want the code,

certainly. But we want Rankel too. Now, there's an agent, or a courier of some sort, coming over to convey this new code into his hands quite shortly.'

'This is information from Dusseldorf again?' He nodded. 'What does "quite shortly" mean?' I said.

'It means probably some time within the next few days. If we can find him, this courier, this agent, whoever he is, and if we can stick to him close enough and long enough, he's going to lead us to Rankel.'

'Where do I make my début?' I said.

'Your début will be either at the dockside or the airport, wherever the fellow lands.'

'What happens if he's a channel swimmer?' I said.

'Well, that's up to you. There are other means, yes; but present indications are that one of the ordinary travel routes is likely to be used. Probably through some other country—Portugal or Sweden, possibly; we don't know yet. Wherever he comes from, your job will be to pick him up and to keep your teeth in his coat-tails from the moment he lands——'

'Till death us do part?'

'Well, that'll rather depend on the way you handle it.'

'In other words, I've simply got to keep tabs on this man until he delivers the goods; is that all?' I said.

'I doubt whether you'll find it very simple, but that's what it amounts to—yes.'

'Long time since I played follow my leader,' I said. 'What happens, by the way, if my leader turns out to be a woman?'

'Well, what does happen?' Herrick said. 'That, if you want to know, is one of the reasons why I thought of you rather than Campion, as you suggested or Sykes or Bosanquet.'

'What were you thinking of—my hot Latin blood?'

'No; I was thinking that Campion is a don, and that he looks like one.'

'Well, he can't help that,' I said.

'Exactly.'

'I see. And Sykes,' I said, 'is a vegetarian, if I remember?'

'He is,' Herrick said. 'And Bosanquet, of course, lives with his mother.'

'Has anyone ever seen Rankel?' I said.

'Not so far as we know.'

'And I suppose it'd be idle to suggest we know anything about his appearance, or what he does with himself?'

'Quite idle, I should think,' Herrick said.

'Sounds like child's play to me,' I said. 'When do I get all these details?' As if they were going to help me.

Herrick said I should probably get them in a day or two, as soon as there was any definite news about the courier leaving Germany. Then he asked me for the number of my identity card. I could have made a better shot at the year of Persimmon's Derby, so I hauled out my card and passed it over to him. He wrote the number down but he didn't say anything to damp my curiosity. Mine not to reason why, so I shoved the card back in my wallet again and went on itching.

It was nearly half-past nine when we got to Hammersmith. I was going home to Chelsea, so Herrick got out. I wound the window down and said good-bye to him. He gave me a breezy little smile, but no word of sympathy. Then his bus came, and he got on it and disappeared.

CHAPTER

3

BLAKE STUDIOS, WHERE I LIVE, IS A SORT OF CLOSE OFF KING'S Road. You go in through a wide passage that runs underneath the upper part of the building, and there are the studios at the back. They're built round a small open square with grass and trees in the middle of it, and there's a flagged pavement running all round.

On one side of the passage, as you come in, there's a little old house crammed in between the studio block and a larger house. At some time or other the little house was disembowelled to make room for a garage underneath it. I can imagine a nice little eighteenth-century doorway being torn out by some Goth to make room for his beastly car. It so happens, incidentally, that my own car just fits into the place very comfortably.

Up over the garage lives a woman who acts as a sort of *concierge* to the Studios; to me personally she acts as a heaven-sent benefactress: does all my shopping, cleaning, mending, and so on, and keeps the duns at bay. The name of this paragon is Mrs. Wellington, and, judging by appearance, her descent from the Iron Duke runs straight as a die.

After I'd dropped Herrick I drove home and put the car away. There were a few letters and some calls to see to before I started work, but when I did get down to it I found there wasn't much edge on my appetite for writing. So I went into the kitchen presently and made some coffee. When I came back I turned on the radio for a bit; then I turned it off again. I read through what I'd written and scratched out most of it; then I began again. Usually the studios are pretty quiet. But to-day, I don't know why, there seemed to be a conspiracy of noises.

First I heard a baby crying somewhere; then a man with a tin whistle started up at the end of the street, and someone kept running a stick along some palings; then the telephone began to ring in one of the studios opposite, and it went on and on ringing. I noticed I was noticing these things, which in the ordinary way wouldn't have disturbed me in the least. I just couldn't settle down. Perhaps it would have helped if I could have started making some sort of plan. But until I got my marching orders, I didn't even know which way I should be going. So there was nothing for me to do except possess my soul in impatience.

At the end of two or three days I had got through just about two-thirds of my usual output, and that was only by slogging at it. I walked up and down, reading through what I'd written since breakfast, and I was glad I hadn't had much to eat: the stomach turns more easily when it's empty. Usually I'm rather pleased with what I write—for about twenty-four hours afterwards; then it begins to take on the bloom of cold gravy. It was a bad sign, starting off with the bloom there already.

I decided to chuck it and see what an hour's Dickensian pacing round the metropolis would do. When I get badly stuck sometimes it has the desired effect on me, as it had on Dickens. Maybe I should come whizzing back later on and dash off another *Chuzzlewit*.

There was no visible brightening of this possibility by mid-day, so I bent my steps towards the Sheridan Club. They bent pretty easily by this time; the loaves and fishes I had had for breakfast might have been enough for the rationing scheme outlined by St. John, but they left me ready for a good square meal after I'd had an hour and a half's walk.

The porter popped out of his glass cage as I went into the Club, and he handed me a telephone message: somebody had rung and asked for me about ten minutes earlier. They had left a number—wasn't one that I knew—but no name, and wanted me to ring back.

As I dialled the number, I wondered if the red light was about to go up at last. I waited, listening to the bell buzzing at the other end, and I tried to tell myself I was feeling perfectly calm. A girl answered: I gave her my name and she put me through to a man with a set of highly-polished vowels. He asked me the number of my identity card; I fished it out and told him. The next question was how long should I be at the Club, and I told him that too.

'Right! I have something for you. I'll send it round,' he said. Then he rang off.

In the ordinary way I should probably have hung around over my coffee and talked to someone at the long table. Instead of this I got through lunch like an absent-minded wolf; then I paid my bill and shot back into the lounge. I sat there for a bit, holding the evening paper up in front of me. If war had been declared again, I didn't notice it. I kept telling myself it was ridiculous at my age to be so much on the *qui vive;* and I kept right on it with both feet.

Presently the porter came and said there was someone waiting for me. I went down to the door and saw a man there with an attaché case and an umbrella. He looked like a commercial traveller and spoke like a ventriloquist. I told him he needn't bother, the porter was deaf. He looked distrustfully at the old man's bat-ears, and then he asked to see my identity card. But I was too quick for him: I had my wallet out already, and it was open under his nose. He took a look at the card, then he gave me a receipt to sign, and pulled a sealed envelope out of his case and handed it to me.

I took the envelope upstairs to the library. It was a fine and private place, the library; it gave you the feeling of being in an air-conditioned tomb. This impression grew on you if you happened to come across a body in one of the chairs; sometimes you'd see the same body there week after week, but usually *The Times* spread out over the knees would have been brought up to date.

The room was empty, and I climbed down into a chair by the window and rang for some coffee. Then I opened the envelope. Inside there were two pages of typewritten stuff, and attached to them a first-class single ticket to Liverpool, and a note from Herrick in his small, neat writing. The note said:

These are your instructions. They should not be difficult to memorize. You know what to do with them—and, of course, with this letter.

I don't think I need emphasize the very great importance attaching to this case, nor the confidence I feel in your ability to handle it with discretion.

That was all.

When the waiter had brought my coffee I settled down to read the instructions. This was the gist of them: I was to go to Liverpool and wait there for the arrival of a cargo boat called the *Joaquin Alvaro;* she was due from Lisbon the day after to-morrow. There would be eight passengers on board—two women, a child, and five men.

My man was described in detail: age, about forty; medium build; dark hair and moustache; pale complexion; a discoloured tooth in the upper jaw. He could speak English fairly fluently but with a German accent. It was not known what name he was going by, nor what his business was supposed to be; probably this would have something to do with printing. Then there was a description of his clothes: black hat and shoes, dark suit and overcoat, and a 'grey or mauve' scarf. They were the main items; and there was also a well-worn brown fibre suitcase, U.S. make.

The instructions which came after this were more or less a repetition of what Herrick had told me already. I was given a completely free hand as to the way I carried out the job. If I needed any assistance, 'financial or otherwise,' I was to ring the number I had spoken to before lunch. At all costs I was to avoid communicating with the police 'or other officials or authorities with whom, if it became known, your association might give rise to suspicion, and so endanger the pursuit of your enquiries.'

It all sounded rather didactic; I smelt Herrick in his pompous vein, and I felt fairly certain that he had worked out the instructions himself, down to the last detail. The most helpful item came at the end. My salary would be paid to me once a month in cash; and so that I need not declare its source, it would be free of tax.

I re-read this paragraph a couple of times: then I rang the bell and asked the waiter to bring a glass of port.

When I felt sure enough of the details to get rid of everything, I threw the papers in the fire and watched them burn; then I carefully raked through the ashes.

Somehow I felt more at ease now that things had really started, and I knew what I had got to do. That's to say, I knew what my objective was, and I knew the first step towards it, though I knew nothing more. It was up to me now to try and make some plan of campaign.

The difficulty was that the hunted, not the hunter, was paradoxically the one who would have the initiative; at least, up until the last moment. I should have to go wherever he chose to lead me; so my strategy would have to be the devising of some situation or some relationship which would make it possible for me to keep an eye on his movements without arousing his suspicions. And as they, presumably, would be floating right on the surface, it looked like being a fairly ticklish job.

First of all, it would mean finding out, indirectly if possible (you'd be surprised to know the oblique use I've made of chambermaids in my time, and of waiters and taximen and porters)—of finding out not only the obvious things, like his occupation—his ostensible occupation, that is—and his habits and preferences, and so on. It would mean also finding out what his weaknesses were, and converting them to my own advantage, using them to anæsthetize his own interest in me once we got acquainted.

To do this, of course, I should have to rig up a pretty good alibi for myself, so that if he became at all inquisitive there wouldn't be any loose ends about anything he might find out.

How all this was to be developed would depend entirely, of course, on how the situation shaped itself when we came together, what manner of man he might turn out to be, and what his interests were, and so on.

There was really very little that I could safely arrange now, except this broad strategic outline. My tactics, to begin with, anyway, would have to be largely a matter of improvisation.

Dame Wellington was seeing about things in the kitchen when I got back. I told her that to-morrow I should be going away for a few days. It sounded more plausible than saying I hadn't the remotest idea when I should be back, if ever. We fixed all that had to be fixed, and then she went away.

I heard the six o'clock pips on the radio next door just as I settled down to start writing. At eleven I heard Big Ben, and the announcer saying good night. I was in the kitchen then, making another jug of coffee and finishing a snack that I'd raked up earlier in the evening.

By a quarter-past two I had filled a second ashtray and had worked off all my arrears; and I still had a good bit of stuff in hand; so, if anything should happen to interrupt my output, editorial *hara kari* would be kept within reasonable limits.

CHAPTER

4

THE ATTRACTION OF A LARGE INDUSTRIAL CITY IS DIFFICULT TO appreciate unless you happen to be one of its citizens, or, I suppose, an industrialist. But somehow Liverpool seems different. Strictly speaking, of course, it's more a mercantile than an industrial area; all the same, there's something about the city which redeems it from the fate that places like Birmingham and Sheffield share in my estimation. Maybe that if you know where to look for them, the charms of Liverpool aren't so formal or so obtrusive as they seem in some other towns. (You don't *have* to look at the cathedral, after all.) There's a dignity and elegance about some of the suburbs, for instance, even when they're pretty near decay, which you don't often find in a city of Liverpool's size.

But even Liverpool's charms may seem slightly exhausted if you get there too early on a damp morning. I'd had quite a lot to do in London at the last minute, and I had ended up by catching a night train, which arrived before most Puddlians had even thought of breakfast. I got a bath and a shave first of all, and then, when I'd had something to eat, I began to feel a bit better.

It was still early enough for a morning haze to be drooping over the city, and as I walked down towards the docks, the sun looked like a dim red bulb switched on high up over the Mersey. The shipping offices hadn't opened yet, so I walked along the quayside and enjoyed myself in a landlubberly way, staring at the ships and smelling the smells of the port. Presently a clock struck nine, and I turned and walked back along the quay. When I came to the office I was looking for, I went in. The *Joaquin Alvaro*, they said, was due about midday.

I went away and killed time for a couple of hours; then I collected my bag from the station and went back to the docks. I found the *Joaquin Alvaro's* berth; but there was nothing anywhere near it on the quayside that would have hidden a ship's cat, let alone a human being. The nearest cover was a bus shelter, about fifty yards away; so I went along to it and sat down inside.

My plan was to wait for a little while, and then, in case the boat docked early, to get hold of a taxi—they weren't allowed on the quay itself; they had to stand on the other side of the road, about twenty yards away—and keep watch from inside it. Or if I couldn't see from there, to squirm along the landward side of the quay and just make use of whatever human cover I could find.

I sat in the shelter for some time, glutting myself on the charms of Rita Hayworth, whose picture was stuck up inside. Presently I noticed a slight bit of bustle beginning on the quay, and when I looked round, there was the *Joaquin Alvaro* being nosed into her berth, nearly an hour ahead of schedule.

I shut my eyes and prayed for a taxi; and when I opened them, there the taxi was on the other side of the road. It had just decanted a fare, and it was moving off by the time I got to it. Just as I was going to hop in, a large van drew up alongside the quay, slap in front of the boat, so that all I could see of it was the funnel. I told the driver that I wanted him to wait, but he didn't seem to care for the idea, and it cost me five bob to persuade him of its advantages. Then I scooted back surreptitiously onto the quayside.

A minute or two earlier the place on shore where the *Alvaro* was coming in had been more or less deserted. Now quite a few people had gathered to watch her; but the crowd, if you could call it a crowd, was still a good deal too thin for my liking; so I waited till a few more gapers had attached themselves to it, then I edged my way in among them.

Presently the gang plank went up, and I saw the Customs men go on board. And just at that minute a boy came by with a covered handcart. He stopped only a yard or two away, and then he dived in among the crowd. So I moved up behind the hood of the cart. The flap at the back was rolled up, and inside the cart there were some empty baskets. I put down my bag—I'd hung on to it in case of accidents—and I leaned up against the tailboard so that I could clean my nails. There was no one near enough to see my penknife going through the hood, and with a slit three or four inches long, I had a perfect view.

The beauty of the scene began to pall, though, after about a quarter of an hour; also I'd started to develop a neurosis about the boy coming back and leaving me in the cart by taking it away. No one had come ashore yet. Two or three people, looking more like passengers than crew, had showed up on deck from time to time. I guessed they were probably waiting for the Customs men to get through with them. There were two tanned youths with rucksacks—I'd spotted them already, hanging about below the bridge—and there was an elderly mixed couple; the man had a beret and a spade beard, and he looked too like a genuine antique to be what I was hunting for. If he was wearing a disguise, it must have been the best since the Trojan Horse. Anyway, I decided to risk it, and count him out; so that took care of four out of the eight on board that I had to account for.

Presently there seemed to be a general livening up on the lower deck; and then the passengers began to move in a bunch towards the head of the gangway. The tide was high, so the angle of the gangway was fairly steep. I could see the passengers would have to take it carefully climbing down, which would give me a good chance to look at each of them as they came ashore.

Just as the first of them, a woman with a small girl, was starting off down the gangway, the van that had been the cause of my trouble with the taxi moved off. But it was too late, much too late—I just saw a party of G.I.s piling into the taxi, and away they drove. All I could do was to thank God I hadn't lost more than five bob; not yet, anyway. If I wasn't careful, though, I could see I was going to lose something worth a lot more; but so far he hadn't shown up.

The next ones to come off the boat were the elderly couple; and then, just as I was looking every whichway for the two who hadn't appeared yet, the boy nipped back into the shafts of the handcart, and it began to move off. If the sensations I had at that moment were the usual sensations of being caught *in flagrante delicto*, I must watch my step in future. I picked up my bag and slid into the fringe of bystanders.

One or two of the ship's crew hopped off next; then a mild, slightly Jewish-looking man came down, rather gingerly. The black hat and coat were there all right, and the moustache; and he had a scarf that might have been either mauve or grey; but from where I was I couldn't tell much about it, or about the bag he was carrying. I was worried for a minute; the Jewish look might have been my imagination; it certainly didn't fit in either with the details or the probabilities of the case. Apart from this, though, he looked as if he was what I wanted.

I'd got my nose half-way to the ground when I noticed another pale man, with a dark moustache and a black hat and overcoat, setting off down the gangway behind the first one. Either of them might have been the right age or build for my desire, and they both had the right kind of luggage. I began to think in double time, and as the first man got near the bottom of the gangway, I eased out of the crowd into the road.

The second man seemed to be having a bit of trouble with his case, thank God, and he was being helped. Number One spoke to a sea-dog near the gangway as he landed, and the dog waved his paw in a vague sort of gesture taking in most of the Outer Hebrides.

I went quickly ahead behind a brace of lorries parked by the kerb; then I cut back between them on to the quay. It was nice timing: Number One had to brake sharply, and our two cases took most of the impact. I apologized, panting as if I'd run a mile, and I grinned with all my teeth. It worked like a charm. He grinned back, and though I'd never understood it till that moment, I realized the enjoyment then of being a sadist: his teeth were rotten, the whole lot of them; unusual for a Jew; and there was no doubt at close quarters, that that's what he was.

He began to say something, but I wasn't there by that time. I was hopping back along the quay with all eyes rolling.

Number Two couldn't have got very far, but I couldn't spot him anywhere; and I began to have the first of a series of inward spasms which were going to seize me quite a few times before I got to the end of this business.

I threw a jug of iced water over my imagination, and I started again. The directions Number Two could have moved in were limited, and he'd hardly had more than half a minute's start. He hadn't come towards me, that I knew; and there was no subway he could have gone into. I also felt fairly safe in ruling out a vertical ascent. If he'd crossed the road, he must still be in sight, because there wasn't a doorway or turning in either direction for at least twenty yards.

I looked out between the line of cars and up and down the opposite pavement. There was a good sprinkling of pedestrians and standers-about, but I couldn't see anyone carrying a bag. There were three directions left; one was towards the bus shelter; another was back on board the *Alvaro;* and the third was over the quayside. If he'd gone that way, the sea-dogs were taking it very calmly. He might have doubled back on board, but as I couldn't think of any good reason for this, I ruled it out for the moment, and I kept on towards the bus stop. There was a man going that way who was carrying a bag, but he had no hat and his overcoat was over his arm.

Ten or a dozen people, mostly women, were standing at the stop. I went into the rear half of the shelter and looked them carefully over through the partition. I still couldn't see what I wanted. There were only three men, all told: a clergyman, a sailor, and the man with the overcoat over his arm. His bag was on the seat beside him; it had a zip tag like mine, and the tag ended in a small disc. I just saw what it said on it—The 'Boston'—U.S. pat.—then he whisked up the bag and moved off towards a bus that was stopping outside. Everything seemed to happen at once then.

I suddenly saw the ends of a mauve scarf hanging out of his overcoat pocket; and at the same moment he put on a hat, a black one, which had been hidden by the way he had been carrying his coat. By the time I got round to the bunch who were waiting to get on, he was well up in front; then the conductor chopped off the tail of the queue, and the bus moved off, with all that I held most dear standing inside.

My luck was still holding, though; I think it must have been caught in a cobweb. I saw a taxi draw up across the road, and I skipped death by a fraction of an inch as I hared after it. A woman was still sitting inside counting her change. She looked an unassuming sort, but perhaps I brought out the worst side of her nature by the way I manhandled her on to the pavement and bawled at the driver.

We followed the bus, keeping some way behind it, for about ten minutes. Sometimes, when it pulled up, we stopped too, or else we ambled past and then let it catch up on us. Now and then we nearly lost sight of it in the traffic, and those were the moments when I'd have one of me spasms again. I could only hope and pray that my fellow wasn't a suspicious type—it seemed highly likely that he would be, all the same—and that my manœuvre wouldn't be as noticeable to him as it seemed to me, sitting in the taxi.

I'd hardly been on the job half an hour; yet already I'd broken two golden rules. First, to avoid startling a suspect. What if Number One had turned out to be the man I was looking for? Not only had I jumped out on him like a banshee; I'd jumped out so that we had come face to face. That certainly wasn't the kind of risk that Herrick had meant me to take. I tried to keep my conscience quiet by telling it that nothing I could have done would have side-stepped the dilemma. My conscience snapped back at me that that seemed a pretty poor excuse, and where was my ingenuity?

And now here was I breaking the second golden rule into several pieces. My man had got away to a good start because the steps I had taken to make sure of being able to keep track of him hadn't been long enough. (The taxi I was in now could only have been called an act of God.) And now I was letting my man, or at any rate, his bus, out of my sight altogether for seconds at a time. Still, whenever it stopped, I could see who got in and who got out of it, and I could see that he was still inside.

We came presently to an industrial suburb, and at last I saw him get out. It seemed a bleak and unrewarding sort of place to be industrious in. The blitz hadn't improved its appearance, and as the sun had gone in, and the morning haze had turned into a sort of thin overhanging fog, there didn't seem much to commend the spot to strangers.

The place where the bus had stopped was a wide cobbled road junction. Two roads running off to the right looked as if either of them might have led you to infinity by a rather dingy route; a third road humped itself up into a huge cantilever bridge running over a mass of railway lines; and a fourth road led straight on.

I saw my chap looking out for the name of this fourth road, and then I saw him set off along the pavement. I sat in the cab till he had gone some way; then we went after him.

On one side of the road there were buildings that looked like works or warehouses; on the other side there was a long hoarding with gaps in it where bombs had torn it apart. When we got about twenty yards away from the fellow, I paid off the cab and started to walk. A factory hooter had just let off its mid-day whine, and there were enough people about to keep me fairly well covered. Once, when we came to a place where the factories ended and shops began, I saw the man ahead stop and look in at the window of a junk store. I was pretty close to him by this time, so I ducked into a doorway and made a bit of play lighting a cigarette. Then he went on a few yards, and all of a sudden he turned in under a little archway leading to a passage. When I got to the passage I looked along it—but he had gone.

He couldn't have reached the end of it; it was at least twenty yards long, and as one wall was blank, the only place he could have gone was through a door about half-way down. There was a symbol of hope in the shape of three brass balls hanging up over the door; but they didn't give me the kind of confidence I needed, and God knows I needed some. For all I knew, I might walk slap into him inside; and how should I laugh that off the next time we ran into each other? I thought quickly what would be the best thing to pop, and the least suspicious; then I went in.

There he was, with his back to me; he was leaning across the counter, which was divided up into compartments. There was no one else in the place, and I stood at another compartment and I took out my cigarette case. I started to empty it, and then I remembered that in my bag I'd got a silver flask which I've never travelled without. It's seen me through many a crisis, that flask, and I thanked God once more for the far-sighted relative who had given it to me when I came of age. There was still a thimbleful of Scotch left in it—I can't think why—and as it seemed unlikely it'd still be there when I redeemed the thing, I knocked back what was left.

We both waited for some moments in silence. Neither of us could see the other, except our mutual backsides if we looked out along the partitions. The pawnbroker seemed to be busy in the more respectable front part of the shop. I could see him through a glass door, talking to a customer.

The pledge department lit rather dimly; it was like a witch's cave; it had that sour, fusty sort of smell that witches have, and it was crammed with every kind of foresworn possession you could imagine: bundles of clothing, cameras, musical instruments, china, silver, typewriters, sports gear, and God knows what else; bicycles hung from the ceiling like bats, and forests of sticks and umbrellas grew out of the darkness.

When the customer in the shop had gone, the pawnbroker came towards the glass door; his hand was actually on the handle when he caught sight of both of us. I don't know what it was—he didn't bat an eyelid, but there was something, the fraction of a second's hesitation, perhaps—which told me he had recognized the man standing further along. The man may have given him some sign, perhaps; I couldn't see from where I was; but certainly he'd made no sound.

On the corner of a showcase in the shop there was a little stack of what looked like trade cards. The broker picked up one of these cards quite casually as he came through the door, and I saw him jot something down on it. I guessed it must have been some figures, or some initials, perhaps; it was too short for anything else.

As he came behind the counter to where I was standing, he

held the card to his lips, edge-on, and whistled against it under his breath. I couldn't see what he had written on the card because I didn't get a chance to look. He had large dark eyes, and he kept them screwed on me—I didn't think suspiciously; it just seemed like an habitual stare. To look at he reminded me of Kreisler; I don't know he would have sounded on the fiddle.

'Yes?' That was all he said.

I handed him my flask, and he looked at it under the light, still whistling very softly.

'Fifteen shillings,' he said.

'Fifteen bob!' I said. 'Cost me that to have the initials put on.'

He didn't say it was a lie. He just handed the flask back. I started to argue . . . anything to keep a foot in the place.

'Fifteen bob,' he said.

I began to pull a hard luck story. He listened quite sympathetically, even if he was bored by it; and he stood propping himself up against the counter with his arms stretched out on either side of him.

Behind him on a shelf there was a big silver tray. I happened to glance at this tray just for a moment; at that moment, I saw in its surface an interesting reflection. I saw two fingers nip the card out of the broker's hand, then disappear; it was done in a split second.

The broker never took his eyes off me. I finished my spiel as quickly as I could, and he heaved a sigh at the end of it, not as if I'd really touched him—more as though he felt fed up with life.

'Give you eighteen' six,' he said.

I took it; and as I turned to go, I saw the apple of my eye had left already. He must have moved like oil in a bottle; there hadn't been a sound. I should have to ask him how he did it, if we ever got better acquainted; and with that end in view, I stubbed my cigarette on the floor, and strolled out of the shop. Then I shot back along the passage like a bullet.

CHAPTER

5

IT WASN'T ENTIRELY LUCK THIS TIME THAT I SAW HIM WALKING on ahead of me. When you're thinking quickly enough, the point where reason and instinct overlap is pretty well indistinguishable; I might have turned left, towards the unexplored end of the passage. The reason I didn't was because of my impression that this wasn't going to lead anywhere worth going to; besides, that was only part of my reasoning, if you could call it that. This man had come a good way to get whatever he was after, and it didn't seem likely that he'd hang about in the neighbourhood just for the fun of exploring. The obvious move for him would be back towards the centre of things; and even someone as sharp as he'd got to be, couldn't help doing the obvious thing now and again. Where the cunning came in was knowing the right moment to let someone see you doing it.

I guessed that pretty soon the obvious thing was going to involve his catching a bus back to Liverpool; and as the chances of my picking up a taxi in these parts seemed fairly remote, the only useful thing I could think of doing for the moment was to try and imitate Micawber.

There was quite a queue at the bus stop, and I saw my man tag on behind it. By the time I got there, enough people to fill two buses had joined up behind him, and I could see it was going to be more and more difficult to be like Micawber as time went on. Near the stop there was a street market, so I made a slight détour towards it, and went into retirement behind a bookseller's barrow.

I watched my fellow trying for the first bus that came along, but he couldn't make it. Then a second bus came, and this time he did get on. The queue had swelled out a good way behind him by now, and a lot of them were left. Then an empty aircraft lorry came by, and the queue broke. Half a dozen chaps swarmed on to the tail-end of the lorry as it went past, and I felt, in more ways than one, like a drowning mariner as somebody yanked my bag on board, and another good Samaritan hauled me up by the scruff of the overcoat.

I moved up towards the front of the lorry, and I tagged on to a group leaning over the driver's hood. As an observation post it was first-rate, only it was a bit more conspicuous than I cared to be. So I took my hat off and turned my collar up, and I nestled in among the crowd as close as I could.

Once or twice we came uncomfortably near the bus, and I could see my quarry standing inside. When we got towards Lime Street, there seemed to be a general movement to get off, and I saw him struggling to get his bag out from under the stairs. As we slowed down near the station, I nipped off the back of the lorry, and I made for the protective covering of the pavement. The bus stopped a little way ahead, and I watched my man being disgorged in a flux of passengers.

He went into the station, and I saw him take a ticket at the down line booking office. I took one myself—for London, and hoped it'd do. If he got out somewhere on the way, Rugby, or Crewe, perhaps—though why, except for love or death, should anyone get out at Crewe?—I could do the same.

When I picked him up again, a few seconds later, he was quizzing the indicator. Then he went to the main line down platform and spoke to the man on the gate; it looked as if he wasn't a chap who took things on trust. The train wasn't in yet, so then he went and had a look at the bookstall. He seemed to have a thoroughly methodical German mind; he began at one end of the stall and worked slowly along till he got to the other; he must have stopped *en route* about five or six times, and each time he seemed to read whatever he was looking at from cover to cover.

By the time he got to the end of the new Vogue Knitting Book, he'd spent the best part of half an hour just browsing. In the end, all he bought was a newspaper and a pocket magazine. After that he went back to the platform again; the train was there now, and he walked along about half-way and then he got in.

It was a non-smoker, his compartment, next to the communicating door between the Firsts and Thirds. I went and sat in the next compartment. Presently he got out and stood a little way away on the platform.

I was worried by that communicating door. As long as it was unlocked (I knew that it was because I'd tried it) this would give him a possible way of escape which I couldn't cover. The seats near the corridor in my compartment had been taken by a pair of nuns, and I couldn't think of any way to eject them, short of committing some form of indictable offence. So I could only see my man if he actually came along the corridor past the window. If he took it into his head to move beyond the communicating door into the Firsts, or even further back on the train—there was plenty of room elsewhere—I should probably lose him for good. So somehow I'd got to get the communicating door locked.

I was standing in the corridor, taking no chances, even though all I could see was his shadow on the platform, when the guard came through the train. I stood near the communicating door, and I made myself as awkward as I could. The guard had to squeeze himself past me, and he looked as sour as a lemon about it.

'Sorry if I'm in your way,' I said. I don't go in for the heavy sarcastic line as a rule, but I fairly reeked of it this time; and as he went through into the Firsts I gave it to him again.

'It'd be asking too much to leave that door open, I suppose?'

'Not allowed,' he said; he didn't even glance at me.

'I thought not,' I said. 'Who is it makes these damn fool regulations?'

'You got a first-class ticket?' he said. He could have made it even ruder if he'd kicked my teeth in.

'No, I've got a third,' I said.

'Well, what d'you want to come through here for then?'

We just glared at each other for a few seconds, and then he slammed the communicating door and locked it.

As soon as we had started I made for the dining-car—it was nearly two o'clock and I was hungry again—and I grabbed a seat near the door so that I could sit with my back to it.

I was paying my bill, about twenty minutes later, when the mystery came past my table and sat down further along by himself. For the first time, while he was looking at the menu, I had a chance to size him up. He was paler and a little older than he'd seemed at first, and there was something, I don't know what it was, the shape of his head perhaps, or the proportions of his features, which told you straight away that he wasn't English. What struck me was that he looked rather pleasanter than I'd imagined him to be. He wasn't particularly good-looking, but he'd got a sympathetic air, an air of sensibility about him, which I had to admit was not unattractive.

I checked on him again as he went back past my compartment; and two or three times during the journey I went out and stretched my legs in the corridor, just to keep an eye on his reflection in the window.

I felt reasonably certain that up till now he had no suspicion whatever of being watched. Nothing in the way he looked or the way he behaved suggested he was in the least alert or uneasy. It would have been difficult, even for an innocent man, not to have shown somehow that he was aware of being shadowed, if he knew it. Anyone with a loaded conscience would almost certainly have given some indication; only a very slight indication, perhaps, but just enough to show a glimmer of their suspicions. They might have done something to check whether their suspicions were true, or else to reassure themselves that they'd been mistaken. This fellow hadn't even looked about him once, or given the slightest sign of haste or indecision. In fact, his whole manner, right from where we started on the quayside, had been perfectly normal in every way—except for that one tiny incident in the pawnbroker's. If it hadn't been for that, I might almost have begun to think I was on the wrong tack again.

By the time we got to Euston it was dark. It wasn't actually raining, but the pavement was glistening from a fine drizzle; you couldn't feel it, you could just see it when you came under a lamp, that was all; but it was wonderful how quickly it damped your spirits.

As I followed my magnet out to the courtyard, I wondered what sort of variation I could play this time on the pursuit-by-taxi theme. I needn't have bothered. I saw him walk straight out of the station with his bag and cross over into Euston Road. He stopped under a lamp and spoke to a policeman. How near that copper came to promotion in those few seconds, I don't suppose he ever knew.

I didn't need the aids of sorcery to tell myself that we were making for one of those boarding houses that are scattered all over Bloomsbury like holes in a colander. Twice we stopped *en route*, and the fellow asked the way again. I was so anxious to keep up with him that the first time, I came round a corner too quickly, and there he was facing me; he wasn't more than a few yards ahead, and a woman was telling him the way. So I sheered off across the road, and then I had to slow down to let him get ahead of me again.

The street was one of those wide and pleasantly proportioned Bloomsbury streets—the sort of street whose original elegance, or whatever's left of it, emphasizes the neighbourhood's decline and fall. Still, I wasn't much bothered by that aspect of it at the moment. What I was bothered about was whether there was likely to be room for both of us in the place he was making for—wherever that might be. When we got there it turned out to be the Bamborough House Hotel, 'private and commercial.' That fitted me all right, fitted my instincts at least, if not my calling. I felt they must have a bed for me, too.

I hung about for a few minutes till I saw a light go on in one of the upstairs windows. The blinds were drawn in most of the rooms, and in this one a woman came and drew them down as I was watching. She hesitated for a minute as she was drawing them, and turned round, as if she was talking to someone behind her; I guessed my man was being shown the ropes. I gave him another couple of minutes to shake down, and then I went inside.

A radio was playing somewhere, and the same woman I'd

seen at the window was coming down the stairs. She went in behind the desk, and looked at me with her head on one side and an expression which I imagined was meant to be welcoming. She was a fat, neat, colourless kind of creature, middle-aged and wearing glasses. There was a lot of powder on her face and not enough lipstick.

I didn't really have time to take the place in properly. All I noticed was that the light was too bright, and the smell of cooking was too strong, and there was too much grained woodwork and too many plants, and a good deal of baize, and brass which needed cleaning. I asked if she had a single room.

'How long would you be requiring it?' she said.

I wondered why she used the conditional, and how she came to manage an accent which was so genteel she could hardly get the words out without a spoon.

'A few days,' I said; 'a week, possibly.' How the hell did I know?

'One on the fourth floor,' she said.

My chap's window—if it was his—was on the third.

'Nothing a little lower down?' I said. I could see the refusal getting ready in her mouth. 'I'm not very good at stairs, I'm afraid. Got a bit of shrapnel knocking about in the leg.' It came out so pat I could almost feel where me old scar would have been, if I'd had one. At the same time I gave her what was meant for a winning smile; and it won. She looked at the register, and then she said:

'I have a room on the third. It's at the back, though, I'm afraid. That's the best I can do.'

Her head fell over on one side again. I recognized this now as a sign of interrogation; so I took the room, and she turned the register round for me to sign. The last entry in it was: 'Walter Speyr, Austrian subject, of Linz,' and there were particulars of his papers. His room number was Number 16. It was rather a good handwriting, cursive and fairly firm; not at all the sort of spidery effect most foreigners seem to produce.

I signed the book, and the woman came out from behind the desk and rang a bell. A boy in a dirty linen jacket shot out from somewhere like a jack-in-the-box, and she pointed to my bag and led the way upstairs. It was one of those cat-and-dog relationships between her and the boy; you could spot it in the first ten seconds: I guessed he was the cat. He had a thin, cheeky face, and I liked the look of him. Just to show where my sympathies lay, I winked as he picked up my bag, and he grinned back at me.

I could still hear the radio all the way upstairs: I didn't mind it, but I wanted to be able to listen to other sounds as well, if there were going to be any.

The room was just a back room in a commercial hotel: faded walls, a couple of rugs on the parquet lino which didn't quite hide the worn place by the wash-basin; and the usual cheap suite. That was about all, except for a slot meter in the hearth, and a copy of the rules and regulations tacked on the wall by the light switch. The only concessions I could see towards the idea of a home-from-home were a Schweppes' ashtray on the jerry cupboard by the bed, a strip of lace paper under the glass top of the dressing-table, and a badly foxed print of some military epic by Lady Butler, which was hanging just out of level over the mantelpiece. The light was shaded so that you could only see properly if you were lying in bed: then it shone full in your face.

I said 'thank you' to the suzeraine, and she went outside and waited till the boy had put my case down by the window. He turned round as he was going out.

'Anything else, sir?' he said.

'Not yet,' I said.

He looked fly enough to spot that I might have had some mental reservations. As a matter of fact, I hadn't any in particular; but he seemed the kind of little fish it might be useful to improve acquaintance with, and I wanted to keep him on the hook.

I looked at my watch: it was getting on for seven o'clock. Feeding time was 'seven sharp,' according to the suzeraine. I was ready to eat all right, but the question was, how was Walter Speyr's appetite?

I opened the door and looked to see how the numbers of the rooms ran. If 16 was where I imagined, it was to the left, somewhere round the corner in the front of the house. I walked along quietly, following the numbers, and treading hard into the haircord carpet to see if any of the boards squeaked. There was a light under the door of Number 16, and two or three times I saw a shadow go across the floor. A yard or so along the passage there was a little pantry, and peeking about inside it, I found a way out on to the fire escape. I always think it's as well to know the geography of a house if you're staying in it; and for all I knew, I might be here till crabbéd age overtook me.

I went back to my own room, and I left the door not quite shut; then I started unpacking. I could still hear the radio faintly from downstairs, and every few minutes I stood still and listened. All I could hear was that intangible heart-beat you get in a house that's full of people; and, presently a clock outside which struck seven. In the distance there was a ground base of noises out of the street which you wouldn't have noticed unless your nerves, as well as your ears, were stretched to catch every sound.

After about ten minutes, I heard a door opening and shutting along the passage; then someone went downstairs. I walked along and looked over the banisters. It was Speyr all right; he still had his coat on, and his hat was in his hand.

I came on cautiously, keeping out of sight as well as I could. I heard him stop on the first floor landing, and I waited. Then I heard a door being opened. After that there was silence. I stood on the stairs and wondered what the next move was, whether I should make it or leave it to him. The problem ironed itself when I heard someone coming down from the landing above.

On the spur of the moment I could only think of one possible reason why anyone should be hanging about where I was, in mid-stairway; and that would be to have a look at a faded chromo of Albert Moore's 'Blossoms.' I couldn't imagine anything calculated to arouse deeper suspicion, so I set off back towards my room again. I passed the cause of the interruption on my way. It was a grey, unmemorable cause, and it left nothing in my recollection except a smell of stale musquash.

I kept my eye over the well of the staircase as I went up,

slowly, towards my own floor. When I got there, I waited about for a bit, and then suddenly I got a bluebottle's view of Speyr, a good deal foreshortened. He crossed the first floor landing out of sight, so that all I could see was his hand on the banisters as he went downstairs.

I dashed down again quietly to the first floor, and as I got there I heard the voice of the suzeraine:

'Is that Mr. Spear? . . . Oh, Mr. Spear, supper's supposed to be at seven, you know.'

Then I heard Speyr: 'So? Pardon; for meals I shall be mostly out.'

He had a pleasant, polite voice, but it was a good rounded German accent, with plenty of *umlaut* and rinsing of teeth on the 'sh' syllable. Then I heard the suzeraine again:

'Oh, I see. Well, we like to be told, you know.'

I could fancy the bitter-sweet smile that went with it.

'So?' Speyr said. 'I am sorry.'

Then I heard the flap of the swing door as he went out.

There were four rooms on the first landing, but there was nothing to show which of them I'd heard him go into, except that one was a negative possibility marked 'Ladies' Room.'

I tried a door towards the back of the stairs. It opened on to another flight which was cluttered with housemaids' impedimenta and gave off a smell of kitchens. Just as I peeped through, the boy in the linen jacket shot up from below. We smiled.

'It's downstairs, the Gents', sir,' he said; and then he tore on upwards.

I shut the door and went back towards the other two rooms. The first was a kind of sitting-room-cum-mortuary. It was silent and it was dank, and it had a single pitiless light hanging from the ceiling in a mauve shade. On the sofa, or even on the table for that matter, you could have laid out a dead guest quite tastefully, and nobody would have noticed anything out of the ordinary. I couldn't imagine any reason why Speyr should have broken off his trip downstairs to come and sit in this hole.

The room next door seemed more promising. It was called Writing Room—I presume because there was a card-table in it covered with a piece of plush, with a blotter and an inkstand on it and a box with a few sheets of paper. There was an ash-tray, too, with some cigarette ash in it; new ash. And there was ink still wet on one of the pens. The paper on the blotter was old and indecipherable, but there was a loose half-sheet lying beside it; this looked fairly new, and I turned it over hopefully. There was a poor impression of someone's writing, so I folded it up carefully and put it in my wallet.

I looked in the waste-paper basket, but it was empty. Then I looked in the fireplace, behind a paper fan arranged with some artificial catkins. All I found was a heavy crop of cigarette ends and a broken gin bottle. I guessed I should just have to be content with my piece of blotting-paper. So I turned the light out and went downstairs.

The suzeraine was in the office behind the desk.

'I'm sorry,' I said, 'I'm afraid it's rather late to let you know, but I shan't be in to supper.' There seemed no harm in trying to keep on the woman's right side, if she had one, and I tried out the old winning smile again. 'I really didn't realize the time,' I said. 'Awfully sorry.'

Whatever inhibition I aroused in her bosom, and it looked as if it had room for a good many, it wasn't the same as Speyr seemed to have brought out.

'Never mind,' she said, and she grinned at me roguishly in a way that made my flesh creep.

I went back upstairs and I lay down on the bed and lit a cigarette. And then I remembered something; I remembered that ash-tray in the writing-room downstairs and the new ash in it. And I thought of Speyr on the train, sitting in a non-smoker. Why? There'd been plenty of room in some of the other compartments, I remembered noticing that.

I was still thinking about this when the clock outside struck half-past seven. What I needed just now was a plan of action. My objective was clear enough, but the means of attaining it looked pretty vague at the moment. So far I'd not had to rely on anything but common sense and ingenuity; and once or twice I'd been damned lucky. But for that taxi in Liverpool, I might have lost the job already. This kind of *ad hoc* approach might do all right as long as I was merely tailing someone. But if I was going to get to know Speyr, which looked like the next step, I should need a new foolproof identity; one that would leave me my own master, so that I could come and go pretty freely without arousing his curiosity.

How I could shape this idea to fit was going to depend on what I could find out about him, and how quickly I could find it out. If I left it too long he might begin to notice my adhesive personality and start having ideas about it; and it seemed better they should come from me than that he should think them up for himself.

Well, what did I know about him so far? Damn all. His name, and that probably wasn't his, anyway: that he came from Linz, or said he did; and that he was apparently a non-smoker. There was also the fact that he could move in a way that would make a python sound like an anchor chain; might be useful to know this, but it wasn't much good as a topic for scraping acquaintance.

You can deduce all kinds of things, and with some degree of certainty, if you look at a man long enough and close enough. His teeth and his skin, the condition of his hands and his shoes, whether his socks are hand-knitted or machine-made, the lining of his overcoat, the presence or absence of certain things visible in his pockets, the type of spectacles he wears: none of them seem particularly important by themselves. They only have something to say if you take them as parts of a whole man. But my total observations of Speyr hardly amounted to more than fifteen minutes, mostly of his back-view and from a distance of yards.

I got up off the bed, and I put a clean handkerchief in my pocket, and then I was ready. Putting the handkerchief there reminded me of something: I remembered I'd still got that piece of blotting-paper in my pocket. I took it carefully out, so as not to crush it, and I went over and held it up to the mirror. The hand looked pretty much like Speyr's hand, what I could remember of it from the register downstairs, but it wasn't easy to read what was written. As far as I could make out, what it said was:

'*O.K. for* 16*th at* 12.45. *Bis dahin.*'

It looked as if it was signed C; and then there was a postscript, which was even more difficult to decipher:

'*I think often of Goronwy's.* (That was the best I could make of it.) '*How long it seems already.*'

Whatever it was all about, I couldn't deal with it now or I should miss an appointment with myself downstairs.

The door locked itself as I shut it behind me, and I put the key in my pocket. I could still hear the radio as I went downstairs: someone with the voice of a eunuch was singing *Basin Street Blues.*

I stopped at the bottom of the stairs, and tried to disentangle the sounds in the office from the other sounds going on around me. There were noises off from the kitchen behind a baize door; a woman in the 'phone booth under the stairs was yammering about some theatre seats; and in the office I could hear the voice of the suzeraine, and now and again the click of a typewriter.

Beside the door of the passage leading to the office there was a board to hang the keys on. It was hidden from the office by a partition of frosted glass. I could see the suzeraine's shadow against the glass but she couldn't see me.

On the board in front of me I saw the key of Number 16. I held my breath, and I gripped the key hard to stop it clinking against its metal tag; then I lifted it without a sound. As I turned to go upstairs, the boy who had carried my bag smashed his way through the baize door carrying a couple of syphons. I jumped out of my skin and back again without his seeming to notice anything, and we grinned at each other; then I went on upstairs.

I waited at the top to get my breath; and when it came back, I walked along the passage to Speyr's room and let myself in.

CHAPTER

6

I STOOD IN THE ROOM, DEBATING WHETHER TO SHUT THE DOOR or leave it open. When you're minding your own business, you don't need to keep your ears as well skinned as when you're minding someone else's: then they're liable to be skinned for you, if you don't do it yourself. So I left the door open, very slightly.

The room might have been my own, except that the furniture was arranged differently; and instead of the battle-piece over the fireplace, there was Millet's *Vespers.* On the table beside the bed there was a black brief-case. It was a cheap-looking thing with a lock you could have broken with your teeth. Without moving the position of the case, I tried the catch through my handkerchief; it was locked.

Underneath the case I noticed the corner of a magazine. I took out my second handkerchief and lifted the case up carefully to have a look: it was the magazine Speyr had bought at the bookstall in Liverpool. Beside it, there were two books in German, *Cristinas Heimkehr*, by Hofmannsthal, and a tattered paper copy of Beethoven's *Briefe;* another of the books I've got on my shelves and always keep meaning to read. Inside the cover, in pencil, it said: 'From J.'

I put the case back carefully; then, of course, I jogged it, and in saving it I knocked Beethoven off the table, and a bookmarker, a small buff card, fell out of it. I knew what it was before it touched the floor; there was the pawnbroker's name and address on it: 'E. Arnholtz, Jeweller and Watchmaker'; and in smaller letters underneath, as if it were an afterthought, it said: 'Loans.' On the other side there was a telephone number in pencil. I wrote it down, and then I put the card back in the title page and rearranged the case as it was before.

I looked all round the room, inside the cupboard, using my handkerchief again for the handle, and on top of it. Then I got down and looked at the underside of the mattress; and then I felt along the top of the pelmet board. I tried the empty bag with the 'Boston' tab on it; it was a genuine bag all right; no funny seams and no hollow handles. It didn't look as if there was going to be anything worth finding in the room, except possibly in the brief-case; and to find out what was in that I should need to know a lot more about Speyr than I'd picked up so far. It looked as if I should have to frisk the whole room and just see what came into the net.

It's really as much a work of art, frisking a whole room quickly and thoroughly, as it is to get a man's watch off his stomach while you're shaking hands with him. I didn't have all the Artful Dodger's experience, perhaps, but I'd probably had the advantage of a more scientific training. I went through every article of clothing in the room, from the turn-ups of the spare suit hanging in the wardrobe to the lining of a tie in the dressing-table drawer.

About every half-minute I stopped and went over to the door and listened. There was nothing to hear, except the ordinary noises of the house, and the thump of my heart as I stood there holding my breath and straining my ears. The door of the little pantry along the passage had been left open, and when I had come by, I had made sure of the door to the fire escape being unlatched, too. I wouldn't want to have to use the axe hanging up beside it, if I was in a hurry.

There was nothing of any interest in Speyr's clothes. He hadn't brought much with him, and what there was was pretty well worn. Some things were marked with a W.S., but that didn't prove anything.

There was very little on the dressing-table, only a razor and a stud-box and a pair of hair-brushes that needed combing out. There was no sign of anything odd about the bristle plates, and the backs seemed all right, too; and there was nothing of any consequence in the stud-box.

As I was looking to see what was in it, I knew all of a sudden that I wasn't alone any longer. There may have been some tiny sound or movement, perhaps; I don't remember. I *knew*—there was no need for me even to turn my head—I knew that someone had come quite quietly into the room.

I stood stock still, and everything inside me seemed to do the same. Then I moved my eyes, nothing more, and over my shoulder in the looking-glass I saw Speyr standing in the doorway.

I put the stud-box back and turned round towards him, and as I did so, he slid into the room and shut the door. He was still wearing his hat and coat.

'This is my room. You are here, why?' he said.

For some reason, maybe a streak of ham in me somewhere, I'd expected him to sound a bit more casual, more insinuating. He spoke with a nasty edge on his voice, like a schoolmaster, as if he'd caught me cribbing; and just as if I had been, I didn't know what the hell to say.

We stared at each other; then he snapped out at me again: 'Why?'

I was wondering whether I looked enough like the ordinary hotel rook to make him believe me. It seemed worth trying; anyway, the only alternative would have been the truth.

'Well,' I said, 'I'm not going to pretend this is a mistake or anything. What can I say?—except that I'm very sorry.'

'So? That I find you, you are sorry, huh?'

'Of course. But I mean I'm sorry that—if I'd—I mean——' Dammit, I didn't know what I did mean. 'Look, I've not taken anything at all,' I said. 'I've taken absolutely nothing. Search me, if you like.'

I held up my arms to let him come and dust me over.

He looked at me for a long while; and then he smiled for the first time; and for the first time, too, I noticed his discoloured tooth. Then he took off his hat and threw it on the bed, and pulled out a cigarette case, a green leather one, and he held it out towards me.

'Cigarette?' he said. 'Ah! I forget: you smoke only Turkish, huh?'

He took a cigarette out of the case and stuck it so that it dangled between his lips, and all we did was to go on looking at each other.

Close to, there was something a little sensuous about his face, but there was something gentle and reserved about it too. Except that he was decidedly a menace just at this moment, I could imagine him having considerable charm, particularly for women, if he cared to use it. He wasn't caring to use it now.

'This is true, no?' he said. 'You smoke only Turkish?' He put his head a little on one side, and looked at me pretty sharply. 'They are strong, Turkish. You notice in a small place at once the smell. *Im leihhause*—Arnholtz' shop, huh? On a train, the lavatory compartment, you notice. Such mistakes always you don't imagine—so small.'

I got some feeling into the roots of my tongue at last, and then I said—and I wasn't trying to be funny, I really wanted to know——

'Any others?' I couldn't see much use in keeping up a pretence of being innocent. It seemed to me about my only chance, and a pretty thin one at that, was to keep him talking; at least I might find out how much he knew. And he did go on talking:

'Was also your cigarette case: you should not have changed your mind.'

I said: 'How did you know I changed it?'

'One mistake more—was in front of you a big tray from Arnholtz, was like a mirror.'

If I'd been in the mood for irony, I might have laughed. All I wanted to do was play for time. What I was going to do with it if I got it, God knows. But it'd be as fine a test of my resource as any I'd had so far.

'Why was it a mistake to change my mind, though?'

'You are going to Arnholtz, why? You need money. So: you know before you go already in the shop what is best to show him, huh?—not wait till you are there inside.'

As he was saying this, he walked slowly over to the dressing-table, and he stood there just touching the glass top with the tips of his fingers, and watching the movements of his hand as if he was playing some sort of game. It was the first time he'd taken his eyes off me. He still had the cigarette hanging out of his mouth, and he still didn't light it.

I didn't move. His other hand was in his trouser pocket, and I began to have a ridiculous superstition about it staying there. Outside, in the distance, I heard the clock strike eight.

'I thought you didn't smoke,' I said.

He cocked his head up sideways when I said this.

'So? Ah!—because I was in non-smoking? This was my mistake,' he said, and he smiled at that.

I said to him: 'Why didn't you change, then?'

'You are keeping me in sight, yes?—and I you, since I realize already you follow me. If I change, so we should lose each other.' He shrugged, and smiled again.

He couldn't speak without gestures, and most of them he made with his head. I hate gestures, and I hated that god-damned accent of his, too; and that dangling cigarette—that annoyed me as well. I was still more annoyed, though, at how easy it had been for him to make a monkey out of me. Still, it had certainly convinced me of one thing: I should need to be a damn sight more clever in future—if there was going to be any future. I didn't know what that depended on at the moment, so I said nothing and just waited.

He pulled a lighter out of his pocket at last, a little cheap, red thing, and as he put it up to his cigarette, the cigarette dropped off his lip.

I don't know what it was—instinct, I suppose—that made me stoop for it. I just heard the swish of his arm as it came down, and I pitched straight on to my knees, and blacked out.

CHAPTER

7

IT WAS QUITE DARK, AND I COULD HEAR SOMEONE KNOCKING somewhere. Then a woman's voice, a long, long way off, said, 'He's gone out.' Then the knocking stopped. Presently another voice said someone was wanted on the 'phone. I couldn't hear who it was. Couldn't be me, though, because I was here, in the dark. I could see something, all the same, even in the dark . . . a clock, only I couldn't focus it; but I could hear it ticking. I tried to look at it closer, to see what time it was; there was such a hell of a pain in my head though, when I moved, that I gave up and just lay still.

Then, after a bit, I put out my hand in the darkness to see if I could reach the clock. . . . I touched it . . . it was on my wrist all the time—my wrist-watch. Made me jump . . . and when I did that someone sliced round my skull with a cheese-cutter. I tried turning slowly, slowly over on my back. There seemed to be a leg or a table or something in the way; no good pushing it, though. So I gripped the top of it and pulled myself up gradually on my knees. That took another slice off, a clean round slice off my scalp. Still, I could rest my forehead against my knuckles this way . . . just rest and hold on for a while, and try to sort things out. It was still dark, but the voices had gone away, and I could just rest now.

Things began to come back presently. Who was it had had a lighter? It was Speyr, wasn't it? And his cigarette fell on the floor . . . that was it . . . and I went to pick it up. When was all this, though? How long ago? Eight o'clock; I remembered that. While we were talking the clock outside had struck eight . . . or was that my imagination? I pulled my head back gently, very gently, so I could see my watch. It didn't register at first, didn't register properly, only by degrees. Nearly a quarter-past eight . . . quarter-past? Was that all?

I waited another minute or two; then I got up off my knees and leant against the table. It was the same dressing-table; I could feel the glass top dead cold against my hands. I got my bearings from the light shining under the door and through the keyhole, and in a little while I braced myself and began feeling my way across the room.

I found the switch, and before I turned it on, I covered my eyes, and let the light come in gradually through my hands. Even so, my head cracked like a dropped flower-pot when I moved; and all at once I felt sick.

I got to the bedside table just in time: after that I lay down on the bed for a little and kept my eyes shut. When I felt a bit better I sat up, slowly. First thing I noticed was that the brief-case wasn't on the table by the bed any longer; nor were Beethoven's *Briefe*, and there was nothing on the dressing-table either. I got up off the bed and went and looked in the drawers; they were empty, too—all of them; so was the wardrobe.

I looked in the long glass and straightened myself up a bit; then I listened at the door, and as the passage seemed clear, I turned out the light and went back to my own room.

I still felt pretty shaky, and after I'd fixed the light so it didn't shine slap in my eyes, I lay down on the bed and lit a cigarette. It tasted like the straw out of a camel's litter. Perhaps I had got concussion after all. I threw the cigarette away and tried to think without it.

Whether this was too drastic a remedy, I don't know. Any-way, my thoughts drifted off on a jive of their own, and I began thinking a long way back, to those early days in the war when the first batch of us had been secretly whisked off to a huge house in the country. This was the place where, at Herrick's knee, we had been given our first lessons in stealth and decep-tion. I remembered his always making us look for whatever seemed the logical issue of the problems they set us, and his teaching us to ignore any instincts or inclinations that might lead us away from that issue. I asked myself what was the logical thing for me to do at this moment. And I thought of

Mr. Dick, when Miss Trotwood had asked him what to do with David Copperfield. His answer was 'Wash him'; which so clearly was the thing to be done that only a man of Mr. Dick's simplicity would have thought of it.

All I had to connect me now with Speyr was a telephone number; I didn't even know who it belonged to. Mr. Dick's advice would obviously have been to ring up and find out. So I got up off the bed and went over to the wash-basin. I washed my face and rinsed my mouth out, and then I began to feel a bit better.

After that I went carefully through my pockets; only one thing was missing: that was my diary. Still, there hadn't been anything in it to identify me by; at least I'd taken care of that. If Speyr had hoped to find out whether I'd taken the number Uncle Arnholtz had given him, he ought to have looked at the ten-bob note in my wallet. Looking at it again, I could hardly make out what the number was because I'd woven it with such care into the design.

I went down into the hall, and what did I find but that same woman still jabbering in the call-box. I hung about outside and hoped she was telepathic; if she was, she'd be liable to bounce out of the box at any minute and slap my face. But she didn't, she stayed there waffling for ages.

I stood and looked at the advertisements hanging up in the hall, advertisements for theatres and Turkish baths, and car hire services. I looked at the letters stuck on the letter-board, waiting to be claimed; and then I saw one of them said on it 'Mr. Speyr.' It was just a folded note, not a proper letter. The board faced the desk, unfortunately, and the suzeraine was still there, gabbing away to someone in the office. She had her back towards me, though, and so, at what I felt to be a safe moment, I tweaked the note out and read it quickly, then I tweaked it back again. It was a telephone message torn from a printed pad. It was timed 8 p.m., and it said:

Mr. Wirth is away. Sorry he must postpone meeting you till tomorrow. Will expect you at 7.30.

I looked at my watch: it said a quarter to nine. The message had come at eight, so there had been plenty of time for Speyr to have seen it. But if he had seen it, he obviously wouldn't have put it back on the board again—or would he? Not unless there was a good reason. I couldn't think of any reason, but I was getting cagey in my old age, and I didn't like to rule out the possibility straight away. If he hadn't seen the note, he must be well on his way to some earlier appointment with Mr. Wirth, whoever he might be.

The woman in the telephone box came out then, and she explained to me how terribly sorry she was that she'd kept me waiting; you could see how deeply she felt it by the way she grinned, with a mouthful of teeth like piano keys.

I went in the box and shut the door; then I opened it again to let out the sweet, smoky smell, and I dialled the number I'd written on my ten-bob note. The girl who answered won my heart with her opening words.

'Astoria Hotel, good evening,' she said.

'It hasn't been so far,' I said. 'Have you got a Mister Wirth staying there?'

'One moment—I'll give you reception,' she said; then there was a pause. I thought perhaps I'd picked up enough for one day; still, I clung to reception like a lost child to its mother.

'Mister Wirth is away,' reception said, presently.

'Back when?' I asked.

To-morrow, reception thought, but didn't know for certain; so I rang off.

When I came out of the box, the suzeraine had turned round, and was draping her bust over a ledger. I went up to the desk.

'Excuse me,' I said . . .

The get-out cost me fifteen and six, and the suzeraine's good opinion. I pulled a long story about a friend I'd just spoken to on the telephone needing me urgently. The suzeraine listened, and then she said: 'That's a god-damned lie, and you know it!' She said it entirely with her eyebrows.

I went upstairs and collected my things; then I shook the dust of Bamborough House Hotel off my feet for evermore.

CHAPTER

8

EVEN SO, MY SHOES STILL NEEDED CLEANING WHEN I GOT HOME, and while I made some coffee, I got out the box and did them over before I went to bed.

It was a great thing about Mrs. Wellington that she'd inherited the Duke's passionate interest in matters of the commissariat. All I needed for breakfast next morning was in the refrigerator; and by the time the excellent woman showed up, just to see that the place hadn't been gutted overnight, I'd finished my toast and my *Times*.

She was the queen of discretion, Mrs. Wellington, and I hated not being able to tell her my arrangements for once; I always told her my arrangements. I felt she'd think it was a want of confidence if I didn't; but there really wasn't anything I could say for the moment, not about my day-to-day movements. Of all the people I might have to try to fool, she looked like being the most difficult, because I knew I shouldn't enjoy it.

My immediate plan was very simple: it was just to have a look at Mr. Wirth's home ground, preferably while he was standing somewhere else. It was a plan that had only two snags: first, it involved, among other risks, the possibility that it might not give any results; and I had to judge my chances of success against this risk. If Mr. Wirth should come in just while I happened to be making my unofficial tour, then my lucky star would certainly go out; and with it, probably the last chance I should get of keeping on Speyr's trail. On the other hand, Speyr obviously hadn't come over just for fun and games; and as his first move had been to fix a meeting with Wirth, the man was obviously a bird to be watched.

You can learn quite a lot about a bird by looking at its cage; and on the whole, the risks involved in trying to get a look at this one's cage seemed worth taking. I couldn't know less about him than I knew at present; therefore I should be bound to find out something more.

The second snag was how in God's name I was to do the job. I felt I should be nearer to God, perhaps, if I went along to the Astoria Hotel; so, a little before seven, I got out the car and drove along there.

I parked the car in front of the hotel, and I went in through the grill room entrance. Then I cut upstairs to the balcony which looks over the lounge, and I took a table behind one of the pillars, so that I could just see the revolving doors below without being spotted by anyone coming through them. I ordered a drink, for appearance's sake really—the chances were I should need to keep fairly sober—and I sat and watched the doors for nearly twenty-five minutes. Then, just after half-past seven, I let out a silent shriek of triumph: a party of scallopped taffeta débutantes tittered through the doors with an escort of adolescent guardees; and, bringing up the rear, rather incongruously, was Speyr.

I could almost have felt sorry for him, only I still had a bruise on my scalp like a pigeon's egg, just to remind me how we felt about each other. He looked a little bit shabby and lost and provincial, standing there; I guessed he knew it, and was trying not to show it. Then he made for a chair facing the lifts; he only remembered when he got there that he still had his hat on.

Nearly fifteen minutes went by and nothing more happened, except that he got a bit restless as time went on, and so did I. Every time the doors went round, or the lifts opened up to let in a fresh bunch of faces, he stopped pretending to read his newspaper and looked carefully at what was being brought in.

I'd moved round the balcony now, so as to be behind him. It put the entrance out of sight, but I had a better view of the lifts. You might have found their great bronze doors in any Florentine *palazzo*, though not the types that filtered in and out whenever the doors slid open. One of these types dropped a newspaper as he stepped out, and the lift-boy handed it back to him. It was such a tiny incident and so quick that I nearly missed it; but out of the corner of my eye, and almost as it happened, I noticed Speyr was on his feet and was going over quite casually towards the lifts.

The man with the paper was short, with a large pale face and rimless glasses. From where I was it was difficult to tell his age; he was bald from the chin to the back of the neck, and he might have been anything between forty and fifty-five.

He didn't look up, he just stood there, reading the paper for a few seconds, and it wasn't till Speyr actually spoke to him that he looked round; and then he seemed quite genuinely surprised and pleased. Very nicely done, it was; a pleasure to watch.

They shook hands, and then the chap took Speyr's arm and steered him over towards the cloakroom. Speyr gave his hat and coat to the boy, and then he and his new-found chum went into the bar.

For the next ten minutes or so I was downstairs tearing myself into three equal parts as I tried to cover all three exits from the bar. Big Chief Pale Face, or Pale Chief Big Face, whoever he was, looked a fairly *bon vivant* from ten yards away, and I guessed the inner man would probably come next on his list: it was after eight o'clock now, and he was on mine already. Sure enough, in a little while I spotted the two of them going out through the door leading to the grill room. They weren't alone any longer, though; there was a third party with them.

He must have joined them in the bar some time ago. I remembered now that I'd seen him when he came into the lounge, and he'd struck me then as a type I don't much care for. He looked like a good mixer, a public school motor salesman, the kind with enough breeding to make matters worse. He had a hustling sort of air, which probably didn't deceive anyone except himself; and when he had come in, he had just tossed his things over to the cloakroom boy without waiting for a ticket, and then had breezed straight along into the bar.

As the three of them came out I managed to get a closer

look at him. He wasn't at all bad-looking, with reddish-gold hair which would have had me panting if he'd been a girl, and large eyes that looked curiously light for his kind of colouring; a type that I imagined could be very attractive to some women; only there was something slightly coarse about him; I don't know what it was; maybe that his neck and his wrists were rather too thick. He looked a little older than he would like to have been taken for, I guessed; something over forty.

The bar had emptied by the time they came out, so I went in and ordered a drink. The barman was trying to read horse news in a late *Star*, and not to let you see what he was doing. As I came up to the bar, he looked at me with virginal innocence, and very neatly slipped the paper off his knee under the counter.

'What's good for the three-thirty?' I said, after I'd drunk a little.

The fellow looked all round before he answered, as if the Gestapo might have been after him; then he leaned over slightly, and, without looking at me, he said: 'Silver Jacket.'

Another inch further off, and I wouldn't even have seen his lips move. Still, the question seemed to have warmed his interest; in the next few minutes he volunteered one or two other bits of useless information, all to do with horses, and all said with a kind of ventriloquial vacancy. It was catching; my face was a wall by the time I could get a word in.

'Show me that paper a minute,' I said. He slid the folded *Star* out as if it might have been a filthy picture. I drooped my eyelids, as that seemed to be the vogue, and I glanced down over the counter at to-morrow's card. I noticed there was a horse running somewhere called Featherbell.

'I've only got this shirt I'm wearing,' I said, 'but it's going on Featherbell for the four o'clock.'

'Featherbell, eh?' He slid the paper out of sight again. 'Ta,' he said.

'That chap in here just now,' I said, 'with those other two, he gets some of the gen now and again—if you know how to work it out of him.' I took another sip, just to wash out the taste of 'gen.'

'The Swiss one, you mean—the gentleman with glasses?'

'The one with the loose hair,' I said. 'He doesn't do too badly out of it.'

'He doesn't, eh? He's to do with pictures, though, isn't he—antiques or something?' I was drinking, so I didn't have to thank him for it. 'Don't reckon much on that kind, though, do you? Like pictures that talk best, eh?' He suddenly grew confidential again. 'Still, his floor valley, he says there's pictures up there on the fourth floor, you wouldn't believe what they was worth. Four and five thousand pounds a time, some o' them! Gen'lman told him so himself. Do you believe it, though?—just for painted pictures—five thousand quid, eh? Wicked, isn't it? Still, shows there's some mugs still goin' around, doesn't it?'

It seemed a bright, philosophical sort of note to end on, so I made a deprecating sound into the bottom of my whisky; then I said good night and I left him. I'd got enough to go on with, and I hadn't had to ask any questions, either.

I went across the lounge to the reception desk. I didn't want to seem too inquisitive; there might easily be trouble enough without my making any. So I asked the desk clerk to ring Mr. Wirth's room. He was an odd, mystical-looking chap for a desk clerk, and I hoped he wasn't clairvoyant.

'Very well,' I said, when he'd given up ringing, 'p'raps I'd better leave a note. What is it, the room number—four something, isn't it?'

He checked it on a board before he had time to think.

'Four-six-three,' he said.

I went away, looking as if I was going to write a note: then I dodged back into one of the bronze Italianate lifts, and I asked the Anglo-Saxon operator for the fourth floor.

Four-six-three seemed to be a good mile or so from the lift, on a corner where two corridors met in the shape of a T; the door was in the long arm of the T. I could see only one way to open it, and that would have been with a key, which I hadn't got. So I bounced round the corner on a carpet that was so thick it came up over the ankles, and I took a look at the short arm of the corridor. A few yards along there was a casement window which opened out on to a well, and at right angles to this window there was another belonging to four-six-three. The diagonal between them was about four or five feet, and down below there was a drop of sixty or seventy. A few of the windows in the well were lit up, but it still looked very dark—and very deep. Somewhere there was a girl crooning away to herself about a white Christmas.

I could see that the window of four-six-three was open; not very wide open, but I judged that if I stood up on the sill I was leaning against, I could just reach out over the well far enough to push up the stay of the other window with my foot. I stood still and listened for a minute or two; not that you would have heard a mechanised column going past on a carpet that thick. Then I pushed the window back, and I got up on the sill.

I've never cared much for heights at any time, and standing up there in the dark seemed suddenly to bring out all the limpet in me: I could hardly force myself to move. The flesh on my soles felt like the skin of a lizard as I stretched my leg out towards the other window. And then, after what seemed like a couple of hours, I touched down on the opposite sill.

There I was, spread-eagled in the dark, sixty feet up, and some damn fool had to choose this moment in the whole of time to go turn a light on in the window opposite. I could see his shadow moving on the wall inside the room, and I could hear him talking to somebody; and I could still hear the girl down below going on about a white Christmas. Just at the moment, though, I wouldn't have been interested if Christmas had had all the colours of the spectrum in it.

I kicked up the stay of the other window, then I gave myself an almighty shove, and I swayed over in the darkness towards the opposite sill. As soon as my fingers touched the cold metal frame, I gripped it as if it were a cheque for twenty thousand quid; and then I swung myself neatly through the window, slick as an acrobat and scared to death.

I sat on the ledge, sweating and with my heart bumping like a jeep in a ploughed field. Then I felt about with my feet, and presently I touched down on a tiled floor.

It seemed to be a bathroom, and I sneaked my way carefully round in the darkness till I came to the door. It was shut, so I opened it quietly, and I put my hand round and felt for the switch in the next room. But I was too late. Another hand was holding the switch already, a woman's hand. I pushed it down hard, and as the light came on, I smacked my other hand over her mouth and then jerked her free arm up behind her back.

She was a chambermaid, a pretty, plump little partridge with large dark eyes that seemed darker than they really were because her pupils were dilated. She looked a trusty, sensible sort of girl, I thought; or was I just being hopeful? Dammit, what else could I be?

I took my hand away from her mouth cautiously. When I'd touched her at first she'd given a sort of soft yelp, and I thought she might be going to let it out again; but she didn't. I had her pinned against the wall with her arm twisted behind her, so I let it go a little, and I said to her:

'Now, if you'll be a sensible girl, and not try anything funny, I'll tell you what's going on here, shall I?'

She didn't answer; she just went on looking frightened and a bit indignant; so I gave her arm a little more freedom.

'I didn't mean to hurt you,' I said. 'I'm sorry if I did.'

She rubbed her elbow, the pinioned one, just to show what a cad I'd been; but she still didn't say anything.

'Look, I haven't got much time,' I said. 'I've got to try and explain something to you which I don't expect you to believe; still, I'd like you to try to. It may sound fishy——'

'Smells fishy, too,' she said; she had a slightly flat, north-country accent.

'Now, don't be silly. I'll talk, you listen,' I said. 'What were you doing here in the dark when I came in?' She didn't answer, so I said it again, very brusquely this time, and, after a second or two, she said:

'Waiting.'

'What for?' I said.

'See who you were.'

I guessed she must have heard me when I kicked up the stay

getting in through the window. She had guts, this girl; most girls would have leapt out into the corridor and yelled for help.

'What's your name?' I said.

She wouldn't answer for a moment, just stood there, looking rather sour and suspicious; then she said: 'My name's Florrie, if that means anything to you.'

'Now look, Florrie, I know what you think I am,' I said; 'just an ordinary hotel rook, don't you?'

'And what do you think you are?' she said.

'The only thing I can tell you is——' I tried to think of something that would sound convincing and innocuous at the same time. 'Well—I'm on a certain mission, let's put it that way.'

'Funny way for a missionary to come in,' she said; 'through the window.'

It seemed to me this was going to be a rather difficult approach. Things might be going to get unpleasant at any moment. Dammit, they were unpleasant already, and I couldn't afford to waste time.

'All right. What's a rook usually up to?' I said.

'Thieving,' she said. She enjoyed saying it, too.

'And what if I were here to leave something instead of taking something away?'

'Such as?' she said.

I was beginning to like this girl. The kind of head she had on her shoulders might be useful, sooner or later. She was shrewd without being smart about it; and she was straightforward, and obviously sensible enough to be able to keep a secret. These were just first impressions, of course, quick and superficial; but often, in this sort of situation, you have to trust to first impressions and act accordingly. If you don't—well, you may not get another chance.

'Such as what?' she said.

'This, for instance.'

I pulled some notes out of my case—I didn't count them—and I held them out towards her. She looked at them, then she looked at me, then back at the money again. I could see she was fighting the good fight with herself—whether to slap my face or to let nature take its course. She looked at me again, but she didn't make any move about the money. Then she said, in a rather quiet, sceptical way:

'What is it you really are after?'

'Nothing—at present,' I said. 'I'm on a sort of reconnaissance, if you like. The chap who lives here in this room, he happens to interest me, that's all.'

I put the notes on a table; then I went over to the door. It opened on to a square yard of hall leading into the corridor outside. I locked the door and took out the key. Florrie looked a bit alarmed again when I did this, but she didn't say anything, so I took the words out of her mouth.

'Whatever's he going to do now?' I said. 'Watch me, if you like. Nothing dangerous.'

I looked quickly round the room to size it up. The floor valet, the friend of my friend the barman downstairs, was certainly right about the pictures, unless they were fakes. In that case, they were pretty good fakes. If not, the sum they must have been worth would have been more than tidy; I should have called it immaculate. There were only a few paintings hanging on the wall: there were a couple of Renoirs and a Sisley and a Corot, and one which might have been a Boudin, a beach scene. I wasn't sure of the others; they were all beauties, though, every one of them; and there were about a dozen or more stacked with their faces to the wall.

Apart from the pictures, the room looked like any other sitting-room in a private suite: everything pretty comfortable and quite impersonal. The only thing that interested me at all was a small writing-table; even that hadn't got much to give away, though. There were a few business papers in the drawers, but all they told me was that Wirth had a picture gallery in St. James's. I could feel Florrie watching every movement I made as I whipped through the drawers.

There was another door, half open, on the other side of the room. I said to her:

'This the bedroom?' She nodded. 'Come on,' I said. She waited till I began going over to her before she made a move, and she kept her eye on me as she went through the door, very unwillingly. 'You're all right,' I said; 'gentlemen prefer blondes.'

'And what about you?' she said.

'You'll be all right,' I said. 'You sit on the bed and be quiet, that's all.'

There wasn't much to go for in this room, either. No trunks; no papers, that I could see; only a dressing-table and the clothes cupboard. There was a handsome set of studs in one drawer, and a cheque book and some loose cash. I let Florrie see that I didn't want any either. There was nothing in the suit pockets or in the shoes; but in the drawer of the bedside table I found a Leica camera. Florrie watched me while I looked it over.

'*Sprechen sie Deutsch*?' I said.

'Eh?'

'D'you know anything about cameras?' I said.

'No.'

'Nothing?' She just shook her head; so I told her what the German markings on it meant. I didn't say that it might easily have been bought in Oxford Street. Then I put it back, and I started going through the clothes in the drawers. In one of them there were some underpants, and one pair had something heavy wrapped in it. I kept an eye carefully on Florrie as I unrolled the pants on the bed; inside there was a nice little automatic.

When she saw it her eyes popped for just a second, but it was long enough. She tried to look unconcerned when she saw I was watching her. The gun was a Luger .32, and there were four cartridges in it.

'Know where this comes from?' I said. She didn't know. 'Comes from Essen. You know where Essen is?'

She looked at me rather sharply. Then she said: 'I know Essen.'

'How d'you mean, you know it?' I said.

She didn't answer for a second; then she said—and she hesitated a little——

'Well—I don't mean exactly I know it. I mean, like, I had my friend shot down over there in the war, see.'

'Your boy friend?' She nodded. 'You mean he was killed?' She nodded again.

There was nothing to say to that; nothing that would mean anything, anyway. I showed her the words Luger, Essen, on the stock of the pistol, and the cartridges in the magazine. She still didn't seem anxious to give very much away, but she did look a little less uncompromising after that.

'What would anyone want with a thing like that?' she said, '—living in a place like this.'

'Target practice, I expect.'

'Eh?' For the first time she looked as if she might be going to smile, but it didn't last.

'Don't be daft,' she said.

'All right, you think of a better one,' I said. I rolled the pistol up in the pants again and put them back in the drawer. Then we went into the sitting-room again.

I looked all round, just to make sure there was nothing I ought to have noticed and had missed, and on the mantelpiece I spotted an address book. They used to teach us at P Branch, in the elementary course, that the two places where a man is most vulnerable are, first, in the lower abdomen, then in the address book; because an address book's about the only place where you can count on him to put down the whole truth and nothing but the truth. In a case like this of Wirth's, where you know damn all about a man, half an hour with his address book could easily be worth a day of his company. So I said to Florrie:

'Florrie, I'm going to need some help. D'you think you could borrow this book, just for an hour? I need it, and Mr. Wirth wouldn't miss it if he was out, would he?'

That made her very cagey again.

'Well—I don't know, really——'

'Look,' I said, and I said it with some feeling, slowly, 'do you still think I really am just an ordinary hotel rook? Because if you do, you'd better get the house detective, and get him straight away, because I'm not here for long.'

I picked up the telephone and held it out to her. It took her a few troubled seconds to make up her mind . . . but in the end she just shook her head, and I put the receiver back again.

'Right! If we're going to trust each other, let's make a job of it,' I said. 'I've told you all I can about myself——'

'All you said was you was on a mission,' she said.

'So I am. I'm trying to find out certain facts about certain people. It's information I want, not valuables.'

'And what d'you expect to find out about Mr. Wirth, then?'

'I never "expect" to find anything. It's the unexpected I'm after. You wouldn't "expect" an innocent man to have a gun, would you?—or to keep it hidden in his under-pants?'

She looked at me—a sort of sideways look—trying to make things out.

'What *are* you, then?' she said. 'You're not a copper, are you?'

'No, not a proper copper,' I said. 'More or less on the same side, though. How about you?'

She stood there chewing her lip while she thought about it.

'Look, Florrie,' I said. 'I need someone here who can help me keep an eye on Wirth—someone I know that I can trust absolutely not to gossip and not to lose their head.'

I let it go at that. It seemed a line worth trying, the sort of points a girl like her would probably like to be flattered about. For twenty seconds or more we just stood there, sizing each other up. Then she gave a sort of little sigh, and she said:

'All right; I can try it.' She didn't sound very happy about it. Still, I knew she had come down on the right side of the fence, and that was all that mattered for the moment.

'Good. Well, keep your ears open. Do you get any time off during the day?'

'Two till four, as a rule,' she said.

'And d'you know The Honeypot in the Strand?' She nodded. 'I'll be there at half-past three to-morrow,' I said.

I went out into the little hall and listened at the front door for a moment She stood and listened with me.

'Half a tick; I'll peep out,' she said. She peeped out, and then she jerked her head for me to get along.

'You coming?' I said. She shook her head.

'Got the bed to see to.'

I slipped outside and went off towards the stairs. When I'd gone a few yards, I heard the door open behind me. Why, I don't know, but it gave me a slightly uncomfortable feeling all of a sudden. I looked round, and Florrie was standing there. She beckoned to me, and I went back.

'Here—you left this,' she said. And she pushed the notes I'd offered her into my hand, and then shut the door.

CHAPTER

9

IT CUTS BOTH WAYS: AGAINST THE INTEREST AND, IF YOU'RE NOT too blasé, the excitement of a job like this, you often have to set off hours of boredom. You don't have to mind waiting for circumstances to shape your next move, instead of being allowed to shape it yourself. And the more active you are by disposition, the harder it is to wait and to go on waiting indefinitely, if you have to, for something to happen. That's only when you can't see far enough ahead, of course, to plan things out properly. But there are other times when everything seems to cut and dry itself as you go along.

This began to look like the kind of case that wanted to make its own opportunities without any help from me; so if I should happen to miss any of the cues, I knew I shouldn't get them given to me again.

After I'd left Florrie I went downstairs into the lounge and along the passage beside the grill room. I stood there for a while behind the glass partition, so that I could see into the room without being seen from inside. Presently I saw them, my three caballeros, over against the far wall. They were still eating; so I went back into the bar and got a drink.

The oracle of the turf had gone off duty, and I went and sat at a table so that I could keep the main door to the grill room covered, and would still be able to side-slip into the lounge if the caballeros should take it in their heads to start coming back through the bar.

I must have sat there, I should think, about twenty minutes, all the time on the *qui vive*, but without really realizing it. There was a calypso band playing in the restaurant beyond the grill; I could just hear it—or rather, I noticed whenever it stopped playing—and people were moving in and out of the bar; but somehow I didn't really take them in as I would have done in the usual way, out of my unnatural curiosity.

Every so often I got up and checked the position of things in the grill room. Presently I saw Wirth signing his bill; so I went back and sat down again, and I waited there, ready to duck out into the lounge in case they came my way. But they didn't; they went straight out into the corridor and past where I was sitting on the other side of the screen. I wanted very badly to take a look at the unknown quantity, but I didn't get a chance. They went by and turned across the lounge towards the lifts.

I gave them what I guessed to be enough time and distance; then I got up and went into the lounge. The three of them were just stepping into the lift. I walked over and looked at the indicator: it reached 4 just as I got there. I hung around till it came down again, just to make sure it was empty, then I went over to the news stand. I bought some cigarettes and an evening paper and a copy of *Time*, so it wouldn't hang too heavy on my hands; then I went back into the bar to wait.

I took a stool at the buffet end of the bar, and looked at my watch; it was twenty-past nine, and that inner man had gone back to the conversation about food. I shut him up with a slice of pie and some salad; then I pushed some lager after it; and just to make sure there'd be no further remarks, I took the barman up on a suggestion about cheese.

I kept *Time* propped up in front of me while I ate, and every so often I turned over the pages. Once in a while I even read a few lines at the top of a page; if I read on any further the lift doors went out of my line of vision.

At the end of about an hour I was bored stiff with seeing those doors open and shut, open and shut; and then, when the clock over the lifts showed nearly a quarter-to-eleven, they opened once more and Speyr stepped out with the golden-haired man of mystery. There was no sign of Wirth.

Speyr gave in his cloakroom check and they got their things. The mystery man had a camel-hair overcoat, as I'd have expected, and a spotted scarf. Then they went outside together.

I'd paid my bill, so I said good night to the barman and went out through the side entrance. I stopped in the doorway to scout round, and there they were, making for a car parked not ten feet from where I'd left my own.

I had to let them go, and then I made a dash for it; but by the time I'd got started, they were well away and getting out of sight in the traffic. It was tricky; I didn't want to lose them, but I'd got to keep my distance. I soon spotted a conspiracy among the traffic lights to try and mess me up whenever they got a chance; and at Marble Arch they nearly managed it. By the time I got round to the corner by the west gate of the Park, there was only just the dot of a tail-light to follow far off down Bayswater Road. I offered up a prayer to St. Christopher, which he took, and he got me safely over the next mile in about seventy seconds. By that time the car ahead was just turning off into a side street; so from there on I followed pretty cautiously.

We were in the Bayswater boarding house country now; every street looked like the one before, and every house like the one next to it; and all of them looked as dingy as each other.

When we got into one of the terraces near Paddington, the car in front of me stopped; and for the first time the traffic lights gave a sign of co-operation; they blocked me comfortably about thirty yards away; and I sat there and watched Speyr and his friend go into one of the houses.

I parked my car a little way away, then I walked back slowly past the house they'd gone into, just to give it a look over. There was a lighted sign hanging over the doorway, which said, rather hopefully, 'Hotel Excelsior.' I hung about for a little while, and then I went in under this strange device and had a look round.

It was scruffier altogether than Bambrough House, and I didn't imagine they'd offer much objection to my having no luggage, if it turned out I should need to spend the night there.

The front door was propped open with an old shell-case, and through an inner glass door I could see a shabby-looking hall. I pushed open this inner door, and I cocked an ear for some sound of life; but there didn't seem to be any. There was an open hatch in the wall with a card pinned over it which said 'Office.' But there wasn't anyone inside, and you couldn't blame them; there was a dismal, decaying atmosphere about the whole place.

I came in quietly, and I eased the glass door back to stop it flapping; then I stood there, listening to the silence and debating whether to ring the bell by the office and see what sort of apparition it might call forth, or whether to chance my arm upstairs and leave the dead in peace below.

The staircase was straight ahead of me, so I went on up. At the top of the stairs there was a passage running left and right, with rooms on either side of it; it looked as if two houses had been knocked into one, and the passage made through both of them.

The shorter end of the passage was more or less in darkness. Down the middle of it there was a narrow strip of carpet; it was thin and ragged and wouldn't have deadened the steps of a cat. Still, my steps were almost dead to start with; not that there seemed to be anything worth my precautions. Only two of the rooms showed any light under the door, and I wasn't going to bother about the others; not to begin with, at any rate.

Judging by the snores coming from the first room, there must have been a sow asleep inside with her litter. In the other room a man and a woman were talking; the woman, that's to say, was letting fly, and every few seconds telling the man, who hardly opened his mouth, to shut up.

I went back to the top of the stairs and I looked over the banisters; there still wasn't any sign of life down below, so I started off down the other leg of the passage.

One of the rooms was dark inside, but I could see through the open door that it was a sitting-room. There were lights showing under three of the other doors, and I listened for some time at the first, but I didn't hear anything; so I went out on to the second. This time I could hear a woman humming softly to herself and moving about the room. That didn't seem to fit the bill either, so I went across to the third floor. Just as I got there, there was a click, and the door swung open slowly with a creak.

My heart and I stopped more or less as one man, and I pan-caked against the wall. I could hear voices in the room just for a second; then I saw a camel-haired sleeve pushed against the door, and it was shut again. I couldn't catch what had been said, but I could tell by the intonation that one of the voices was Speyr's.

Just where I'd been trying to scrabble through the wall, there was a curtain hanging over a sort of recess; and by the time I began to draw breath again, it was no surprise to me to find I was behind this curtain, along with a lot of buckets and brooms and cleaning things.

I could still hear them talking in the room, but I couldn't hear what it was about. Sometimes there was a gap in the conversation, and sometimes they both seemed to be speaking at once. Then presently I heard something else. I couldn't make it out at first; it was very faint. And then I realized it was a musical box. It played a little chirripy tune of about eight or ten bars, and then it stopped. And then, after a few seconds it went on again, the same tune.

When it came to the end again, they went on talking once more, but I still couldn't hear what they were saying. They talked, I should think, for ten minutes or more; and it sounded as if one or other of them was getting fairly worked up. Then, after a few minutes, I heard the springs of a bed creak, and there was a sort of exclamation—a kind of loud gasp, it seemed like; then there was silence; then a little scuffling noise just for a few seconds, and the bed creaked again.

I waited for at least a full minute without hearing another sound. Then there was the faint creak of someone opening the door, and I heard the light switched off inside the room. Some-body's footsteps went away down the landing, and then they stopped; I guessed they were at the top of the stairs; then they went on down.

I still waited a bit after the footsteps had gone; but there seemed no sense in standing there indefinitely with my face stuck into a cleaner's mop; so after a little while I recon-noitred through the curtain; and then I stepped out into the passage.

The door of the room where they'd been talking was standing open a little way, but there was still not a sound from inside. As I slid into the room I pushed the door to behind me without quite shutting it—I didn't want it to start creaking again—then I turned on the light; and there was Speyr. He was lying on his back across the bed; his feet were pointing towards the door on one side and his head was drooping down almost out of sight on the other; his arms were hanging backwards with his hands touching the floor.

I reached over quickly and lugged him back on to the bed. But I needn't have taken the trouble. He was dead all right. It looked like a case of bare-handed strangling; the finger-marks were still there in the skin round his neck and underneath his ears, and his whole face was the colour of a bad bruise. He wasn't at all a pretty sight.

It was only thinking about it later on that I felt rather a ghoul; there was hardly time to feel anything at the moment. I went very quickly through all his pockets, but there wasn't anything of any use to me in them. Then I saw, lying on the floor beside the bed, a cigarette-lighter, a silver one. It had on it the initials J. Y. E. Speyr's—and I had good reason to remember it, was a little red plastic thing. This J. Y. E. model looked like something worth keeping, so I put it in my pocket.

Speyr's brief-case was lying open on a chair with some letters and files scattered about. I stuffed all these into the case and put it on the bed to take with me. Then I went through the hanging cupboard, and after that through every drawer in the room; there was absolutely nothing anywhere. Except for his brushes, and one or two things he had put out on the dressing-table, all his things were still in his suitcase. I went through that too; and if it'd been a grain of rice that I was looking for, I'll guarantee I would have found it.

I went through the bedding and the bed; and I frisked the curtains, and the inside of the chimney; I looked in every conceivable place where there could have been a musical box; and I knew then that if there had been one in the room, it wasn't there any longer. Perhaps there never had been. If not, my imagination must have been working overtime.

It was while I was just thinking about this that I suddenly felt something touching my sleeve. But my imagination wasn't taking any more; it just showed the whites of its eyes and passed out. But all that had happened was that the curtain was blowing to and fro in front of the open window. The door behind me creaked gently open in the draught at the same moment, and I went over to shut it. As I crossed the room I heard someone coming along the passage outside.

There wasn't even time for me to put the light out. I snatched the brief-case and went down on the far side of the bed like a snake. Speyr's hand was hanging down over the side of the bed, and it touched my neck as I lay there; it was still warm. I hardly dared to breathe, let alone shift from where I was lying; and I could hear my heart pounding as if it were out for the record.

The footsteps went on past the door, and as I looked across the floor underneath the bed, I saw a woman's feet shuffling slowly by in a pair of woolly slippers.

The door was only open a few inches, but it was enough to show the light was on inside. Maybe that was what attracted her attention; anyway, she stopped. Then I heard her shuffling back; and she stopped again. I saw her feet just outside the door; then I heard the door creak again, and I saw it slowly opening . . .

Time stretched . . . and went on stretching, like a piece of elastic: then it snapped.

The woman let out a sort of gasping cry, and then she turned round, and I heard her stumbling away towards the stairs. As she went she began to screech, not like a human being though, like a bird—a bird mad with fright.

I've noticed before that when something dangerous happens, particularly if it happens unexpectedly, the speed and cutting-edge of one's common sense operate like the slash of a razor. What you do instinctively—or what seems instinctive, anyway —would take some careful thinking out in the ordinary way. There were several mistakes I could have made now; I could have turned off the light; or I could have shut the door; or made some other move that would have shown there was someone actually in the room when the woman had looked in. But I didn't do any of these things. I took Speyr's case, then I whipped out his handkerchief and with my own, one in each hand, I pulled up the sash and got out on to the balcony. I threw his handkerchief back into the room, then I pushed the sash down again from outside, and I ran along past the windows of the house next door. I could hear the woman still screeching and blubbering in the distance. I don't suppose the whole thing took more than about thirty seconds; but they were thirty of the most unpleasant I've ever spent.

The balcony ran straight along from house to house, and next door a big TO LET sign was tied on the front of the balcony. When I got behind this sign I was out of sight from the pavement—it was only about fifteen feet below—and out of the radius of the street lamp opposite. Beyond the empty house I could see another, with a broken window. The only thing to stop me getting there was a woman dawdling about on the pavement with a dog. You can never tell with either species how long it'll take 'em to make up their minds, and neither of them seemed to be in a hurry . . .

I looked back when I got to the broken window, and there they were, both of 'em, still undecided.

There was no board on this part of the balcony, but the house seemed to be empty all the same. The window opened easily enough, and I stepped through into the room. From what I could see of it, by the light of the street lamp shining in from outside, it looked as if there'd been a bomb somewhere nearby; but they didn't seem to have done much in the way of repairs; the place smelt damp and unlived-in, and half the ceiling seemed to be on the floor. I trod carefully over all this mess and got outside on to the landing; then I began to feel my way down the stairs.

At the half-landing I could see a slit of light in the hall where the lamp outside was shining through the letter box. Just as I began to fumble my way down the second flight, towards the ground floor, there was a piercing whistle somewhere. It sounded quite close, rising and falling; and then there was suddenly a burst of song, and that was blotted out by a snatch of talk and atmospherics: somewhere in the house someone was fiddling with a radio. After a few seconds they hit on some French dance music and they let it go at that.

Nothing I should have enjoyed more in the ordinary way, but I didn't feel much like dancing at the moment, certainly not by myself. All the same, I think the music must have had a slightly intoxicating effect, because I suddenly did a sort of accidental *glissade* in the darkness, and it was only by a miracle that I didn't crash down the stairs.

The music stopped dead; I stood absolutely still. Then, quite quietly, a door opened in the hall by the side of the stairs, and a man stood there silhouetted against the light of a gas fire in the room behind him. I saw him cock his head and listen, and he looked down the hall towards the front door. Then he called out:

'Emmy? That you, Emmy?'

The light in the room was off, so I couldn't see his face. He had no coat on, only a sort of cardigan, and he was wearing bedroom slippers. He looked as if he might have been a caretaker.

When Emmy didn't show up, he turned his head round rather stiffly and looked at me instead. We stared at each other, and neither of us said anything. A black cat curled itself round his legs and jumped up between the banisters on to the stairs. He clicked his fingers and called to it softly:

'Tib, Tib, Tib—where you goin', Tibby?'

Without taking his eyes off me, he reached out to get hold of the cat; but he wasn't even in the right direction, because I could see now that he was stone blind.

The cat was curling itself round my legs and was purring. He went on calling it, and presently it went back and got through the banisters again. He must have felt it as it went by, because he stooped and picked it up. Then he went back into the room with the cat in his arms, and he shut the door.

I waited till *le jazz* had started up again; then I went on down to the front door and let myself out as quietly as I could. A few yards away the woman with the dog was still standing there, like Patience hanging round a lamp-post.

I went back past the Hotel Excelsior, and as far as I could see, the place looked as if nothing had happened since I had left. When I got to the corner of the street, though, I turned smack into a copper; he was coming along pretty quickly for one of his kind, and there was a man padding along beside him with only his shirt and trousers on. As I looked back I saw them both go into the hotel.

CHAPTER

10

BY THE TIME I GOT HOME IT WAS ABOUT HALF-PAST ELEVEN. So many things had happened so quickly that it might have been days, not just a matter of hours, since I'd started out. And where had I got to? Seemed to me as if I was almost back where I'd begun. How had I gone wrong? I'd kept my teeth in Speyr's coat-tails till death us did part; only, as usual, death had barged in before anyone was ready. Still, as long as a few faint traces of the scent were left, it gave my nose something to twitch on. And now, of course, there was Florrie's nose as well; not that I was counting much on her olfactory powers.

I got myself a drink, and I sat down to try and think things out. But it didn't work; they just wouldn't come out; they stayed jammed up like a wire puzzle, with bits and pieces sticking out in different directions and refusing to come together. There was nothing as far as I could see in Speyr's papers—and I went through them pretty thoroughly—to throw any light on the subject. The silver lighter didn't seem to help much either. There was nothing you could identify it by, except that there was an odd triangular pattern chased on the sides.

The letters in Speyr's case seemed mostly to do with business matters; it looked, as Herrick had said, as if he'd had something to do with printing. Most of the letters were in German, though some were in English from English firms. But none of them explained any of the things I wanted to know.

That pawnbroker, for instance, dishing out secret addresses: just where and how did he fit into the picture? and what was Wirth's game, with his Renoirs, and his gun tucked away in his underwear? And why should Speyr, of all people, the goose carrying the golden egg, why on earth should he have had his neck wrung?

Speyr's papers didn't seem to give a clue to any of these questions. In fact, the only thing among them that looked like being of any interest was a postcard with a British stamp on it; it was postmarked S.W.3, and the date of the mark was eight days old. The card was addressed to Speyr at the same address in Linz as he had written in the register at Bamborough House. All it said on the card was:

How about the Villa d'Este? 12.45 *on the* 16*th*, *unless I hear from you.*

It was just signed 'J,' like the inscription in his Beethoven's *Briefe*. The card was dated the same day as the postmark, but there was no address to show where it had come from.

I looked at my evening paper; it gave the date as the 15th, which was probably the only objective statement in the whole thing. I was disposed to believe it, anyway; and as the time was now just after twelve, here it was, the 16th already.

Before I went to bed I wrote out for Herrick an account of what had happened up to the time I'd left the Astoria. I didn't say anything about what had happened after that, or how I'd managed to get hold of Speyr's papers. I merely said 'here they are.' I saw no reason either, to mention the lighter that I'd found, because that would have involved going into events at the Excelsior Hotel; and the last thing I wanted just now was to get involved with the police. For one thing, if it got about that I might be a material witness in the case, that would be the end of my usefulness to Herrick; and for another, I wasn't too happy about being, as it were, a fore-and-aft accessory to Speyr's murder.

For once, I suppose because I was still a bit on edge, I didn't sleep very well, and I was up and waiting for the boy when he came with the newspapers. But there was nothing in them. Impatience had been gnawing at my vitals for quite a time, and had made a pretty good meal by now; still, it wasn't to be satisfied yet. So I consoled myself with the idea that the longer the papers kept quiet, the more likely it would be that J, whoever J might be, would stick to the Villa d'Este appointment.

I wondered whether J meant a man or a woman. The handwriting on the card might have belonged to either. The only way I could think of deciding about it was to turn up at the Villa d'Este and see what happened. If it meant *the* Villa d'Este, I should be a bit late. If it was some little suburban cot—there must be thousands called the Villa d'Este, to the lasting curiosity of their inhabitants—I should miss it altogether. For me the only practical possibility looked like a little restaurant that I knew called the Villa d'Este, which was in Greek Street. So I rang up and booked a table there in the name of Winter, that being the first that came into my head—I suppose because I was looking out of the window at the bare black trees in the studio garden and at the patch of cold sky showing over the roof-tops.

When I went out I went first of all to the bank and drew some money. Five of the notes, nice new crisp ones, I put into an envelope, and I sealed it up. I felt pretty sure that Florrie wouldn't take a farthing if she knew I was giving it to her; not without a great song-and-dance, anyway. But if she had been able to do what I hoped she had done, it might well be worth the reward. In any case, she would have been taking quite a risk, and I didn't see why she should have to have taken it for nothing; after all, it was the Treasury's generosity, not mine.

The next thing I did was to get an evening paper. The story had broken quietly in the stop press: 'Unknown man found dead in Paddington hotel . . . death believed due to foul play . . . investigation by C.I.D. officials proceeding, etc. . . .' That was all.

It was a curious feeling, not altogether a comfortable one either, to know that every copper I passed after that was on the look-out for Speyr's killer; or probably would be in a few hours. And what alibi had I got, in case they made a mistake? It'd be no use to invent a story, however ingenious it might be. The one thing I needed—and any story would come to pieces without it—would be corroboration; which would be the one thing I couldn't get. For about the twentieth time I went over the whole thing second by second. I still couldn't spot anywhere I'd gone wrong; except perhaps in the very fact of being so confident. Still, I knew that it would have been a damn sight worse to have had doubts at the back of my mind.

I stopped at the Sheridan on my way and gave the porter Speyr's case and my own report for Herrick. Then I rang the number he'd given me, and the same chap answered as before. He still wasn't taking any chances with his vowels; every one was a neat ellipse. I asked for the stuff to be collected.

I'd said in the report that I hadn't given up hope altogether; but looking at the facts on paper, I'm bound to say there didn't seem much in them to give Herrick a great deal of confidence. I still had a few threads on my fingers, I said. I didn't tell him they looked as if they were of purest gossamer. I felt it was pretty obvious.

As I walked back towards Soho the sun struggled out and gave an invalid's grin. It didn't last long; it just took that bleak, chalky look out of the sky for a little while, but it reminded me that, sometimes there are other seasons besides the beginning of winter, even in England.

I don't know if you know the Villa d'Este. It's got a small place just inside the door where you can sit and wait and ask three times for a drink before anybody brings you one. Because I was early I got a dry sherry under the record. I sipped it and sat looking at a picture of *the* Villa d'Este by an artist who obviously must have had other means of support.

Very soon people began to drift in. Some of them went straight through to eat, and some of them sat about where I was, waiting, but rather more hopefully, I imagined. There was only room for about a dozen people to sit, and by a quarter to one, according to the clock on the wall, there was a quiet-looking American boy with two loud English girls; and there was a frog with bulging eyes and the Legion of Honour in his buttonhole; and a Wren; and a hatless man in corduroys and thick spectacles, who was armed (for attack, I guessed, rather than defence) with a paper copy of *Vers et Prose*. There was a nice-looking girl dressed in brown velvet and with the same sort of eyes; and there was a thin middle-aged Jewish woman who seemed burdened with sorrows; one of them was obviously her son who was a grumpy-looking chap with glasses.

Every so often a waiter peered at us through a curtain, and after a bit I asked him, loud and clear, whether Mister Winter had arrived.

'Not yet,' he said.

I sat back and tried not to look impatient. I tried not to look anything, in fact, and not too carefully at anyone. All I could do was wait, and try to spot something which might suggest I wasn't on a wild-goose chase after all.

By about one o'clock most of the bunch who had been waiting had been claimed; a few others had come in to take their places, and now they were gradually being collected, too. All of a sudden there seemed to be only four of us left—the girl in brown velvet, and the American with his two honeys. Then another American blew in and took these three in [illegible]

I began to wonder if I hadn't better chuck it. If by a[illegible] chance J was this girl opposite, the odds were she might be in for a bit of trouble, and I should probably be the cause of it. Somehow I didn't like that idea. Somehow, too, I seemed to be getting soft; so somehow I should have to kick myself in the pants without letting her see. If she was J, it'd be more than a miracle; it'd be a sign for me to forget my upbringing and do what I'd got to do like a swine, if it had got to be done that way.

The waiter looked at us round the curtain again. I said to him:

'Mister Winter did book a table, I suppose?'

He checked it on the list.

'At quarter-to, sir,' he said.

It was quite genuinely by accident that I happened to catch the brown velvet girl's eye just at that second, and in a rueful kind of way we half-smiled at each other: it looked as if we were both being stood up. I said to the waiter:

'I'll give him another few minutes.'

The man nodded and slid his head back through the curtains like a tortoise going into retreat. I pretended to fiddle with my watch. The girl looked at hers—she'd looked at it half a dozen times already—and compared it with the clock on the wall.

'That's slow,' I said; it was, incidentally.

We both smiled again. Then, I suppose because she felt a bit embarrassed—she was sitting straight in front of me, facing the light—she took out her mirror and had a look at herself. And as she opened her bag I saw on the flap a gold J as big as a meat-hook.

I gave myself another minute to calm down and think out the next move; and while I was doing this, she looked at her watch again, and then she got up and went through the curtains into the restaurant.

A couple of women came in just afterwards, and I followed them inside. The girl was sitting over against the far wall, looking at the menu. It seemed as if the two women who'd just come in were going to be unlucky. The waiter shrugged at them as if he was ducking a smack on the neck; this apparently meant the place was full.

'All right. Give these ladies Mister Winter's table,' I said. 'I'll find somewhere.'

I went over to where the girl was sitting—she was still reading the menu—and I said:

'Would you mind very much if I sat here? My table seems to have gone.'

She sort of murmured and smiled, so I sat down; and when she'd finished with the menu she handed it over to me.

'What's good?' I said.

'Spaghetti, if you like it,' she said.

I liked it; and while I was waiting for it, I flicked some crumbs off the cloth and a plate with them; the plate was an accident.

She saved it neatly. I noticed as she put her hand out that there weren't any rings; didn't tell me much, except that it was quite a pretty mitt without any.

'Well caught,' I said.

'Not much room on here, is there? How about disposing of this?' she said. It was a bottle of mayonnaise.

'Unless you want to polish some of the furniture,' I said.

So in this and that way we got talking. She was obviously better trained in spaghetti than I was. She flipped hers round her fork like an old hand, and she could hold a glass at the same time. I needed one hand for the fork and one for the plate, and I could have done with another to keep my head in line.

If either of us felt any curiosity about our hosts not having turned up, we seemed to get over it pretty soon. Now and again she looked past my shoulder down the room for a second or two, but I couldn't kid myself that she showed the slightest sign of expecting anyone or of feeling anxious. She seemed to be doing merely what I was doing—looking casually around.

I still didn't really believe she could be the J that I was looking for. J's a common enough initial, after all, and somehow I couldn't see her and Speyr together. There was nothing in the least provincial about her, not as there'd seemed to be about him. And I still couldn't get out of my head the nasty picture that I had of him lying there on the bed, with his blue face and the whites of his eyes watery and bloodshot.

The idea of this girl being mixed up in any sort of monkey business, let alone murder, didn't seem to fit in at all. She was very calm, very self-possessed, considering the way we had met, which presumably wasn't the sort of introduction she was used to. She might have been anything between twenty-five and thirty; something like a Goya to look at, only the make-up was better; a type I find it only too easy to fall for, dark and very pretty, and yet, without looking in the least hard-faced, with something slightly sardonic in her expression. Maybe it was the eyes, maybe it was the mouth; I don't know: or maybe it was my imagination because I happen to like them that way.

As I say, there were no rings on her fingers and no bells on her toes either; but she should have had music wherever she went because, as I found out pretty soon, it undoubtedly meant a good deal in her life. It seemed that we shared quite a number of affections—and prejudices—in music: Verdi, for instance, was an affection; most of Wagner was a prejudice. All the same, I envied her Bayreuth, which somehow I had always missed; but she had never been to Glyndebourne, so we were quits.

'You going to the Schnabel concert?' I said.

'I love Schnabel,' she said, 'and I love Mozart; but I won't queue, not even for nylons.' She smiled.

I only realized then how seldom that happened; not that she seemed sulky, exactly, but she had a sort of unspecific gravity; it was hard to define, but it gave her a dignity and detachment which I rather liked. And somewhere or other I guessed she'd got quite a good sense of humour tucked away.

'If you don't think it altogether too brash of me, and you'd really like to go, I've got two seats,' I said, hoping to God I could lay hands on a couple somewhere. So after a certain amount of polite this and that, it was fixed.

'You'd better have my number,' I said, 'in case anything goes wrong.'

I gave it to her in the hope of getting her own number back. All I got, though, was her name, which was Jackson—Miss Jackson. I told her mine, the second name which I'd dropped at the font and hadn't bothered to pick up again till this moment.

She wouldn't let me pay for her lunch—which, considering I'd got damn all out of it, seemed fair enough—and outside we said good-bye.

CHAPTER

11

IT WAS JUST AFTER TWO; I HAD AN HOUR AND A HALF TO KILL before I needed to be at The Honeypot. Whenever I've got time on my hands I usually go to have a look at some pictures; so this time I thought, why not at Wirth's? If the pictures up in his room at the Astoria were anything to go by, I might run into something quite interesting: might even run into trouble. So I walked down through Soho, and as I went along I first got a whiff of roasting coffee, and then of baking bread; and sometimes the smell of an *epicerie* smelling like they smell in France. It was cold, and the wind had swept the pavements clean and dry. All it had left were those little polygot groups which seem to sprout without the slightest encouragement all along Greek Street at any time of the day or night.

Going from Soho to St. James's isn't just exchanging one social *milieu* or one set of habits for another: it's a long distance journey between the cosmopolitan and the English temperament. The neighbourhood of Wirth's gallery was the antithesis of Greek Street. It was in a secluded well-bred little thoroughfare, and the gallery had just one picture in its window—a big warm Vuillard, and I wanted it.

I went inside and looked round. There was a large room in the front and a smaller one behind it; and at the back, up a few stairs, there was what I imagined was the office.

In the front room there was a mixed exhibition of French paintings, and in the back room there were some English water-colours. But either the pictures weren't up to scratch or I wasn't. I sat for some time in front of a painting of St. Cloud by David without really taking it in at all. I realized that what I was really thinking about was how much, or rather, how little, I'd picked up during lunch; and I wondered whether it was that J hadn't got much to give or whether I'd been missing things.

It wasn't a very productive train of thought, and presently it was interrupted by Wirth walking in from the street. He went through into the back room and up the stairs into the office. So I moved into the back room too, but as he'd shut the office door behind him, I just had to look at the water-colours.

There were two by Samuel Palmer that looked good enough to eat. One of them was sold, and I had a sinking feeling in my cheque book as I stood and looked at the other. I don't know whether Wirth sensed what I was thinking. Anyway, he came back into the room presently and stood idling about in the background. I could feel him getting ready for a few words, and I was looking at the Palmer again when they came to the surface, in a very soft, hoarse voice.

'You enterested in Semuel Palmer?' he said.

The intonation was more marked than the accent, but I couldn't tell exactly what the mark was: Mittel-Europa was the best guess I could make. At close quarters his face looked like the face of a big pale baby—a baby with rimless glasses and little hard honey-coloured eyes. He had a very clean, spruce look about him, partly due to his tailor, and partly because he was as hairless as a Dutch cheese.

I didn't like him, and that wasn't just being subjective; he was unctuous, and at the same time too damn knowledgeable; though that was unfair perhaps; he didn't only know about pictures—he certainly did that—he felt about them too, as if they were things to be loved. Maybe he was right. Anyway, he spoke sense about them, not just sales talk.

'Wait, I show you sumpting,' he said, and he slid up into the office, and then came back again with a large piece of brown paper. He put it down on the table as if it were a sheet of spun glass; then he turned his face close to mine and looked right at me, like an owl looking at its breakfast. I tried not to laugh. He nodded silently, then he opened out the brown paper, and inside it there was as pretty a Palmer as ever I saw, rich and ripe, and yet curiously sombre. It was an evening landscape, full of golds and pinks and thick green lichens and shadows that looked as if he'd washed them in with burgundy. There was absolutely no sign of life though, just a feeling of desolation and the aftermath of great heat.

I looked at it a long time. I should be a damn fool not to buy it, I knew. So did Wirth, but we neither of us said anything. He was too good a tactician, and I was just dumb with the enjoyment of looking at it. Then I said to him:

'What's it worth?' He told me the price. 'Not how much,' I said, 'what's it worth?'

From staring at me like an owl, he looked suddenly like bursting out crying, full of injury. 'I wouldn't give that for it if it were a Botticelli,' I said.

He tried to look indifferent. 'No?' he said.

'No. I tell you what I'll do though,' I said, 'I'll make you an offer.' And I made it.

'You're choking,' he said.

I hadn't noticed anything; still, I let it go. He shook his head, *molto doloroso;* then he sliced my offer and I sliced back, neither of us moving a muscle. And so, after a bit of this and that, I got it, my lovely Palmer; and it hangs up here in front of me while I write, just as a reminder of all this business, in case I should ever forget it.

We discussed framing and mounting. I had pretty definite ideas, and so had Wirth. We compromised on having it mounted his way, but I was to come in and have another look at it before we finally decided on a frame.

'Coupla days I have it mounted so goot you won't rekernize,' he said.

'That's what I'm afraid of,' I said: 'Still . . .' I didn't really mind, as a matter of fact, because it gave me an opening to keep up our acquaintance.

'I ring you,' he said.

Then it suddenly struck me—my being a new customer, he'd want a cheque; and giving a cheque would mean giving my own name. I didn't like that very much, and I tried having no cheque book with me. I might have known it wouldn't work; he was so damned obliging, there was one laid out on the desk for me before you could say knife; and when I'd written the cheque, the suggestion of putting my address on the back was just touched on. There always comes a time in matters of this sort when you have to fall back on the truth and just hope it'll bear your weight; so I wrote my address.

For all he knew, we parted friends. What annoyed me was not so much having to tell the truth about myself—he might not have been any wiser if I'd told him a lie—it was having let my private feelings, and greed at that, rush me into a position where I hadn't any alternative to the truth.

All the way to The Honeypot I was kicking myself, and by the time I got there, my conscience was black and blue.

The Honeypot's the kind of place where high tea seems to be the *plat du jour* whatever hour of the day you go there. At half-past three the place wasn't full, but there were four or five people there who seemed to feel an urge for Hamburger steak and chips. For me the smell of steamy food and tea in urns was as good as a meal—or as bad. I sat up on a stool at the counter and asked for a cup of coffee.

There was no sign of Florrie. So I decided to give her half an hour, and then, if she hadn't turned up, I'd go along to the Astoria again later.

I hadn't doled out more than a couple of minutes when she came in. She came straight up to where I was and sat on the next stool. I asked her what she'd like. She wouldn't answer me directly; she spoke to the girl behind the counter instead.

'Got any Horlicks?' she said.

Now that we were together, in public, she seemed to feel rather shy about it. As soon as the girl had gone for the Horlicks, she pushed an envelope along the counter under cover of her bag and slid it into my newspaper.

'I copied it all out, what you wanted,' she said. She spoke very quietly and she still wouldn't look in my direction. 'I didn't like to borrow it in the end,' she said; '—you know.'

It was better than nothing.

'Fine. That's excellent,' I said. 'I've got something for you too.' I pushed over the envelope which I'd put the money in. She looked suspicious at once.

'What's this?' she said.

'Don't open now; wait till you get home,' I said. I could tell without looking at her that she was quizzing me pretty sharply; I took no notice. She hesitated a long time about the envelope; and then in the end, rather reluctantly, she put it in her bag.

The girl came back and planked a mug of Horlicks down in front of her. Florrie waited till she'd gone away, then she said:

'Here, I got the wind up though. He came in once; I didn't expect him.'

'What happened?' I said.

'Nothing. Don't think he spotted anything. Hope not, anyway.' She smiled rather abruptly; then she leaned over with her nose in her mug and said: 'Here, after you left last night he came upstairs again, and there was two other fellas with him.

I didn't say anything; I let her carry on. She happened to have passed them just as they were going in the door, and she'd taken a good look at the shorter one because he was new to her. The other chap, the tall one, she'd seen before; he was often up there. She hadn't seen anything more, but some time afterwards she'd heard them all three talking.

'What did you hear?' I said.

'Well, I was in the service pantry, see; that's next door. I couldn't tell actually what they was saying; just sounded like they were having a row or something.'

'Why d'you say that?'

'Well, you know . . . the way their voices were.'

'And you didn't hear anything else?'

'All I heard was when they left. I was in the passage again, and Mister Wirth, he was just showing them out. He said something about they'd meet again this evening.'

'Where? D'you suppose he meant at the hotel?'

'Well, he said somewhere about six, I think. He usually comes back about then.'

She was full of the drama of the situation, a bit too full. I could see the first thing I should have to teach her would be how to relax. No one except me could have heard a word she said. A couple of women and a child were sitting at a table munching; and further down the counter a chauffeur was picking his teeth over a pool's forecast; there was no one else in the place, yet all the time she was talking, she kept glancing this way and that way. Finally I said to her:

'Now look: take it easy, Florrie, there's nothing to worry about, really,' I said.

Poor kid, you could see she'd worked herself up about it and it was starting to worry her. She smiled at me over the top of the mug.

'Hope it was all right, what I did,' she said.

'You just carry on as you are, with your ears pinned back. You're doing very nicely,' I said.

She gave that funny little smile of hers again, and she sat there stirring her Horlicks as if it was a Christmas pudding. Presently she looked down sideways at the newspaper under my elbow.

'Hullo, 'nother murder,' she said. I saw her eye had lit on the stop press; she was craning round to read the end of it. 'Doesn't say how he died.'

It was on the tip of my tongue to tell her.

'You'll have to wait for next week's instalment,' I said. I finished my delicious cup of synthetic coffee and I got down off the stool. 'Now, look, if anything funny happens——'

'What sort of funny?' she said; she looked a little apprehensive just for a moment.

'You've got a sense of humour,' I said. 'If there's anything you don't like, anything you need to tell me about urgently, just call me at this number and say something—so that I'll know. Say you've got toothache or something. Understand?' I tore off a corner of the newspaper and wrote my number on it. 'Don't lose it,' I said.

'And ask for Mr. Cornelius, eh?'

She said it looking so innocent that she had me off my guard for a second. Then she gave a flickering sort of smile, and she pointed to the inside of my glove lying on the counter. You could just see the name inside, written across the back of the wrist; it was so small and so washed out, though, that I'd forgotten about it altogether. Then she said:

'Not yours, maybe?'

'You just keep on believing that,' I said. Then I paid the bill, and I folded my newspaper over her envelope and pushed it down into my coat pocket.

'So long,' Florrie said; and I left her with her nose well down in her cup.

It looked like a question of killing time again. For once I thought I could see ahead for two or three consecutive steps, and it seemed a good chance to try and work out some way of negotiating them without breaking an ankle; or perhaps having something else broken for me.

The difficulty in a case of this sort is always the same: you can't make a long-term plan of action. What you've got to be is not really a strategist, except in the broadest sense; you've got to be an opportunist. You need ingenuity and the patience of Job quite as much as you need the theorist's broader vision. But that's just one of the little differences between this kind of job in fact and in fiction. When it happens in fiction the trouble is that nobody's still for five minutes, unless they've been slugged. The narrative flows at the pace of an antelope, and nothing ever stops happening, except in the hero's cerebellum; and like the rest of him, that's usually so tough you wouldn't risk a sledge-hammer on it; though God knows, it's often a temptation.

What usually happens in fact is that there's an endless amount of hanging about with nothing to do but watch and pray, mainly for something to start. And when it does start, it probably happens at a snail's pace; except now and then when the snail seems to work itself into a frenzy and events come on in a rush. Only that very seldom lasts long, and pretty soon you find you're back watching and praying again.

It looked as if I should have to do a bit of both in the next hour or two. If Florrie had heard Wirth correctly it seemed that the next party meeting was to be in his room at the hotel at six o'clock. If so, it might give me a chance to find out one or two things I was beginning to get curious about.

I'd killed an hour and a half since lunch, and now I'd got to do the same again. This time the kill took place in the smoking-room of the Sheridan. I sat there, deep down in one of the plum-coloured leather armchairs, and I filled my lap with all the magazines in reach. I decided I'd keep Florrie's envelope till I got home. There was no action I could take on it now, anyway, and I wasn't keen to brandish its contents in public.

The smoking-room was very peaceful, except for the rasping breath of an aged man of letters sleeping near by. Presently I ordered tea; and soon after five o'clock I staggered up, flushed with buttered scones, and I walked back through Covent Garden to the Astoria again.

This time I gave in my hat and coat; then I went upstairs on to the balcony again and took the same table I'd had before. I ordered the same drink and I looked at the same paper; or it might have been the same for all that I noticed on its front page. I was really more intent on the froth of human kind that kept bubbling up every time the revolving doors went round.

At a quarter to six—I'd just looked at my watch for about the tenth time—the doors rolled once more and Wirth came in on the tide. He stood looking round the lounge for a few seconds, then he went over to the desk and got his key.

I saw him say something to the clerk. The clerk shook his head, and Wirth went away and got into the lift. Not a very sensational incident; still, it encouraged me to wait on for a bit. I guessed his question had been whether anyone had asked for him, and the man had said no.

And then, soon after six o'clock someone answered my prayers. He came thrusting in from outside with that busy, self-confident air which looked so big and meant so little. And just as he'd done the night before, he shied his hat and his camel-hair coat at one of the boys without waiting for a ticket, and went straight on into the lift.

After a little while, I walked downstairs and went and stood near the cloakroom. Trade was pretty brisk, and the boys were too busy checking clobber in and out to notice me standing there. But I kept an eye out for the house-dick—I'd been hanging about the place long enough during the last twenty-four hours to be a matter of some interest to anyone who happened to have a nosey disposition—and with the other eye I stripped the cloakroom still I spotted the hat and coat I was looking for. Then, when the boy who had taken them was giving up another party's clothes, I tackled his *alter ego*.

I fumbled about in my pockets and the *ego* stood there waiting for my ticket. When I couldn't produce it he tightened his lips and started to hunt for my things. Just to lend a hand, as the other boy was still busy, I slipped in at the side of the counter, humming to myself, and I twitched a likely-looking model off one of the pegs. It was a soft green felt, and it had the initials J.Y.E. inside, so it couldn't be mine. Mine hadn't any initials in it; and, come to think of it, it wasn't green either; it was brown; and there it was all of a sudden.

'Here we are,' I said to the boy.

'Okey-doke,' he said, which suggested only one answer, in the circumstances, and that was *tempora mutantur*. Still, I'm never the one to start an argument, so I just thanked him for shuffling me into my coat, and I left it at that. I found the ticket just as I was leaving; it had been in my pocket all the time, so I handed it back to him.

'Okey-doke,' he said.

Outside in the street I bought an evening paper, but there was very little in it. The story which I'd read earlier in the stop press had worked its way on to the front page, but no more details had been added.

There were some letters on the mat when I got home, and a card from some optimist who had hoped to sell me a vacuum cleaner. When I'd been through the letters I sat down at my desk and I pulled out Florrie's envelope. At the back of the envelope—I imagine they had been caught up somehow in the flap—there were half a dozen Health and Unemployment stamps, about ten bob's worth, all told. There was nothing I could do, except keep them till I saw her next time. So I put them in my wallet and took her list out of the envelope.

It was written in pencil, and the writing was very weak and untidy, as if she'd scribbled it all down in a hurry. It looked as if there might have been a couple of hundred names and addresses. Under E there were only about six; none had all the initials I was looking for—J.Y.E.—but there was a Jimmy Earle, with an address somewhere in Sheen; and underneath it in brackets—'Earle's Garage,' with a different address; then two more telephone numbers without addresses.

Under J there was not a single thing of any interest. A few of the other entries, mostly shops and business places, I knew by name. But Earle still looked to me the most promising. Whether it would keep its promise I couldn't tell until to-morrow.

By the time to-morrow came I had other things to do before I could start to find out. Problems of food and drink and clothing had to be gone into with Mrs. Wellington; there were letters to write or to leave unanswered; and there was this and that to see to. First of all I had to ring a man about a dog that I hoped would be able to smell out a couple of seats for the Schnabel concert. The man said the dog said, well, perhaps if I went along . . . so presently I went along. The dog wore glasses and spoke with a Scotch accent, but looked like a French poodle. Still, he was as good as his bark, and I got my two seats.

Then, as the place where he hung out was close to the Astoria, I thought I'd go along on the chance of finding Florrie and give her back her stamps.

As I went past the bookstall in the lounge I slid my eye over the midday paper, and suddenly it caught on something. It was a full-face photograph of Speyr. The morning papers hadn't had anything new on the story, but now the headlines were saying: 'Paddington Crime: victim identified.'

I read the story as I went up in the lift. The inquest had been opened and adjourned. 'Evidence given by the police . . . now revealed . . . victim was Carl Friedrich Becker, one-time prisoner of war . . . had escaped from Llandfrith Camp, Monmouthshire, in October, 1944. Becker, a 'star' prisoner, had earned privileges for good conduct . . . had avoided recapture . . . since disappeared . . .' and so on.

The lift doors slid open at the fourth floor on a lot of new possibilities. As I walked down the corridor—it seemed as long and as empty as a Dali dreamscape—the only sound I could hear was the whirring of my own thoughts.

When I got to the service pantry next to Wirth's suite, I peeked in. A waiter was standing there in front of an electric cooker; he had his back to me and he had got a chafing dish in his hand, and while he chafed, he hummed a Crosby number.

I walked back towards the lifts. I'd nearly got there when I heard someone behind me coming out of one of the rooms. I turned round, abstracted-like, as if I'd forgotten which way I'd meant to go; and about half a mile away I saw Florrie coming towards me. It wasn't till we got a few yards away from each other that she seemed to recognize me. Then she suddenly veered away through a swing door leading on to a back staircase. She was holding the door open for me when I came along, and I followed her out on to the stairs.

'I was looking for you in the pantry,' I said.

'You'll get me the sack if you're not careful,' she said—'if they catch you prowling around after me.' She wasn't joking either.

'I wanted to give you these,' I said. I gave her back her stamps, and I told her how I'd come across them. She seemed grateful; then she said, rather awkwardly:

'I don't know why I did it, what you asked me the other day. I was sorry about it afterwards. I don't want to get myself in trouble. If I was to lose my job——'

'If you lose your job, I lose mine too,' I said, more for the sake of interrupting her than because of it being quite a possibility; that only struck me, really, after I'd said it. All I knew was that unless I could talk her out of it here and now, not give her a second to try and justify herself or to think twice, she was going to slide. I wasn't worried so much about what she knew: I'd still bet on her being trusted to keep her mouth shut. But she was the only person at present who could keep an eye on Wirth for me; and now, it seemed, her feet were getting cold, so I'd got to do something about their circulation.

'Yes—well, I'm sorry,' she said. 'Was silly of me in the first place, only . . . I don't know; I'd rather not have anything more to do with it, that's all.'

She was quite quiet, amiable about it, in fact, but suddenly obstinate and a bit prim, like she had been when I first came across her in Wirth's room. I didn't say anything for a second or two. I lit a cigarette and watched the flame shuddering in the draught coming up the staircase.

'I didn't think you'd have been so easily scared,' I said. I leant back against the handrail and went on looking at the flame of my lighter.

'Don't know about being scared,' she said, 'not particularly.'

I didn't know either, but she'd answered just quick enough to show the edge of the idea had gone under her skin. 'It's just that . . . well, I don't really know what it's all about, and I don't like it, that's all.'

'What in particular don't you like?' I said.

She paused. 'Don't like being had for a mug, for one thing.'

'Should have thought the boot was on the other foot,' I said. 'I had a sort of notion you were a fairly dependable type.' I puffed out the flame of my lighter slowly, and I watched it slowly dying. I wanted her to suppose there was nothing in it for me, either way, whether she agreed to play ball or wanted to stay out of the game. I could see if I tried to rush her in her present state of mind, she might easily stick her heels in and stay where she was.

'Well, I don't like spying,' she said flatly.

'No, nor do I,' I said. 'What do you think I'm doing this for?'

'I don't know what it is you are doing,' she said. She looked at me more easily to-day than she had yesterday. 'And I don't want to know either; not now.'

I could see we weren't going to get very far this way.

'All right,' I said; 'we all make mistakes sometimes.'

'Well, I said I'm sorry,' she said.

'I didn't mean you.'

She looked at me quickly, rather resentfully, and she said, 'Doesn't suit you being sarcastic.'

I hoped she was right. 'I never was more serious,' I said. 'The mistake I made was thinking you'd got a good memory.'

CHAPTER

12

IT WAS NEARLY THREE BY THE CLOCK IN THE LOUNGE, AND BY A quarter to four I was in Richmond, walking along Sheen Lane with cat-like tread. That, at least, was the psychological approach; it wasn't meant to show.

The road where Jimmy Earle lived (if he did live) was lined with houses that looked as if they'd been pushed up in the 'twenties by some speculative builder; a speculator in architecture as well as in economics. Still, the results might have been worse. It was a quiet-looking road, outwardly respectable and pretty well cared for. Not many of the houses showed any signs of individual taste; yet, except for the architecture, which was hardly the residents' fault, it was an unpretentious-looking neighbourhood.

Most of the houses were detached, and no two looked alike, thank God. Each of them had a neat bit of garden or a gravel sweep in front, and a garage at the side, or tucked down underneath the house; and each had another garden away at the back. Some of the gardens in front had rustic pergolas and concrete bird-baths, and one or two had beastly little stone elves dotted about the place.

I walked straight past the house where I hoped Earle lived, and I took in as much as I could see in covering about fifteen yards. It was a house standing by itself, with a garage built out against one side. It looked pretty much like all the other houses; there was a fake lantern hanging in a fake porch, fake weather-boarding upstairs, fake bottle-glass in some of the windows, and—well, you know the sort of thing.

I turned the corner at the end of the road, and I made a circuit of the area; and when I came back to the house again,

I walked up the stone-flagged path and rang the bell. I could hear someone indoors whistling; when I rang, the whistling stopped. Presently a boy of about thirteen or fourteen opened the front door. He was pale, with a round face and freckles, and he had a huge bush of tow-coloured hair on top of his head. He stood there, looking at me through a cock-eyed pair of glasses.

He opened the door only half-way, so I couldn't see much of what the house was like inside. But while we were talking I was getting a quick impression, so that I could resolve the details later on. The hall was the kind of place a house agent's delicacy leads him to call a 'lounge,' meaning a sort of vestibule-living-room. It had a parquet floor with rugs on it, and there was a narrow side-table by the front door with a pewter dish and some ration books on it. On the wall, above the table, there was a bastard rococco mirror.

As the boy opened the door I pulled back the bow of chance as far as it would go, and I let fly.

'Good afternoon,' I said, 'Mrs. Earle at home?'

'No, she's not in,' he said. He was quite polite, but there seemed to be something a little sharp, a little thorny about his manner; I don't know what it was, exactly.

'I see. Any idea when she'll be back?' I asked, partly because I wanted to know, partly to play for time, so that I could size him up and the house as well; or as much as I could hope to see of it in about sixty seconds.

'Not till this evening,' the boy said.

I brought out the card the vacuum cleaner man had left on me while I was out.

'P'raps you'd give her this,' I said, 'would you?'

As we were talking a shabby-looking old girl showed up behind the boy, and edged her way out of the front door. She had a shopping bag in one hand and an empty milk bottle in the other. She put the bottle down in a corner of the porch, and she said to the boy:

'Bye-bye.'

' 'Bye, Mrs. Knight,' he said.

He opened the door a bit to let her get past, and I saw then coming in by the ordinary way. I got over the wall and dusted myself down; then I turned in at the gate and walked up the drive.

I'd forgotten the Knight watchdog, and as soon as it heard me, it started to yap again. I knocked at the basement door—I couldn't find a bell—but the only result for about a minute was that the dog went on yapping its head off. When it had almost decapitated itself I heard Mrs. Knight 'sh-shing' it; and then she shut it away somewhere and came and opened the door. She opened it just enough to give me a beady squint, and I followed the bottom of the door smoothly with my foot, just in case she should turn out to be a slammer.

'You Mrs. Knight,' I said; I made it rather heavy on purpose.

'That's right,' she said, and her eyes changed from beads to boot-buttons. I flashed my identity card at her, keeping it well out of the light, and I said:

'I'm a police officer. I believe you may be able to assist certain enquiries I have to make. There's just one or two queries I'd like to put—just a matter of routine, that's all. You're not bound to answer nothing, of course, not if you don't wish.'

I tried to make up for the violence I was doing to my syntax by speaking in a rather easy, kindly sort of way. She didn't say anything for a moment. She obviously wasn't the sort of woman who was used to thinking much before she spoke, but I could see her now, poor old girl, trying to weigh up the situation before she said something she might be sorry for later on. Evidently she thought injured innocence would be the safest line. She tried looking very tight-lipped and withdrawn.

'Nothing to do with me—I'm sure o' that. I never bin in any trouble—never. Got enough troubles of me own.'

I soft-soaped her a bit, and when she dropped her guard for a few seconds I slid into the house, and I shut the door gently behind me.

'P'raps we could just have a chat about it for a minute or two,' I said.

She raked me over for a long time in the light shining out from her room, and then she led me along a stone passage towards the door. The room was quite neatly kept, but it didn't look very clean, and the furniture was rather shabby. Bits of bric-à-brac were dotted about all over the place, and I noticed a powerful smell of washing-up and stale tobacco. On the wall, over by the window, there was a big patch of damp looking like a silhouette of Voltaire. Underneath the window there was a sink with a dripping tap, and there was an old gas cooker in the fireplace.

Seeing her in the light she looked a little younger, not much more than fifty, I guessed. Her hair was still dark, but her skin was raddled, and the front teeth were missing out of her upper jaw, so that her mouth fell in like an old woman's.

She pushed her shopping on one side of the table and told me to sit down. She was still trying to keep up the air of innocence, but instead of being injured about it, she was just being cautious now.

'Won't be a minute—you wait here,' she said, and she went off into another room. I guessed it was her bedroom, and I guessed what she'd gone there for: the next thing I heard was the bottle chinking against the glass. I leant over and looked through the crack of the door. Sure enough, there she was with her head back. I called out to her:

'Why don't you bring it in here?'

So she did; she brought in a bottle of gin and a tumbler. 'All right, I don't touch it,' I said; 'not on duty.'

She didn't say anything; she just planked the bottle down on the table and looked at me as sour as a quince; and I sat there feeling like Tantalus. She still glared at me when I offered her a cigarette, but she took one, all the same; then she poured herself out a drink.

'Wasn't it you was round there,' she said, 'talking to the boy this afternoon?'

She looked at me with one beady eye nearly shut. I thought probably she would have recognized me, so I didn't deny it. She sniffed.

'Thought so.' She nodded into her gin; you could see she was aching to know what it was all about, but I wasn't saying anything, so she had to. 'Someone in trouble, then?'

'No trouble, no. Just checking up about a car, that's all.'

'Oh.' It was obviously a disappointment.

I faked up some palaver about an accident, and Earle being wanted by the police as a witness. The boy at the house, I said, hadn't seemed to know much about it.

'No; don't s'pose you'd get much change out of 'im, not young Paul,' she said. 'He's close, he is.'

'Don't know, looks quite a bright lad,' I said. I guessed the most profitable routine would be for me to edge the conversation round so that she should pull it and I could do the steering.

'He's all right,' she said. 'Spoilt though, that's what's the matter. Got that leg.'

'I know, I saw it. Hard luck on a kid, a thing like that.'

'Sorry for him, mind you,' she said, as if she expected me to doubt it. 'Sorry for 'er too sometimes, I am really.' A kind of moody look came over her face. 'What a life, eh?' She gave a great sigh, then she smacked her lips and took another pull at the gin. I waited. 'I see a few things you know, and 'ear 'em.' She looked sharply at me, and then she nodded in a way that was obviously meant to be full of meaning; only I couldn't make out what the meaning was. 'There's lots o' women wouldn't stand for it, you know. My first husband, he raised his hand to me once—never again!'

I looked at that trap of a mouth, and couldn't help admiring her first husband's restraint.

'And why does she stand for it?' I said.

'Young Paul, that's why. Makes a proper baby out of him sometimes, fussing him the way she does. Carts 'im off to school, fetches 'im home again—course he can't play no football, not with that leg—takes 'im along the Odeon up the road instead, every Wednesday like clockwork. Mad on the pictures, they are, both of 'em. S'not the way to treat a boy, though, is it?—even if he isn't like the others—fussing 'im like that all the time.' She paused for breath and a sip. 'Still, what else's she got? Can't blame 'er, I suppose. Wonder at 'er stickin' it though sometimes, I do really.'

She took another drink, and then she sat there for a long time staring at nothing with her eyebrows raised.

'Here, you know what?' she said. 'I'm not one to go telling

tales of people; still, there's a limit, you know, to what you can stand by an' see done without saying what's in your mind. Oh, yes!' She looked at me very defiantly again, and then she went back to the gin. 'I'm tellin' you,' she said, 'I'd have left him long ago, Paul or no Paul. Wouldn't stand for it, I tell you straight. S'posed to have a weak heart, she is; don't wonder. Seen her once or twice after he's had a go at her—wicked! Just 'cause she dare back-answer 'im now an' again. I'd give 'im a few back answers!'

I couldn't see any reason to doubt it, so I kept quiet. She got up and went over to the sink to get a saucer to put her ash in; so I did her a good turn by pouring a bit more into her glass while she wasn't looking.

'What's it all about?' I said.

She shrugged her shoulders.

'Same as happens to all of us, I guess: not so young as she was. Well, we all come to it, eh?' she said, with another huge sigh. 'Reckon she wasn't bad looking a few years back. An' what's she ever got out of it, eh? Talk about the give an' take of married life! Flat of 'is 'and and the week's money, that's about all 'e's ever given her.'

'Up the spout, is he?' I said.

'Don't you believe it! He does all right for himself. New clothes, new cars, all the time.' She took another drink. 'Yes, he doesn't do too badly. 'nother petrol place of 'is he's opening down the Chertsey Road somewhere, I b'lieve. That's the way to do it, eh? Find out what we all want an' can't do without.' She picked up the gin bottle and nodded, with the nearest thing I'd seen to a smile.

Then, for about a quarter of an hour, she went off on the philosophical tack. I wasn't in any hurry, and I didn't want to start asking questions as long as she was willing to talk. Presently she got round again to Paul and his 'Dad.'

'Only good thing you can say for him, I reckon, he is fond of that boy. Mind you, I've heard him give him the rough side of his tongue once or twice. Oo, an' you should o' seen the way the lad looked at him! Still, I will say it for him: he's fond o' the boy.'

She went at the gin again. It was beginning to show now; she couldn't keep her eyes straight.

'In the war, too. That's another thing. One of the patriotic sort; first to enlist—so he could make sure of a soft job before they all went.'

'Hope he was lucky,' I said; I tried to make it sound like a lead.

'He was lucky all right. Did the whole war on his bloody backside.' She stopped; and then she said suddenly, as if it had just struck her—and she tried to fix me with a steely look at the same time, only she couldn't manage it—'Here—you're a bit nosey, aren't you?'

'That's what they pay me for,' I said. 'Where was he stationed, remember?' She didn't unfortunately.

'Dunno; out of London somewhere. Where was it—up in Wales or somewhere? I dunno.' I let it go; and presently she started up again. 'When I think of 'im before the war——' she snorted at the idea. 'Bloody blackshirt, I reckon he was. Him an' his friends paradin' around! Brought him 'ome one night from one o' them do's with a crack on the head—cost him fifty bob. I'd a' given him six months, straight I would!'

She dried up for a minute. Then she poised herself at me over the table, getting ready to say something big—but all she did was to belch softly, and then she settled herself back in her chair.

'That poor kid, though—he's fond o' that kid.' She waggled her head and began to weep a little. I thought it might do one of us some good, so I didn't say anything; and presently she went on:

' 'is temper tho', that's 'is trouble. Tried it on me once—yes!' She gave that snort of hers again, and straightened up, looking very aggressive all of a sudden. Then she stretched her elbow out towards the table, but she missed it. 'Didn't reckon I was at 'ome, see. An' they were at the pictures, 'er an' the boy; so he reckons he's alone, see, 'cause it was my half day. Only I come back 'cause I'd left me ration book. And then I hear there was someone upstairs, an' I thought it was her come back, see. So I went up like for a chat, you know; an' it was 'im!' She was making a great story of it as far as I could tell. ' 'e was up there with the door open, an' I thought, well, now I'll get a dekko; but I never see in. Minute 'e heard it was me, 'e come out an'—oo, he swore at me! I said, I'm not going to be sworn at like that, not by nobody, I said. An' he slammed the door an' locked it, and told me to get downstairs . . .'

I let her drool on about this and that. She hadn't anything else to say, though, just kept repeating herself. When she finished her drink, I poured her out another, and then another; and after about half an hour she was pretty well speechless. It's not an incident I remember with much satisfaction; it was pretty degrading for both of us, and if there had been a more certain way of lubricating her tongue, I'd certainly have tried it. Whether the means would be justified by the end, I couldn't tell yet, but one thing seemed pretty certain: I wasn't too keen for her to remember any part of the discussion very clearly, and there seemed to be quite a chance she wouldn't remember it at all.

In the end she tried to get up, but she fell down on to the floor. She'd passed out completely; so I picked her up, the poor old cow, and I carried her into the bedroom and put her on the bed. I took off her shoes and covered her over with the eider-down, and then I left her. I didn't turn the light out, just in case she came to; not that it seemed likely. Still, if she did she'd certainly smack into something if she got up in the dark.

Before I went I let the dog out of the room where she'd shut him up. He was whining and scratching and he yapped for a bit. Then he calmed down and ran into the bedroom and got into his basket.

CHAPTER

13

LLANDFRITH TURNED OUT TO BE A ONE-HORSE PLACE IN THE Wye Valley, not far from Monmouth. At another time of the year it would have been as pretty as anywhere you could find round there; which is saying a good deal when the trees are in blossom, but not much when there're only their bare branches to see and the chilly outline of the Welsh hills. All the same, it was a pleasant change from London.

I went up on the night train, so as to waste no time, and I got to work early. I wanted first of all to get a look at one of the local newspapers; that is, at its back numbers for October, 1944. Llandfrith itself was obviously too small to go in for a paper of its own; it hadn't even got a station. But Stowbridge, which was about ten miles away, seemed more promising. Pop. 5,338, the A.B.C. said; so I guessed they'd be fairly certain to have a local rag of some kind. Whether it would give anything except just an account of Becker's escape from Llandfrith—I imagined that would be pretty sure to have been reported—time would tell; anyway, it seemed worth trying.

The office of the local paper, *The Sentinel*, was in a pleasing eighteenth-century building, and the clerk I had to do with in the reference department might easily have come with the office. He was slow in speech, and slow in movement, but he was slowest of all in the uptake. Some people must have asked for back numbers now and again, but you wouldn't have thought so, from the time it took for my request to sink in and the longer time it took to bring the right volume.

It didn't look like a gold mine when it came. Yet, as things turned out, it was one of the few nuggets of any real value that I picked up in the whole of this business; not so much that there was anything of special interest in the paper itself—it was what grew out of my enquiries when I began to follow up the story.

It was there all right, Becker's escape, a full account of it. It seemed that he had belonged to a group of war prisoners who used to be loaned to farmers round about the district, and one day while he was working in the fields at Llandfrith he had just cut and run for it. The only person who had actually seen him beating it had been a landgirl called Lena Bethell. She had given the paper an interview and a rather garbled account of what had taken place and how she had raised the alarm. The farmer whom Becker had been working for was called Maxted, and I couldn't have cared less. On the other hand, the place where he lived rang a comforting little bell in my memory; comforting because it was a conclusive sign that I was still on the right track. That piece of blotting-paper that I'd found at the Bamborough House Hotel had given me quite a lot of trouble to decipher. I had never felt positive about the name on it until this moment. 'I think often,' it had said, 'of Goronwy's.' And now Goronwy's turned out to be the place where Farmer Maxted lived.

I ploughed on through *The Sentinel's* files. For the next few days the paper carried more or less the same story, about how the search was being kept up by the local police and the F.S.P. It was all on the front pages to start with, but at the end of about ten days the story had dwindled down to an inside paragraph, and after about a fortnight, it disappeared altogether.

There were the usual tales about the prisoner having been seen in half a dozen different places at the same time, each account full of circumstantial detail. But there obviously was nothing at all to go for except the story that had broken on the first day—the story Lena Bethell had told.

So I thanked the aged scrivener behind the desk and I left him—probably wondering what I'd thanked him for. In point of fact, it was for Miss Bethell's interview, because what with the old boy's deafness and my dexterity with a razor blade, I'd got the cutting of it in my wallet without having had to put him to the trouble of telling me I couldn't have it.

I bought a copy of *The Sentinel* before I left, and just as I'd expected, the inquest on Becker was featured prominently on the front page; not that anything new seemed to have come to light since yesterday, but presumably the proceedings would revive local interest in the story. I'd kept the copy of the *Standard* too, with Becker's picture in it, because I suspected that if I was lucky here in Stowbridge—and it began to look as if I might be—I should probably need it.

A local yokel put me right for the Llandfrith bus, and as we bowled along towards the place, I read through Lena Bethell's interview again. She was described as an attractive blonde, the only child of parents described as dead. She had been in the Women's Land Army nearly three years, and before that had been a saleswoman in a London store. *The Sentinel's* reporter, with an appreciative sense of delicacy, had described how 'Miss Bethell and her companion, Miss Doreen Shelley, a native of Worksop, were engaged out of doors.' Miss Bethell was then quoted: 'We were forking mangels out of a clamp, and Carl was with us. Mr. Maxted had just carted one load away, and left the three of us alone. I do not really know what happened. We had just sat down for a minute and I imagined Carl was still working. When we got up we could not see him anywhere. I did not think anything of it at first, and then Doreen said, 'Where's Carl?' I then realized he had gone. We called out and looked for him, but could see nothing. I then stood on top of the clamp, where I saw him running away along the road. I called after him, but he did not stop; so I then said to Doreen, 'I believe he has run away. Go and tell Mr. Maxted quickly.'

I wondered whether Miss Bethell had really spoken in such petrified phrases, or whether her account had been streamlined by some obsessional sub-editor. I read the report through several times. But even with my mania for corroboration, I couldn't see anything much to try and corroborate.

We got to Llandfrith a little before midday. The place didn't seem to be much more than a hamlet, but it had got a post office. The post office was fully eighteen inches wide—almost half the width of the whole counter in the little shop where it had its being. Its being turned out to be a neat-faced little woman in a knee-length cardigan of repulsive hue. She had grey eyes that looked faintly humorous, and she wore a toupet; or it might have been a mop that had come loose from a bunch hanging on the ceiling, along with boots and shoes and strings of onions and balls of twine and braces and dried apple rings and God knows what else; all part of a miscellaneous stock which would have made Woolworth look like a man with a one-track mind.

When she spoke, the woman reminded me a bit of Emlyn Williams; as a matter of fact, she reminded me of him before she spoke; perhaps it was the toupet. She told me where Goronwy's Farm was, about a mile from the village, and I set off.

Whether to bless my enterprise or not, I don't know, but the sun was shining agreeably and although there was quite a nip in the air it turned out to be a very pleasant walk.

Goronwy's Farm was a rambling slatey collection of buildings with the farmhouse just beside the road. A sheep-dog the size and shape of a steam-roller bounced out from somewhere —I didn't see where—and had me begging for mercy even before I'd knocked at the door.

A woman opened the door, a comfortable-looking nondescript body in a printed apron. I asked her if she was Mrs. Maxted. She thought about it for a second or two with her eye on me; then decided that she was.

'I come from the London *Standard*,' I said. 'I don't know whether you've seen this?' I gave her a look at Becker's photograph.

'Oh yes . . . t'was in *The Sentinel* this morning, something about it,' she said.

I brought out *The Sentinel* too, just to show I knew of its existence.

'Well, we're rather interested in this story, Mrs. Maxted, about this man escaping,' I said. ' 'Course, it was quite a good time ago; still, anything like an escape always makes a good story. Got rather crowded out of the papers in London when it happened—remember, just when all the fighting was on?

And we thought p'raps there might be a new line on it somewhere now—now he's died in these sort of circumstances. So I wonder—would I be bothering you a lot if I just asked you a few questions about what happened? Probably tired of being asked questions about it by this time, I expect. Still, it was quite a while ago, wasn't it?' I had to pause—for breath. I was anxious she shouldn't have a chance to say 'no.' She looked as though she might, if I let her get a word in, so I played for the same old stake. Time, I find, wears away resistance to most things.

'Don't know that I could tell you much,' she said. She stepped back into the passage and shouted for someone called Will. 'Better you talk to my husband,' she said, 'he'd remember.'

Will stepped out from a room at the other end of the passage. He stood there, outlined against an open door; and beyond the door you could see a yard with the backsides of some cattle and a few hens stalking about. Mrs. Maxted explained the situation.

'Bring the gen'eman inside,' her husband said. He was in his shirt-sleeves and he was wearing a cap; and I could see now that he was eating.

'I'm disturbing your lunch,' I said.

'N'mind that,' he said; he seemed quite cheerful about it.

We went into the parlour: it was full of dark furniture and odds and ends of bric-à-brac. There was a nice little Welsh dresser facing the window, and it was crowded with a collection of jugs and mugs and plates. They looked mostly like Worcester and pretty good Worcester at that. Apart from tactics I would have stopped to enjoy the look of it anyway. I let Maxted see the light in my eye, and I said to him:

'Got something there to be proud of.'

He perked up visibly when I said this. He was a short, shrewd-looking chap, about fifty, very bright and cheerful. He asked me if I knew 'something' about china.

'Enough to know what's good,' I said.

It wasn't true; all I knew was how much you can make any kind of expert think you know by keeping quiet at the right time; so I let him go on. He took down one or two pieces off the dresser and he showed them to me lovingly. I gathered he knew all about glazes and clay constituents and oven temperatures, and so on. Mrs. Maxted stood on the other side of the table and smiled at me indulgently.

'Have an apple,' her husband said. He picked one out of a bowl on the dresser and gave it to me.

'Have a chair too,' said Mrs. Maxted. So we all three sat round the table, and I began to get down to cases.

The facts I wanted were simple and few. But to get at them, if they were to be got, I knew I should probably have to take along a cargo of other information which would be quite useless.

First, I wanted to hear the exact circumstances of Becker's getaway. It seemed inconceivable that at the height of the war a German p.o.w., speaking badly-broken English, could have made off and never have been seen again; not unless he had had some kind of prearranged help. Why in the world should a 'star' prisoner, a man with all the privileges he could earn by good conduct, risk loosing them all by trying to break away?—unless he had known that there was help in the offing? Becker wasn't a fool, obviously. Beethoven's *Briefe* and Hoffmannsthal's plays aren't the sort of thing a congenital chump reads for pleasure. Yet only a congenital chump would have taken the kind of risk he'd taken, without some certainty of bringing the thing off.

I said no more than was necessary—and that wasn't much—to start Maxted talking.

'We was cartin' mangels up in the Long Field—I'll take an' show you the Long Field directly——'

'Who's we?' I said.

'Becker—Carl we used to call him—him an' Doreen and Lena—two girls I had then—and me; and Jake; he's the carter.'

'Just the five of you?'

'Just the five of us. We was comin' back with pretty near the last load—I reckon there'd 'a been one more load for the day—Jake an' I, we was on the two carts an' Carl an' Doreen an'

Lena was up in the field, 'long by the clamp. We had a lot go bad that time, see, so we had to open up the clamps an' fork 'em out. Well, we got down by the gate—that's the gate there, look——' He got up and pulled the lace blind away from the window, and he pointed to a gate leading out on to the road.

'What time of day was this?' I said.

He looked at Mrs. Maxted. 'Five o'clock, would it be, near enough?'

'It was still light, then?' I said.

'Oh, it was still light. I just jumped down, see, to open the gate, an' I hear Doreen calling. I looked round, an' she was coming down across the field, see——' He pointed out of the window again.

'Which way?' I said. The field was a large rolling field; you could see pretty well the whole of it from the house because it lay on rising ground. The gate was right down in the bottom corner, not far from the house.

'Straight down across, down from the far corner. That's where the clamp were, see.'

'And you heard her calling, so what did you do?' I said.

'I didn't think 'twas for me. I thought maybe she was calling Jake for to wait for her. I went on thru'. An' then I hear him calling, see; an' I notice him jump down off the cart an' start running back up the field. So I thought maybe 'twas an accident or something. Then I went back up. An' Doreen was on the ground by the gate there, clean blown, 'cause she'd a cracked rib since a week or two back, see. Still, I didn't wait. I went on up after 'em.'

'And when you got to the clamp,' I said, 'what happened? No sign of Becker, I suppose?'

'Not be that time. See, Doreen, she'd had to come down, see, and we get back up there—a good four or five minutes each way. Then I come back here to 'phone, see. There's a good five an' twenty minutes start for him, 'fore ever the police got here, I reckon.'

He talked on a bit about Becker, what a good steady worker he had been, well-behaved, and so on. And they both of them seemed genuinely quite shocked, he and his wife, about the way

Becker had died. I think it was the sensational circumstances, though, that shocked them, more perhaps than the fact he was someone they had known.

'How about the girls?' I said. 'They still work here?'

'No, oh, no. Got no girls here now. No, they left, when was it?'—he looked at Mrs. Maxted again—'right after the end of the war.'

'That's right,' Mrs. Maxted said. 'Doreen, she went back to Worksop; she'd a boy there. And Lena, I don't know what became of her. We was downright sorry when they went. Two nice girls they were. That's them, look . . .'

I'd noticed there was a snapshot on the mantelpiece, and she passed it over for me to look at. Two girls were tossing straw into a wagon with pitchforks, and there was a man standing in the wagon on top of the straw.

'That's Carl there, in the wagon,' Mrs. Maxted said. It was a pretty poor photograph, but I could see that it was Becker, now that she said so. 'That's Lena on the right there—an' that's Doreen.' They were standing facing each other, the two girls; they both looked about the same height and the same build, and they had the same fair hair.

'They used to live here with you, did they?' I said.

'No; they shared a room over at the hostel, down the village. Real chums those two, they were. Different as could be though, 'cept in looks. That's often the way though, so they say, don't they?'

'Different in what sort of way?' I said.

'Like in character; they was quite apart. Always one for a bit of fun, Doreen was; and Lena like more the quiet type—you know; but always the best of friends, they were.'

'And how did they both get on with Becker,' I said, 'all right?'

'Got on O.K.,' Maxted said. 'Lena, I used to chip her 'bout she an' Carl, the way he used to watch after her.' He grinned, and he helped himself to an apple out of the dish and sliced it in half with a Swedish jack-knife.

'This knife, that b'longed to Lena, didn't it?' he said with his mouth full. He wiped the blade on his trousers, and he handed the knife over for me to look at.

'Fierce-looking weapon for a young girl,' I said. It had two blades, one on each side of the knife; the big blade was about three inches long; it was unused and looked pretty sharp; the little one had been ground down a good many times, but it still had quite a good edge on it.

Mrs. Maxted laughed all of a sudden, in a shame-faced sort of way.

'Well, I never! I meant to post that knife back a dozen times or more an' never done it.'

'You lost track of her, though, didn't you say?'

'Now, yes,' Mrs. Maxted said. 'She wrote a couple o' times, just after she left; that's the last we heard.'

'You don't remember the address?' I said; not that I imagined it was going to be as easy as that to find her.

'I don't, I'm afraid, not after all this while,' she said.

I could probably have taken the knife without either of them being any the wiser; but I liked both of them, and the thought of lifting it, even though it wasn't theirs, didn't appeal to me. Still, with ideas that were vaguely shaping themselves in my mind, it looked as if I might need it some time.

'Maybe you'd like me to give her this,' I said, 'if I come across her?'

Maxted wasn't quite sure whether I was joking or not. 'Have your work cut out finding her, I reckon, in the whole of London,' he said.

'Well, I don't know,' I said. 'Surprising what a nose you develop, if you spend your life following news stories.'

He opened his little bright eyes, and he looked at me incredulously.

'You reckon to find her, then, really?'

'Can but try,' I said. 'That's my next assignment, anyway.'

He didn't know whether to admire the qualities of the ferret in me, or whether to think I was just a liar; so he compromised. He shut the knife up with a snap and handed it over; and he grinned sceptically at me, but he wasn't unamused.

'O.K. Jolly good luck to you, that's all I say. And if you find her, you give it to her with my compliments.

I enjoyed the walk back to Llandfrith; that's to say, I was conscious of the sweetness and stillness of the countryside and of the pale sunshine smiling out of a light, blue-washed sky. But I could hardly say my mind was bent on absorbing the charms of nature. What it was really bent on were the few facts I'd managed to glean from the Maxteds and the odd-shaped web of hypotheses that looked as if it might be spun out of what they had said.

I ticked off the facts mentally as I walked back up the hill. First, there was the fact that only Lena Bethell had actually seen Carl—or said she had seen him—running away. Second, according to what she had said in the report given by *The Sentinel*, she had told Doreen to go and tell Maxted; and Doreen had gone—although at that time she'd got a cracked rib, which presumably wasn't likely to be improved by a cross-country run. Could be that Lena had forgotten that, of course; but she surely must have known about it if they had shared a room together? Then there was what Maxted had said about Carl always watching Lena—but that was hardly fact; might quite well have been Maxted's imagination.

Couldn't count as a fact, either, that the two girls were very friendly. What Mrs. Maxted said they seemed to be, and what they actually were, might easily be different. In the circumstances though, the probability was that Mrs. Maxted was right. Anyway, it wasn't a point that seemed to be of much consequence.

It wasn't really anything that had been said, or left unsaid, but what had been implied—quite innocently as far as the Maxteds were concerned—which strengthened my suspicions about the girls. Which one I didn't know—Lena seemed the most likely—but one or other, I felt pretty sure, must have been associated with Jackson in some way.

The devil of it was I knew so little about Jackson that there was nothing I could use as a cross-check on anything the Maxteds had said. Dammit, I didn't even know—I could only assume—that Jackson and the 'J' that Becker had written to from Bamborough House, were both the same person. If so, of course, the reference on the card to Goronwy's Farm would seem a pretty conclusive pointer at least to Jackson having known about the place.

At present the whole problem seemed to be hopelessly fluid. A few unrelated facts floating like tiny drops of oil on a large expanse of water.

I lunched at Llandfrith, in front of a log fire in the four-ale bar of the Queen of Hearts. They gave me a slice of pie with bread and cheese and a pint of bitter, and what with the warmth and the amiable agricultural company, I couldn't have had a better meal.

The lady behind the bar was a cheerful, saucy fifteen-stoner, and she seemed well chosen to epitomize the name on the sign outside. But really the queen of my heart in Llandfrith turned out to be someone quite different.

After lunch I went back and squeezed myself into the post office again, to find out about buses back to Stowbridge. The lady with the toupet was more than obliging; she not only gave me all the information I needed about buses; she gave me a bit on the side about something that was entirely different and a lot more useful.

There were some newspapers on the counter; they were lying all among the kettle-holders and sherbet suckers and rubber heels and aspirins and what not. One of the papers was *The Sentinel*, and it had a bit about the Becker inquest on the front page, so it wasn't difficult to slide the talk round that way.

Madame Toupet looked a fairly innocent type, but she seemed, all the same, to have a sensitive nostril for gossip. She remembered, for instance, that after Becker's escape—her version of the story differed somewhat from the Maxted's: the two girls had been practically clubbed to death by Becker, whom everyone had known to be a homicidal maniac—after his escape a captain up at the P.O.W. camp had been dismissed. Toupet herself had been very sorry about this because the captain, who apparently popped in and out of the post office at all hours, was so nice; and it was nice to have someone so nice come in now and again. It sounded idyllic. I imagined the dashing captain dashing in for a twopenny-halfpenny stamp and a sherbet-sucker, and then dashing out again, flashing his dark eyes at Madame Toupet.

Only it seemed he hadn't had dark eyes. Toupet was very sensitive, so she said, to people's colouring; possibly, I imagined, because of the overall drabness of her own. The captain 'ad 'ad light eyes and auburn 'air; it was a very, very unusual combination that, very. Auburns usually 'as dark eyes apparently, which I didn't know; something to do with the blood, same as when you're born white and 'as pink eyes. I could see this fascinating theory of genetics could easily be extended until it was time to shut up shop. But all I wanted to know was whether she had the slightest idea what the captain was called. I said to her, because I prefer the prompt indirect rather than the specific reminder:

'Was that Captain Scrubbs? Wasn't there a Captain Scrubbs up at the camp for a while?'

I said this because there was a bottle of Scrubbs Cloudy Ammonia straight in my line of vision; and I felt sure the original benefactor wouldn't have minded my borrowing his name in a good cause.

No, she said, it wasn't Scrubbs, the name. She was all right on remembering what it wasn't, but when it came to remembering what it was, she was stuck. Still, I went on hammering.

'Sounds like a Captain Scrubbs I met up in these parts,' I said, 'a long time ago. Little short chap, thin?'

I was wrong again. Hers wasn't a thin captain or a short one. He was tallish, and he had a nice figure, and this auburn 'air and pale eyes. She nodded rather sentimentally when she spoke about him, and I wondered what curdled emotions were coiling round each other under that *bois de rose* cardigan.

She could never have known how grateful I was for the description she gave me of her hero. I did my best to show it discreetly by buying some Jersey caramels and a half-crown book of stamps. Then presently the Stowbridge bus came, and we said farewell.

In half an hour I was on the way back to London. I sat for a long while looking out of the window of the train. The telegraph wires beside the track rose and fell, a few yards away from the window. Imperceptibly, but quite quickly after we had been travelling for about an hour, the sky lost what little colour it had had, and the countryside in the distance began to darken. I saw out of the window a woman driving some cattle towards a shed; I saw some school-children hurrying home over a foot-bridge; and I saw some rooks wheeling in and out among elm trees in a churchyard. I saw these things, I know, but they must have sunk straight away into the back of my mind because it wasn't until I was thinking over the journey later on that I remembered having seen them. I was so preoccupied with trying to sort out the information, such as it was, which I'd got out of the trip, that these incidents went in at one eye and out at the other.

I was trying to see how this information looked in relation to the pieces I'd got on the table already; and I came to only one conclusion: that if I was patient, and didn't begin to act on suspicion instead of proof—and the stronger the suspicion, the stronger the temptation often is to try and make a short circuit—I might still stand a chance of bringing home what I was after. But if I scared the birds now, by trying to have a show-down with Jackson straight away, the whole flock would probably disperse and never be seen again. It did occur to me, too, that perhaps I might be the one to be dispersed and never seen again, except possibly in rather ill-fitting pieces.

CHAPTER

14

I DON'T KNOW WHETHER I REALLY EXPECTED JACKSON—I STILL thought of her as Jackson—to turn up for the Schnabel concert or not. I got to the place early, a little before three, and hung about in the foyer for a bit. Then I looked round, and suddenly there she was, dressed in a yellow coat and a yellow turban. I'd had a pretty clear picture of her fixed in my mind—at least I thought I had—but seeing her again, I realized the picture wasn't such a good likeness after all. I don't know just what the difference was; something to do, perhaps, with the way she was dressed; perhaps to do with the way I was feeling; anyway, she was very easy on the eye.

It may be that I'm not really musical, whatever musical means. If it means that you're able to find in music the same kind of comfort and stimulus that some people find in political theory, or in religion, or in cats and dogs, or films or football—all right, then I'm musical. But I freely admit my enjoyment of music, or my failure to enjoy it, is sometimes influenced by the kind of company I'm in.

Jackson seemed to be the sort of person who might easily help to increase one's pleasure in listening to Bach, or even Mozart. 'Even' is a matter of taste, of course, and as it turned out, Mozart tasted the same to both of us.

When the interval came we went out and smoked, and we talked about this and that. I noticed, when she pulled off her left glove, that this time she had got a ring on her third finger, a small antique ring; it was French or Italian, I guessed. She still puzzled me, this girl. It wasn't that she seemed purposely evasive, or as if she was trying to keep me at arm's length, but I just felt I wasn't getting anywhere with her, wasn't finding out any more about her than I knew at the beginning. She was amusing and easy to get on with, but somehow she managed to keep the conversation well away from anything that might have given me more than a hint about the Jackson way of life.

Well, then the bell rang, and we went back to our seats.

It was a Mozart concerto. Now, Schnabel chasing himself through Mozart is just the kind of sound I hope to hear outside the Pearly Gates, if I ever get close enough. It shows how far away I was in my mind that I really only woke up to the music in the last movement; and then it was partly because Jackson happened to glance round and saw me looking at her. I wondered what she thought I was thinking. Whatever she may have imagined, she didn't show it. When she wasn't talking her expression was sometimes a little wry, a little uncompromising; but when she was talking she lost this look. Either way it was no hardship to watch her.

It was getting dark by the time we came out. Jackson said to me:

'Must you dash away or have you time for a drink? I thought we might go along to the Minstrels.'

If she'd known me better she wouldn't have had to ask. But I had a lot of work, real work, scribbling, to do by to-morrow morning; and I knew that if I didn't go home and start it I should be making trouble for myself. So I made trouble; but only because Jackson was insistent and I didn't want to seem ungracious.

The Minstrels' Club is off Long Acre, and although it's upstairs, it somehow gives you a feeling of being in the bowels of the earth, if you can imagine its bowels being lined with pink looking-glass. The ceiling and the floor seem almost to touch each other, and the windows look out on to brick walls. If any members of the club really are minstrels, the only way they show it is by hiring a large pale girl, with hair like a lion's mane, to sit and play quietly to them on the piano. And as she seems to have learnt all she knows from a close study of Hoagy Carmichael, the effect, on a musical dustbin like me, isn't at all unpleasing.

Stap me for a thick-eared Goth, if you like, but while we sat there drinking, I found that *Susie Went Away* as pretty and gentle as you please, without making any fuss either about Mozart or Schnabel. And Jackson didn't seem to mind either; she liked it, in fact, and thank God she did, because before we left; it gave me an excuse to ask her round later in the week to hear some of the records I've got of jazz in the early 'thirties.

When we did leave I had a slight contretemps getting my hat and coat off a half-tight minstrel who was trying to climb into them under the impression they were his own. And in the way drunks have, he couldn't let it alone and had to go on and on apologizing.

Jackson remembered, just as we were leaving, that she had a call to make; and so we said good-bye at the doorway and she went back into the club. And in the neat way Providence sometimes has of arranging these things, a man I know was coming in just as I went out, so we stopped to say a few words.

While we were talking there in the doorway, my drunk friend filtered out into the street. The chap I was talking to said his say, and then just as we said good-bye, something happened.

The drunk was about twenty yards away, just near the corner of the street. He was crossing the road—he looked slightly unsteady but nothing more—and just as he got to the kerb, a car, a private car, zoomed up in the dark and seemed to go absolutely straight at him. It all happened so quickly that I don't know whether I yelled out or not. I know the drunk did. He let out a ghastly sort of squeal, and I saw him fly up into the air. His coat seemed to catch up in the back of the car somehow as he came down, and it dragged him about ten yards; then it chucked him off on to the pavement. He hit a lamp-post, and even from where we were standing you could pretty well hear his spine crack as he wrapped himself round it.

The car didn't even slow down. It screeched round the corner and then was out of sight.

The drunk was still jerking a little when we got to him, but I didn't wait. The fellow I was with stayed by him and I gave him my overcoat for a pillow. Then I shot on round the corner.

I ran on, and I yelled to a taxi as it went by but it didn't stop. It was Sunday, so the streets were empty, of course, and there wasn't a thing in sight. Further on, about fifty yards away, there were two or three turnings all close together; the car might have taken this one or that one; anyway, by the time I got there it had disappeared.

I ran back along the street, and when I came round the corner there were half a dozen people standing round the drunk, poor devil. The ambulance was on the way, someone said, and someone else had gone to get a policeman. The fellow I'd been talking to in the club was trying to make the drunk look comfortable, but it was a waste of time.

I knelt down to have a look at him. I don't need to go into what I saw, but something struck me all of a sudden, something so fantastic that the only reason it could have occurred to me must have been that I was getting to accept this kind of fantasy as part of the ordinary run of things.

I noticed the chap was about my height and my build, and that he had on a light suit like mine and a white shirt; I had on a white shirt too. And his hat and overcoat were enough like mine for him to have mistaken them for his own; true, he was a bit tight, but still . . . There wasn't really much similarity, I suppose; but there was a superficial resemblance, certainly; and at twenty yards, in a street not too well lit, someone who didn't know either of us well might easily have taken one for the other. It would have been easier still if they had been expecting that just about that time I should be coming out of the Minstrels' Club.

The police and the ambulance both came along at the same time; and in a couple of minutes there wasn't much left to show that anything had happened. No one, except me and the fellow I'd been with, had seen anything.

An inspector who came with the coppers jumped me into a call-box straight away, and put through a message to Scotland Yard. I told him all I could, which was precious little. I hadn't even had a chance to see the colour or the make of the car.

When we came out of the box I stood under the lamp and they slowly wrote down my version of what had happened. I took them back to the spot where the car had hit the chap and they measured out the distance he'd been dragged. Before

I left the inspector warned me I should be wanted at the inquest, probably the day after to-morrow.

It was after seven by this time; for once I didn't feel particularly like having anything to eat. Still, I went along to the Sheridan, as it was nearby, and I had a bite; then I went home.

In my suspicious frame of mind everything that had happened in the last hour or two seemed to fit together nicely—except for one thing: what was Jackson's part in all this? Of course, it might be that what had happened really was an accident; and that after he'd hit the man the driver had simply lost his head. If so, then that would let Jackson out completely, and would leave me just where I was before, with nothing to confirm my suspicions of her—and nothing to show they were wrong, either.

Somehow the accident theory seemed less and less likely the more I thought about it. There was too much coincidence in it: both of us looking alike, the drunk and I; both being in the club and coming out of it at the same time; and the driver not stopping. If it had been on a deserted country road I could have imagined someone driving on, if they had really got in a panic; but right in the middle of Soho . . . it looked more like a risk that had been carefully calculated.

There was one thing, though, that stuck in my guts. I've got no use for 'hunches' at all, but whatever Jackson might be up to, I simply didn't believe that she'd willingly, or rather knowingly, have acted as a decoy duck for my assassination. That wasn't simply flattering myself either, or flattering her. I wouldn't have put it past her to know quite a thing or two about subterfuge, but I'd have betted my skin, or even more attractive odds, if you'd cared to name them, that she hadn't known what was going to happen outside that club. If she had, if she really was such a cold-blooded, murderous bitch as all that, then I was a Dutchman; and however thrifty, phlegmatic, and clean in my personal habits I happen to be, there's certainly nothing of the blood Orange in me, as far as I know.

Just when I was finishing breakfast the next morning, sure enough, a policeman came round on a bicycle and gave me a summons to show up at the Coroner's Court at half-past ten the next day. It was a damn nuisance; there were two or three threads I wanted to twitch, just to see what was on the ends of them; and now I should have to waste time doing an honest day's work. Still, the threads were slack at the moment, and unless they tightened unexpectedly in the next twenty-four hours there'd be nothing to lose by waiting to see if the inquest would bring up anything I could make use of.

The session opened with evidence of identification by the manager of a hotel where the corpse had been staying. The corpse turned out to have been an Englishman from Rio, who had been over here on business. Then a pale pathologist went into the box and gave medical evidence about the man's injuries and the cause of his death; and after that, a man and a woman, friends of his, who'd been with him in the club, gave evidence about meeting him there, and his getting tight. Then I said my piece, and the chap I'd met on the doorstep corroborated it. The coroner asked us all a lot of questions and took a lot of notes, and that was all, except for the evidence given by the police.

It was a gloomy business altogether; not that I'd expected a floor show. But I wondered, looking round the place, why on earth some attempt couldn't have been made to get away from the branch-line waiting-room atmosphere. Anything that might have given a touch of human warmth to the proceedings or comfort to the emotions seemed to have been barred. Everything was hard and bleak and bare, and the only colour in the place, apart from the geranium tints of the coroner's face, was a sickening *eau de nil* dado. The difference that could have been made by a bunch of flowers or a print on the wall seemed beyond the imagination of those plasma-veined creatures who look after these things.

In the public part of the court there were about a dozen bits of the public. They looked a pretty broken-down lot, most of them, and they seemed so apathetic I wondered why they bothered to come there at all. There was one of them, a youngish chap with a broad pale face and sandy hair. He looked a little more spry than the rest, and seemed to strike a very faint chord in my memory somewhere. But I couldn't place him, and after a bit it began to worry me. Might be just coincidence, of course, that he somehow happened to look familiar.

As a matter of fact, the more I came to think of it, the less likely it seemed that it could have been just a coincidence, and the more likely that—well, what? Why shouldn't it have been a coincidence, after all? I wasn't certain, very far from certain, in fact, that I'd ever seen the chap before. I just had a very vague feeling of recognition, that was all: so vague, that if I had ever come across him before I hadn't the faintest recollection where it could have been. I thought of the Astoria; I thought of Wirth's, of Jackson, of Earle, of the Maxteds—he didn't fit in with any of them. I wasn't happy, though; it worried me a little—not that I couldn't place him, but that I couldn't even be sure in my own mind that I'd ever seen him. Still, that's the kind of thing that does worry me, rotates in my mind like a wheel with a cog missing.

At the end of the proceedings the coroner adjourned the inquest for a week to let the police get on with their enquiries, and I was told I wouldn't be wanted any more. By the time I got outside there was no sign of the chap I'd noticed in court. So all I could do was to let my memory itch and try not to scratch it.

The rest of the day I packed in a lot of work. I went on writing till quite late, and about half-past eleven I went into the kitchen and brewed some Horlicks. Just as I was putting a spoon into the glass, a flash-bulb went off in my memory: it showed me sitting in The Honeypot, with Florrie drinking her Horlicks beside me; and it showed, further along the counter, a sandy-haired chauffeur picking his teeth over a pools forecast. He hadn't picked them during the inquest, and he hadn't worn his uniform there; but it was the same chap all right.

In its way, this was about as unpleasant as anything I'd discovered up till now. The only compensation was the shock it must have given this fellow to see me alive and kicking in the witness box. Still, the feeling of suddenly having the initiative wrenched out of your hands is pretty disconcerting whatever you happen to be doing. And if it's something that might be dangerous, the sensation can be rather nasty. It was certainly nasty enough at this moment, because I realized now that I'd never really had the initiative, that I'd lost it right from that moment when he'd seen us in The Honeypot.

I didn't mind this so much as a blow to my self-esteem; I could take that all right. I didn't especially mind that it meant I was a marked man, though I'd much rather have stayed without blemish. What worried me was that it meant Florrie was marked too.

Already Becker had been strangled like a chicken, which he may well have deserved, for all I knew. But that, and the arrangements for my own cold-blooded slaughter, which only misfired quite by chance, were fairly sharp signs that the opposition hadn't any scruples about going into the butchery business when it suited their plans.

I couldn't see, at the moment, how Florrie was to be got out of the mess. But I could see that somehow or other she had got to be got out of it, and got out pretty quickly. Whatever she did or didn't do now, and whether she was acting for me or not, if the circumstances looked even slightly suspicious, it wouldn't be much good her trying to explain things—not with her skull already smashed in or a round of bullets in her stomach.

From now on I had got to watch every step; not that I hadn't been doing that from the start, of course. But now I'd got to go into a sort of shadow waltz, and instead of watching merely to see that no one spotted me, I'd got to watch myself as well, so that I shouldn't give away the fact that I knew that I'd been spotted. If they once became suspicious of that, either they'd slug me out of hand or they'd lay off and lie completely quiet till the scent dried up altogether. Obviously, there wasn't a hope of diverting their suspicions from me now; not unless I was prepared to chuck my hand in and tell Herrick he'd better put someone else on the job, a new face they wouldn't recognize. But I still had a couple of cards up my sleeve, as well as some relics of professional pride. I still believed it would be worth while playing the rest of my hand, and seeing if I could force them to show theirs.

But first of all there was this question of Florrie. It seemed pretty clear that there was only one thing to be done: she'd have to chuck her job, for the time being, at any rate, and disappear. The case couldn't go on for ever; I hoped not, anyway; and possibly in a few weeks, she could come back again. In the meantime I should have to see that she got another job, or at least that she didn't suffer by losing this one.

The first thing was to get hold of her and see how things could be arranged. It was going to be a bit difficult without putting the wind up her. If I minimized the danger she was in, she'd probably dig her heels in and refuse to take any notice. Still, whether I had to scare her into it or not, she'd got to do whatever she was told.

I should have to find out how she was fixed for relatives and money and so on, and see what sort of a story we could work up that would be fool-proof as well as plausible.

For the rest of the night I made a rather half-hearted pretence of going to sleep. I tried counting sheep jumping over barbed wire; but there were too many with weak ankles, and about one in five came down with a whack that woke me up every time. At about seven o'clock a ram came at the wire full tilt: he caught both feet in it and I shot up off the bed like a rocket.

CHAPTER

15

I DIDN'T SEE ANY SENSE IN TRYING TO GO BACK TO SLEEP AGAIN after that, so I got up and I had an early breakfast. For once I hardly looked at the newspapers at all. I sat there chewing away and thinking over what had happened last night, and what there was for me to do about it, if anything.

I've always made it a practice not to carry arms. Once you start to carry arms, someone's sure to get hurt; so I've never carried them in case it might be me. I have got a little Colt, though, a .25, which I keep to scare the landlord with; and as it looked as if moral persuasion wouldn't cut much ice with the sort of gentry I was coming out against nowadays, I got out the little Colt after breakfast and started to give it a good clean.

I was in the middle of doing this when someone rang me up. I don't even remember who it was now; but I do remember that while I was on the telephone, Mrs. Wellington came in with my laundry. I'd left the Colt in pieces on the desk, but from the way she looked at it you might have thought it was a bloodstained chopper.

While she was busy doing this and that, we discussed the meals I was going to be in or out for, and we touched on the weather and the liquor situation. I needed some more gin for one thing, because it was this evening that I had asked Jackson to come in for a drink, and ostensibly, to hear some of my records—ostensibly, I mean from her point of view.

My motive in asking her round hadn't been entirely musical, and I wondered whether she'd had reservations, too, in saying she'd come. All I had in mind at the moment was to keep on steadily getting to know her better. If things should ever come to the point where I'd got to start making love (what was this, all of a sudden—wishful thinking?) in order to squeeze some information out of her, or to get her thinking along certain lines, or acting in a certain way, I knew I should stand a better chance if I had acted with reasonable decorum to begin with, and hadn't behaved like a wolf. She was intelligent enough to be more susceptible (I guessed so, anyway) to advances which combined lusts of the flesh with a nice appreciation of the intellect. I hoped she wouldn't think I collected gramophone records only because I couldn't afford etchings.

'If I'm not back,' I said to Mrs. Wellington, 'would you let her in, if she rings your bell?'

There's a note on my bell, by the way, telling you to ring Mrs. Wellington's, if I don't answer. If she doesn't answer, you either break down the door or go home.

'I ought to be back about six,' I said.

I put a couple of clean handkerchiefs and a torch in my pocket, and I slipped the Colt into my overcoat; and then I was ready.

It was a crisp, cold morning, and as I walked up the street, I wished it was going to lead me into the woods up at the back of Uncle Arthur's house, and that I could spend the morning tramping round them, potting at the rabbits and the pigeons with Bruce smelling around at my heels. As it was, the wood I seemed to be getting into was darker and thicker, and looked as if it might easily have a lot of very unpleasant traps in it.

I walked slowly, and when I got into King's Road I stopped every so often and looked in the shop windows. There didn't seem to be any reflections, though, that might have suggested I was being followed; still, I wasn't taking any chances.

I went along to the cave where the magician lives who conjures up my supply of Scotch. He's a bit of a character, this old chap; he looks like a gargoyle with white hair and his voice is blanketed with asthma. Over and above the proper price of his stuff, you usually have to pay heavily for it by listening to a stream of waggish talk and innuendo. Still, if he's got the stuff, it's yours—as long as you can stand the becks and wreathéd smiles. He couldn't send round to-day, he said, because the boy was down with 'flu. I told him it was vital I should have something by this evening; I appealed to him as man to man; and after a bit of palaver, he promised he'd bring the order round himself on his way home.

My first move was to get at Florrie, and on my way to the Astoria, I dropped in at the office to leave the stuff I'd written last night. It had to be this morning, of course, that the Editor lit on me just as I was leaving, and pulled me into his room for a long discussion. By the time we broke up it was nearly midday, so there wasn't time to do anything about getting into the Astoria without being seen—I didn't want to be seen, for Florrie's sake—if I was going to catch her before she went off at twelve. By the time she came on again at four, I hoped I should be frying other fish.

The clock on the lifts showed exactly midday as I came into the lounge. I went across into a telephone box, and I asked for fourth-floor room service. I waited. Either there wasn't a fourth floor any more or there was no service. Presently I gave it up.

In the alcove where the telephones are there's a writing-table, and as I came out of the box I slipped a sheet of paper and an envelope into my pocket. Then I went down and wrote a note to Florrie where I couldn't be seen, in the lavatory. All I said was:

Sorry I couldn't wait. Must see you urgently. Got bad toothache.

I signed it 'Dick Barton', and I marked the envelope 'Personal,' and just put Florrie on it.

Then I took a lift to the fourth floor and I walked along the corridor to the service pantry. And blow me, if that waiter wasn't still standing there chafing with his chafing dish. He was all alone with his back to me, just like he had been last time. So I went back towards the lifts where there was a wall telephone, and I asked for fourth-floor room service again.

A Wop accent answered me, and I asked for a waiter in room 472. I chose 472 because it was a good way from the service pantry and round the angle of the corridor. Then I went back the same way, and in a few seconds I saw the waiter coming out of the pantry towards me. By the time I got to the pantry door, he'd disappeared round the corner of the corridor. So I slipped into the pantry and left the note for Florrie where she couldn't miss it, on a shelf near the door. Then I went back along the corridor and down the stairs.

I'd had to risk going through the lounge when I came in. So I went down to the lower ground floor this time, and right along; then I came up through the bar, and I went out at a side entrance.

It was a bit after twelve by this time; and by a bit after one I was having lunch in The Rose and Crown at Sheen; and a bit later I was digesting it in a call-box facing the end of the road where Jimmy Earle lived.

Mrs. Knight, in her cups, had overflowed with a few drops of information that had rather interested me. To-day, for instance, Wednesday, was her half day; and also it happened to be the day when the Earles, *mère et fils*, made their routine trip to the local Odeon. So it seemed a good opportunity, without giving anyone any bother, of seeing if I could satisfy my curiosity about one or two other things that Mrs. Knight had let drip.

Soon after two o'clock I saw Mrs. Earle and Paul come out of the house and turn up towards the main road. The boy walked with a bit of difficulty, and when they came to the bus stop they waited. Then they got on to a bus going towards the big cinema which I'd passed a little while before.

When they'd disappeared I rang up Earle's number, and presently I heard Mrs. Knight's voice.

'There's no one at 'ome,' she said.

It might have seemed like tempting fate to say 'Hooray!' so I kept quiet. And after a while she got tired of saying 'Hullo?' to herself, and she hung up.

At about half-past two I saw her in the distance, coming out of the gate. She walked up towards the main road, and when she got to the top, instead of turning left or right, she kept straight on across the road—straight towards the box where I was standing.

I switched round quickly and muffled myself up as well as I could, and I started an earnest conversation with myself on the telephone. Every minute I expected that she'd pull the door open and tell me to buck up. Then I caught sight of her just beside the window; all she was doing was buying some stuff from a greengrocer's stall; and when she'd finished, she went trundling off and got on a bus. I gave her ten minutes' start; and then I came out of the box and went down the road towards Earle's house.

I'd noticed the lie of the land pretty carefully when I was there before. The runway in front of the garage was hidden from the garden by a tall hedge. A tradesman's passage, with a swing gate at the top of it, ran along between the garage and the house next door; it ran along right to the garden at the back. The house next door was empty, thank God.

When I got down the passage and through a swing gate, I was out of view, unless anyone should happen to come by in a helicopter. But to-day looked like being my lucky day; there wasn't a helicopter in sight. On the other hand, there didn't seem to be any way, short of dynamite, for me to get into the house from this side. The back door was bolted, and the only window I could reach was the larder window, and that had good strong bars on it.

At the back of the house, on the corner, there was a little conservatory built out into the garden. I got behind it, so that I couldn't be spotted from the house on the far side, and I reconnoitred.

Just over the conservatory, on the first floor, there was a window, a sash window, and the top of it was open. I put half my trust in God, and the other half in a dustbin that was standing against the fence . . . it took my weight all right, and from the top of it, I got hold of the gutter which ran round the roof of the conservatory; then, like many a good man before me, I worked my way up from the gutter, and eventually got so that I could just balance on it. If I overbalanced—or under-balanced, for that matter—Mrs. Earle's zinnias and I were going to be cut to pieces. There was a waste-pipe running down the corner of the house, and though I don't think there's much to be said for outdoor plumbing, I said all there was to say, and I grabbed hold of it.

Compared with some situations, before and after this, I didn't seem badly off: I had a foothold of about three inches, as well as this pipe to cling to, and a drop of only about fifteen feet to the ground. I had a feeling, from the state of the gutter, that this might come at any moment. And anyway, as long as I stayed where I was, I could quite easily be spotted from the road, if anyone happened to look in the right direction. So, at this moment, of course, a hospital nurse suddenly had to come rolling by on a bicycle. . . .

She nearly had me head first into the dustbin; but for the ten seconds that mattered, she kept her beak steadily in line with her handlebars; and by that time I'd swung myself round the corner of the house.

I got a good grip on the windowsill with my right hand, and then I brought my left hand round to join it; and I hung there for a second or two, with my feet tucked up behind me to keep them off the glass roof. Except that I hadn't anything to kneel on, it was an attitude of deep devotion. Well, such is the power of prayer that somehow or other I managed to get up on to the window-sill, and by holding on to the top of the open window, I was able to push up the lower half with my free hand and get inside.

I guessed the room I was in was Paul's room. It looked as if it was partly a bedroom and partly a workshop, with a lot of mechanical gadgets all over the place; bits of wireless sets and railway lines, and so on. There was a shelf full of boys' books, and one of the walls was pasted all over with neatly cut-out photographs of machines and ships and aircraft. The door of the room was open, and there was a landing outside with two more rooms and a cupboard that opened on to it.

I went across the room and instinctively, I suppose, I began to move cautiously, rather quietly. Just as I got to the door there was a sound somewhere; it was so soft and so short I couldn't tell where it came from or what it was; the sound of something falling, or dropping on a carpet, it might have been.

I listened, I should think for a full minute; but there was

dead silence. And in the silence, without any sound at all, the cupboard door across the landing began slowly to swing open.

It was too late to start wishing I hadn't come; but I wished it all the same; I desired it above all else. And when the handle of a broom suddenly fell out of the cupboard with a noise like the Alamein barrage, my desire knew no bounds.

There was another extremely unpleasant silence. How long it lasted, I don't know. I only know that when it broke, it wasn't broken by a sound; it was broken, oddly enough, by a sight—the sight of a small white kitten, which came out of the cupboard and looked at me for a moment, and then went off downstairs.

I put the broom back in the cupboard and shut the door. Then I tried the other two rooms on the landing; they were both bedrooms; so I went on up to the top of the house; but I didn't find anything that seemed of interest until I got to the attic. The thing that interested me about this was that it was locked. I hadn't explored downstairs yet, but this fitted in well enough with Mrs. Knight's story to rouse my curiosity.

All I could see through the keyhole was that the room looked as if it was lit by a skylight. Just over my head there was a trap leading to the roof; so I poked up the trap and looked out. Sure enough, there was a little skylight outside, and I got out to have a look. But the glass was opaque—that struck me as odd for a skylight—so I was no better off. I got out my pen-knife and I gouged out the putty round one of the panes; then I worked the glass loose as carefully as I could, so that no mess should fall down into the room below, and I lifted out the pane and laid it carefully on the roof.

It left a hole just big enough for me to get through; but I wasn't at all sure that if I did get through I wouldn't bust the whole skylight trying to get back again. So I lay down and I hung on to the window frame with one hand and worked my way through the hole as far as I could, without pitching head-first into the room. I felt rather like a wombat, hanging there upside down; and I probably looked like one, with my slightly protuberant ears and my bright eyes and the anxious expression on my face.

There wasn't much to see: a wicker armchair and a small table and some old newspapers lying about on the floor, and a lot of cigarette ends; there was a cushion on the chair with its feathers leaking out, and a cup and saucer on the table and a writing pad. The thing I liked the look of best was lying on the cushion: it was a pair of headphones, and they had a lead going off to a handy little transmitting apparatus stuck up under the sloping roof, so as to be well out of line with the keyhole.

It was bigger than an ordinary walky-talky set; big enough to have quite a good range, I imagined; not that I'm much of an expert, but I had learnt a bit about radio during the war. I remembered a set like this which I'd seen at Grenoble, and the girl who had used it had been able to get instructions from England quite easily; up till the time, that is, when the Germans took her out and shot her in the head in front of her mother and her young sister.

There was nothing else to see in the room, and as I felt that my shoulder was slowly being dislocated, I edged my better half—from the trunk upwards, that is—out on to the roof again. I put back the pane of glass and as much of the putty as I could, then I got down through the trap and shut it after me.

I had a look over the rest of the house on my way downstairs; but there was nothing more unexpected than the kind of things that always surprise me about the dwellings of the Philistines: the things that they can put up with about the house, that they have to see every day, and can look at without wincing.

Taste's a matter of taste, of course, but, from the look of her lampshades, Mrs. Earle obviously had too sweet a tooth. There was nothing showy about the place, though; it was all loathsomely discreet, from the *objets d'arts*—(the *art* was discreetly *nouveau*)—to the glazed print on the cover of the telephone directory. I didn't think much of Mrs. Knight's dusting, but otherwise the place didn't seem too badly kept.

At the bottom of the stairs I came down into the lounge which I'd seen the day that Paul had opened the front door to me. My idea up till now had been to let myself out of the front door in the ordinary way; but just on the bottom step I had my mind changed for me. The shadow of somebody outside suddenly showed up in the window of the porch, and I heard a key in the lock.

I ducked through a swing door into a passage; at the other end of it there was another door, and the remains of my common sense told me this would probably lead into the garage. I went straight through, and I stumbled down a couple of steps. The garage was dark; it had no window; and then I remembered noticing before that instead of an ordinary door, it had a rolling shutter that was padlocked on the outside.

I got behind the door and I stood there and listened. For about five minutes, I should think, nothing happened. Then I heard someone open the swing door and come into the passage. I pulled the gun out of my pocket and took a deep breath. From the clumping sound of his walk I guessed that it must be Paul; he was whistling in a soft, toneless sort of way. If I was lucky, he was either going to make for the kitchen or the lavatory. But I wasn't lucky: he clumped down the steps into the garage and turned on the light. Except that we had the door between us, I could have touched him.

He went over to a bench that stretched along the opposite wall; it was littered with all sorts of gear, tools and spares, and so on, and it had a little lathe and a grindstone fixed to it.

I watched him through the crack of the door; he ran through a set of drills, and when he found the one he wanted, he switched on the grindstone. He had his back to me and was stooping over the bench, and while he kept the drill on the stone there was enough noise to cover the sound of my moving out into the passage: only he moved first.

The grinding stopped; there was only just the motor purring, very softly; then he turned round from the bench and clumped over towards a cupboard hanging on the wall behind me. He pulled back the door to get at the cupboard, and we looked at each other: or rather, he stood and gaped, not at me, but at the gun.

I said to him in a whisper, 'Are you here alone?'

He paused, just a fraction too long. Then in a frightened sort of way he said:

'Um—no.'

'Go on, then,' I said, 'why don't you yell?'

He didn't answer; he still stood there gaping. So I brushed past him into the passage; and exactly at that moment, through the fan-light over the swing door, I saw a light go on in the hall.

I jumped back again into the garage, and he stepped away from me clumsily. I half-closed the door and I whispered to him:

'Who's that?'

He swallowed, and then he whispered, 'My mother—she's not well. You better not frighten her.'

I remembered then what Mrs. Knight had said—supposed to have a weak heart. I wondered. He stood there, Paul, just staring at me through his cock-eyed glasses and fiddling with the buckle of his belt.

'Why didn't you stay with her then, if she's not well?' I said.

Now that he saw I wasn't going to go for him he seemed to relax a little; he looked rather sullen.

'She'll be all right,' he said. 'She gets turns like this: just needs to lie quiet, that's all.'

'Where's she lying? In the lounge?' He nodded.

All this time the grindstone had still been purring away; and now suddenly I heard another sound, outside the garage. I went over quickly to the entrance and I listened; a car was backing along the runway. It stopped right up close to the shutter with its exhaust burbling; and then I heard someone get out, and I heard feet on the gravel.

I ran back again to the passage door, but Paul had shut it, and he was standing there in a damn-fool pose, spread-eagled in front of it with his iron leg stuck out. I could have hit him—or rather, I couldn't, let alone shoot him, and he knew it. Whoever it was outside was fiddling with the padlock already, and it didn't seem a moment for argument. I told Paul to move away; he didn't budge, and he didn't say anything. I said to him again:

'Get away!'

He still didn't move, so I grabbed him by the tie and swung him away from the door; but he clung on to the handle and he hissed at me:

'Don't—don't! You'll frighten my mother!'

I didn't want to touch him, the silly little fool, but what else could I do? I caught him round the shoulders and we began to struggle. I managed to open the door, but he kicked it shut again, and he wouldn't let go of me. I was surprised at the strength of the little so-and-so. Then, just as the shutter began to be pushed up, I gave a god-almighty heave and got the door open again. We both fell against the wall behind it, and I stuffed the kid's face into a pair of dungarees that were hanging on the back of the door; and there we stood. We must have looked pretty funny, locked in each other's arms, me hardly daring to breathe, and the kid hardly able to.

I heard footsteps going back to the car; then someone got in and slammed the door, and it backed slowly into the garage. I could smell the sweet smell of the exhaust as it came closer; then it stopped, with its rear bumper about a couple of feet away from us.

The driver got out. I didn't know, of course, but I was pretty sure it was Earle. Instead of turning off the engine, he opened up the bonnet and stood there playing about with the throttle for a bit.

Paul was standing absolutely still now. I'd got his arm up behind his back; I wasn't going to hurt him, if I could help it; but I wasn't going to take any chances either; so I kept his face buried in the dungarees.

Suddenly he took a violent kick at the bumper—but he missed it. He jerked me off my balance, though, for a second, and what happened exactly, I don't know, but like a fool I managed to drop the gun, and as he broke away from me, he kicked it underneath the car.

The engine was still running all this time, and as Earle was pulling down the shutter, I thought perhaps he hadn't heard us at first; then he called out:

'Hullo, Paul, what are you looking for?'

He came back and switched the engine off, and all you could

hear after that was the grindstone purring away on the bench.

Paul didn't answer. For a few seconds I thought I'd really hurt him. He stood there massaging his arm, and he was biting his lips with pain. Then he turned round, and somehow, in his clumsy way, he smacked his iron leg up against the wing. Earle was walking round from the bench and he called out to him:

'What the hell are you doing? Goddamit! Why can't you be more careful!'

I pulled the door right back as he came nearer, so that I was sandwiched against the wall; and I could see Paul looking at him though I couldn't see Earle.

'God!' he said. 'Look at this brand new wing! Clumsy little oaf you are sometimes—you'll ruin this bloody car!'

Paul didn't say a word. His face went very white, though; and all of a sudden he looked like murder. I heard Earle go back round to the other side of the car, still grumbling and cussing.

'And I've told you fifty times not to leave this grindstone running, haven't I?'

I heard him snap the motor off; and then in the silence, I heard him tapping a cigarette on his case and lighting it with a match. Paul simply stood there, I should think for twenty seconds, white to the gills and without saying a word. Then he hitched at the iron on his leg, and suddenly he turned round and clumped off into the house. As he went through into the passage he gave a little sob in his throat.

Earle called after him, but he didn't answer; he just clumped through the swing door and there was silence again.

I heard Earle sigh, and then he swore savagely to himself. He went on messing about at the bench for a little while, then he walked round towards the door; and just as he was going to put the light off—I could see his hand actually on the switch—he noticed the dungarees which had fallen off the back of the door. I couldn't have put them back without showing myself, so there they were.

He stooped and picked them up; then he pulled back the door, and I hit him crack on the point of the chin. As I hit him I brought up my knee good and hard, so it caught him where it hurts most. And he just folded up with a grunt and rolled over on the ground, groaning. It was too dark in the corner for him to have seen what hit him.

I ducked out into the passage, and I saw a door on the left, so I dived in. It was a wash-place, and there was a window in it that looked out on to the runway in front of the garage. I got out and dropped down—it was only a few feet—and I ran along beside the hedge towards the road. It was about ten yards away, and I was nearly there when I suddenly saw the top of a policeman's helmet over the hedge. He was standing talking to someone on the pavement. I stopped, instinctively, I suppose. Probably I should have done better to have kept going; anyway, I didn't. I crouched down against the hedge, thinking what I ought to do.

All of a sudden a racket started to break out inside the house, and the next minute Earle came dashing out of the front door, shouting at the top of his voice. Either I hadn't hit him hard enough or he must have been a damn sight tougher than I'd imagined. He went flying down the path towards the gate. I saw the policeman look round, but I didn't wait to see any more. I turned and ran along the passage at the side of the garage and into the garden at the back. I heard the swing gate bang behind me, and I hoped to God they hadn't heard it too.

Then, just as I was getting up on to the wall at the end of the garden, I saw the copper's helmet over the gate. He came charging down the passage, and Earle was behind him with another man—I imagined the chap the copper had been talking to. The copper was getting his whistle out as he ran; and then I heard it, that dull, shrill note, just as I dropped down on the other side of the wall.

It was a huge piece of waste ground where I came down, all over pot-holes and strands of wire and rubbish, and I kept tripping and sliding all the time. Then I got on to a rough cinder track, which was a bit better, and I streaked for cover.

There were some great stacks ahead of me, stacks as big as houses; they looked like crates and cans and cases; and there were huge coils of rusty barbed wire and old ammo boxes and disused chassis; mountains of stuff, all dumped. There were alleys running this and that way all through the stuff, and I went charging and skidding along like a mad steer.

Away behind me they were all shouting to each other, and I could hear the copper's whistle still going. I stopped for a second and listened; from the sound of it they seemed to have split up: the whistle was away over on my right now, but I could hear voices not far away, and there were feet pelting along on the left. All of a sudden a man shot across the top of an alley about twenty yards away. He caught sight of me and tried to turn, but he skidded and went down on his face.

Just where I was standing there was a huge block of jerry cans, it must have been twenty feet high at least, and the top of it was bulging out. I took hold of one of the bottom cans and I wrenched it away from the stack . . . the sound was like a dress rehearsal for the Apocalypse, and the next minute the whole alley was blocked right across.

I'd doubled on my tracks so many times that I wasn't really sure which direction I was going in now. Still, I kept going—I felt safer that way—and then all of a sudden I came out from the maze, and there right in front of me was a railway. It was about fifty yards ahead over open ground, and I was three-quarters of the way there, when one of them must have spotted me. I heard them suddenly start shouting again. I didn't look round, though: I went flat out till I got to the embankment, and as I scrambled up on to the track a train came slipping round the bend. It hardly made a sound; it came shooting up out of the dusk, and I just cleared the live rail in time. I was panting like a dog already, and what breath I had left went clean out of my body.

Then I found myself standing in the middle of the next track with another train which I hadn't seen bearing down on me. It was so close that I could see the driver in his cabin; I saw him jamming his brakes on and heard him hooting. I jumped back and crouched down between the two trains as they passed each other. I lay there with the wooden guard of the live rail pressing into my back and the ground shaking like an earthquake. The coaches went whipping by with a rolling, roaring sound, making a hell of a dust and draught. I was choked and deafened for a few terrible seconds, then it was all over; and there was I again, with nothing between me and arrest but my own legs.

Beyond the electric rail there were more tracks and strings of goods wagons were being shunted about. I got away on to the far side of some wagons that were standing still, and I looked out from underneath them across the tracks. I saw the Law, or at least, the top of the Law's head, moving along the embankment towards the place where I'd climbed up. Then I saw Earle. He came up on to the edge of the track and stood there peering this way and that in the half-light. Presently he trotted away towards the policeman.

I realized then that I'd been hanging on to what was left of my breath as though it might have been my last. I leaned against the truck in front of me and took it easy for a few seconds. I could hear the noise of wheels and engines and I could hear voices some way off. There was a sound of wagons clattering together, and then a sequence of clatters, growing louder, as a whole string of wagons bumped each other in turn. The wagon behind me gave as good as it got to the one in front, and then the whole string started moving off.

I was just looking out from underneath them when they started to move, and I saw Earle and the others coming back again. The truck passing in front of me was a long flat truck. It had nothing on it except a tarpaulin, and as it started off I climbed up on to the brake-rod and swung myself up from there on to the empty boards. I lay down flat by the tarpaulin, which was folded up and was too big to spread out. It wasn't much of a place to hide, but at least we were moving away from trouble; and in a couple of minutes we were heading at quite a good speed for Budleigh Salterton; or it might have been Saskatchewan, for all I knew.

Wherever it was to be, we went rattling along in the dusk, past rows of grimy suburban 'backs,' past gasworks and building yards, and the sort of places you only seem to catch a glimpse of from a train.

We went underneath a viaduct presently, and in the street lights high up overhead I looked at my watch. It was just after six. I wondered whether Jackson had got to the studio yet. If so, I hoped Mrs. Wellington had been there to let her in. How long would she wait, I wondered? And what excuse was I going to give for being late?—assuming I was ever to see my native heath again.

Then I noticed the train was beginning to slow down; going slow enough, anyway, for me to slip off without risking much except my dignity. So at what seemed an opportune moment—I was guessing really: it was quite dark now—I slid myself over the edge of the truck and let go.

The ground seemed harder and further off than I'd imagined, but I made a safe landing on somebody's allotment, and I rolled over on to a heap of fine fresh manure.

There were lights not far off, and when I'd picked myself up I walked into a rail fence which I hadn't seen in the dark, and got over it into a sort of alley that went along between two walls. There was a solitary lamp to light the place, but there was nothing to see by it. I stood still and listened; there wasn't much to hear either, except the train rumbling away in the distance.

I walked down through the alley into a street of houses, but I couldn't find that the street had a name. At the end of the street there was a main road with buses and pubs and lighted shops in it. It didn't look to me like Budleigh Salterton—or Saskatchewan either.

I found a cab presently and I said to the man, 'Where is this?' He looked at me sideways. 'I mean, whereabouts am I?' I said.

'This is Brighton beach,' he said. 'Where d'you want to get to, chum?'

I gave him the address and hopped in. A few minutes later we went past the Clapham Odeon, and I had at least the illusion that I'd reached civilization once more.

We got to Blake Studios soon after half-past six, and while I was paying off the cab Mrs. Wellington appeared. She was going out, but when she saw me she stopped.

'I let the young lady in,' she said. 'She come about ten minutes ago.'

I thanked her and I hurried indoors. When I got under the light in the hall I saw I was still in a bit of a mess, so I brushed myself over quickly. I called out into the living-room:

'Sorry I'm so late. I got held up.'

There was no answer, and when I went in I couldn't see anyone at first. Then I caught sight of someone sprawled, face down over the back of the sofa. It wasn't Jackson though—it was Florrie. She had been shot through the head from behind, and she was dead.

CHAPTER 16

I'D ALREADY DIALLED THE FIRST TWO NINES BEFORE MY BRAIN began to stop thrashing. Then I banged the receiver down and tried to get a grip on my thoughts.

I had a ghastly feeling, looking at Florrie lying there, that in a way I was really to blame for this. The fact that I had hardly known her didn't prevent me feeling utterly appalled by what had happened, and disgusted, too—disgusted with myself, because it wasn't the kind of case I ought ever to have got an innocent party involved in, least of all a decent little creature like Florrie.

It was obvious that she hadn't had either the instincts or the sort of experience a girl would need, getting herself involved in this kind of business. Not that it was much use reproaching myself about that now. After all, it was more or less for those reasons that I'd counted her in in the first place—because she'd seemed the last sort of person anyone would have associated with what I was involved in. I only hoped to God that she hadn't suffered or had had time to be frightened.

It so upset me, though, so overwhelmed me, that I had to wrench my mind back to get it in line with the situation—to try and work out what was to be done.

One thing was pretty clear: sending for the police now wasn't going to help Florrie, whether they came straight away or in half an hour's time. And it wasn't going to help me either; because half an hour might very well make all the difference between my keeping contact with Jackson and my losing it. She was almost the only bit of the puzzle that I'd got a finger on so far. If I let her slip, the chance of my finding any of the other pieces would probably go for good. And I couldn't shaking, but when I gave the chit back to him he winked and quivered his own hand at me.

'Better put a drop o' water in it this time,' he said, and he went off into a wheeze like a punctured concertina. 'Hullo, you've cut yourself,' he said.

I looked at my hand: there was a smear of blood on the side of it and on my shirt cuff.

'Scratched it just now on a tin,' I said. 'It's all right.'

He went away, and I carted the bottles into the kitchen and then I rushed back in the bedroom and began to change my shirt.

The bell rang again just as I was tying my tie. This time it was Jackson. And I realized, without even feeling ashamed of it, that in spite of my suspicion about her, in spite of what I was feeling at this very moment, I was glad to see her in a way; she looked so pretty and so self-composed—not hard-boiled, mind you, but simply like a girl at peace with herself; and I wondered whether she really was. Anyway, just the look of her had a sort of steadying effect on me, and I hoped I wasn't showing any signs of the inner tumult I was going through.

The pleasure of having her with me didn't last, though. I don't mean she was a bore. It was just that I found myself getting more and more tense all the time, and having to make more and more of an effort not to show it. It wasn't so much the danger of the situation, though that made things uncomfortable enough; it was because the whole thing was so macabre it revolted me. There was this girl, dead in my bedroom cupboard, a warm corpse, and Jackson and I sitting here drinking our drinks, and listening to Benny Goodman and Maxine Sullivan and Fats Waller.

Well, there we sat in front of the fire and talked and gossiped. I must say, she made the time go fairly smoothly, if you could call it smooth, considering the circumstances, because she was so friendly and so engaging and so easy to look at. But she never dropped a word or a syllable that might have given any colour to my ideas about her; nothing that even gave me an opening to explore.

Perhaps she was hoping the same sort of thing would come

from me; I don't know, even now; but she didn't get it. If anything was going to come up that I could make use of, I knew it had got to come up spontaneously. The slightest hint, the subtlest twitch in the conversation, and, if there was anything in my suspicions, she'd see the red light a mile off.

After a while, I hardly knew how to sit still. It really came to be quite a relief getting up now and then just to change a record. Whatever it is that some people find so insidious about the pleasanter kinds of swing, Jackson suffered from it. Suffered isn't the word I'd have used at any other time, because as a rule I feel the same way about it myself; but I was beyond the effect of any soothing harmonies at this moment.

It was getting on for eight before Jackson seemed to realize what the time was. She got up and said that she must go. Even then, she stopped in front of the books and began discussing this and that. Suddenly she put her finger on the back of a book and tipped it half out of the shelf. It was exactly at the place where Florrie's bag was hidden. She looked at the tooling on the spine and said something about it which I hardly heard; and then she let the book slip back into the shelf again. I felt as if I'd just missed treading on a rattle-snake.

She stopped again in the hall and had a glance at the books there; they're mostly foreign books. She pulled one of them out to have a look at it, and I noticed she still had the little antique ring on. She stood and looked at the book for a few seconds before she put it back, but she didn't say anything. I didn't see what the book was till then: it was Beethoven's *Briefe*.

Before she went I slid out a suggestion of our going to hear Verdi's *Requiem*. I remembered seeing it was going to be given at some church in the City, and as Verdi ranked pretty high among our common musical factors I hoped she might fall for the idea without too strong a suspicion of my motives.

She fell for it all right; but as usual, there was nothing to show which way up she had landed. She simply said that she'd love to come; that was all. And the way she said it would easily have satisfied anyone who wasn't in the suspicious frame of mind that seemed to be becoming my second nature.

After she had gone, it took me ten seconds to reach the

telephone; but the telephone beat me. It rang before I got there. My editor wanted a write-up of someone I happened to know, and he wanted it by the morning; not just an outline; he wanted something that would have meant the best part of a night's work.

I gave him the first excuse that came into my head; which was that I was feeling rotten, that I thought I'd got a touch of 'flu. I should have remembered, of course, this wasn't a good argument to spring on a Christian scientist. Anyway, he seemed to have set his heart on my having a shot at the job, whatever I felt like; and in the end I had to say the doctor had been and had sent me to bed. I could tell, though, from the old man's tone that he thought I sounded suspiciously healthy, and he didn't ring off with a very good grace.

I got on straight away to the number Herrick had given me; but everything seemed to be going against me this evening. There was no one in the office, of course, at that time of night, and I had to make three different calls to three different numbers before I could even track down Herrick's secretary. And when I finally did get her I was no better off. I was worse off, in fact—far worse. Herrick had gone to Germany, and wasn't expected back for three or four days at least.

It seemed to me during the next couple of hours that I must have walked about a thousand miles, backwards and forwards, trying to decide what I should do. Whichever way I turned for a solution the thing seemed to become more and more difficult, and my position more compromising.

I began to see gradually what a very tough spot I was getting into. Dammit, I was in it already. If I were to send for the police now, a lot of questions would be asked which would make things a very nasty colour for me when they began to check my answers. I knew the process only too well; that patient sifting, twisting, turning and scrutinizing of every word, every motive; matching one answer against another; checking off what one person corroborated with a statement by somebody else; times, dates, taxis, telephone calls—everything gone over, everything taken to pieces and put together again.

The police surgeon would obviously know, for one thing,

that Florrie had been dead at least a couple of hours, and that her body had been moved. That was the first thing I should have to explain—or else flatly deny that I knew anything about it.

But in either case, Mrs. Wellington, as soon as they asked her, would certainly confirm having seen me come back ten minutes after she had let Florrie into the studio. I don't mean she wasn't the queen of loyalty, Mrs. Wellington. She'd sooner have bitten her tongue out than say anything that might put me in a spot. But all she could do would be to tell the truth; and just as sure as it was that the police would ask her about it, she'd remember that I had a gun, that she'd seen me cleaning it that very morning.

Then there was that old fool from the wine shop; not such an old fool, perhaps, that he wouldn't be able to remember one or two awkward things. That scratch on my hand, and how my hand was shaking; and the blood on my cuff.

Where was the scratch now? That would seem a pretty obvious question, even to the dumbest detective. And where was the tin that I'd said had caused it?

That part of the story, I might be able to fake perhaps. But I couldn't fake a doctor who had ordered me to bed; which was the part of the story my editor would be certain to remember. Just as Jackson would remember that I had been with her, to all appearances perfectly fit and well, all the time the doctor was supposed to have been here. Why I should have lied to the editor was another thing I should have to find some explanation for.

There seemed to be only one piece of evidence that could possibly have been in my favour; which might have been conclusive, in fact. Any expert could prove easily enough that the bullet in Florrie's skull hadn't been fired from my gun: only my gun was now lying underneath the car in Earle's garage.

No; I was in a jam all right, a real jam this time. Even if Herrick backed me up to the hilt—and I wasn't so sure that he would—even if the police were told exactly what I was supposed to be doing, you still could not get away from the fact that every possible clue pointed to my being the only person who *could* have shot Florrie.

Again and again I went over every single point. How did I know, for instance, what Florrie had done with the note I'd left for her at the Astoria? It wasn't in her bag. I took the bag out from behind the books and had a look. More than likely she'd destroyed it; but if she hadn't, and the police somehow got hold of it? No use saying it was a million to one against such a thing. I wanted longer odds than that. If they did get hold of it there were two ways they could interpret it. One would be simply to believe the plain truth about it. The other way would be to see it as an inducement to get Florrie to come to the studio. If so, for what?

There was something else that wasn't in her bag either. That was the money I'd handed to her in the envelope at The Honey-pot. Because it wasn't there didn't mean she must have spent it; and if by any chance she'd kept it, there wouldn't be much difficulty in tracing it; not those nice new notes; they were almost warm when I had 'em from the bank.

The police might believe the truth about them or they might not; they might have all sorts of strange ideas. People use money for such odd things: buying silence, buying talk; buying other people's confidence, or something to give you more confidence yourself; paying for past favours, or favours to come. Still, whatever the police might suspect I'd paid Florrie for, they wouldn't be able to prove their suspicions—any more than I should be able to prove they were wrong. And foul suspicion's entrance in the mind, etc., often breeds ideas in a policeman's mind which wouldn't occur to an ordinary person. With the circumstantial evidence being what it was, and my not being able to disprove a single shred of it, lack of motive wouldn't mean a damn thing.

CHAPTER

17

IT WAS GETTING ON FOR ELEVEN O'CLOCK BEFORE I FINALLY made up my mind what to do. I could see only one way out; only one way that wouldn't involve a pretty high risk of my being charged with murder; and that was to get rid of the body. It seemed a foul idea, I know; a ghastly, cold-blooded arrangement altogether. The only possible justification for it was the risk involved in the alternative.

In a way, it was almost a relief to have made up my mind. And yet, as soon as I had made it up I began, more or less subconsciously, I suppose, to look for moral support—to try and square the plan with my conscience, or what was left of it after the last two hours.

I kept telling myself that, after all, it wasn't as though I had killed the girl. I reminded myself that I had once killed someone, and not in self-defence either. Near Grenoble I had had to stab a sentry; he never even saw me or heard me. I can still see him when I think of it, lying there on his back on the cobbles. He was quite young, not more than about eighteen; and I should think he had never even harmed a fly by the look of him. Yet it never seemed to sit very heavily on my conscience that I'd killed him. *C'est la guerre* and all that, I know; but it was a pretty cold-blooded effort, all the same. So why should it sit more heavily on my conscience merely to hide away a corpse?

Well, anyhow, I had decided now what to do, and I was going through with it. I had a perfectly simple plan, and barring accidents, there seemed no reason why it shouldn't come off. I don't mean there were no risks; the risks of disposing of someone's corpse illegally stand up and stare you in the face.

All I mean was that it wasn't a plan that involved my having to take any spectacular chances; not, as I say, unless anything went wrong. If anything did go wrong, it wouldn't be because I'd miscalculated; there wasn't much to miscalculate. It would simply be the clammy hand of providence intervening.

I went into the bedroom and I lifted Florrie out of the cupboard and laid her on the floor. I undid the mackintosh, very carefully, and I mopped up the blood with cotton wool; then I plugged a good wad of it into the wound and put a layer of gauze over it, in case it started bleeding again; and then I strapped it over with sticking plaster.

There was a woollen scarf round her neck, and I pulled it up and arranged it so as to hide the bandage. Then I dressed her up in the mackintosh, and I carried her out into the hall and sat her on a chair. I went back and got her bag and I slung it over her shoulder, and I pulled her gloves on to her hands. It wasn't easy; she was pretty stiff by this time.

The next move was going to be a tricky one. When I was describing earlier on what Blake Studios are like, I said there was a covered passage between the studio block and the little house where Mrs. Wellington lives, which has got my garage underneath it. In this passage there's a side door to the garage; it's about fifteen feet or so diagonally from the door of the studio. At the garden end of the passage there's a lantern to light the way to the other studios, and at the opposite end there's a street lamp. So the middle of the passage is fairly dark at night, and consequently there's quite often a loving couple there doing their loving.

After I'd got Florrie into the hall, I looked outside in the passage to see if anyone was about. There was no one there, so I shut the front door and went over into the garage through the side entrance. First of all I looked to see how much petrol I'd got; the gauge showed that I should need some more. Then I pulled up the hood and wound the windows up, and I left the door on the near side open. Then I went back into the house.

When I'd put off the light in the hall, I hoisted Florrie up till she was more or less standing beside me, or rather, leaning up against me. I had to bend her arm down firmly to get it round my neck, and I held it there with my right hand; and with my left I lifted her up round the waist. Even so, her feet were still touching the ground when I tried to walk with her. I got her outside, though, and I shut the front door. And just when the latch had clicked a policeman walked slowly across the top end of the passage; then he stopped.

I jerked Florrie back against the wall and I held her there with my arm still round her waist. I pushed my other hand up under her chin to stop her head from sagging, and there we stood. The policeman flashed his lamp down the passage; I watched the beam of light moving slowly along the opposite wall, then across the footway gradually over towards us. It lit on both of us just for a few seconds, and then it flashed up over our heads. After a moment he moved off, and I heard his footsteps going away in the distance. Suddenly I found that I was breathing again.

I hoisted Florrie round the waist once more and got her over into the garage without any further trouble. There was plenty as soon as we got there, though. The car isn't a big one, and there was no way in the world to get Florrie in the back of it with the spare wheel there too. It was taking too big a chance to go without the wheel; if I got a puncture I should be sunk. I couldn't put the wheel in the front either, because there isn't a key for the back; so if I got a breakdown and had to go to a garage, Florrie would take quite a lot of explaining, if anyone happened to find her doubled up in the dickey.

I tried every way there was to squeeze her and the wheel in together. In the end I had to haul her out and fix her sitting up in front. Putting all this down in cold blood like this makes it somehow seem even more disgusting now than it seemed at the time. But then I had had to try and screw down every feeling of decency, every moral scruple I possessed.

Still, I wasn't at all happy about having Florrie in front with me. It certainly increased the risk; although with the hood up, and the side curtains as well, there seemed to be no reason why anyone should suspect anything unusual.

All the same, there was a moment when we stopped to get some petrol that squeezed the sweat out on my upper lip. The man came round on the wrong side of the car first of all; he peered at Florrie through the window—thank God, it was fairly dark—and he must have thought she was asleep. When he came round to my side he nodded at me and grinned.

'Do with a bit of shut-eye meself,' he said.

Except for a few traffic lights, we hardly had to stop again for the best part of an hour. I knew the road like the palm of my hand, and there wasn't much on it at this time of night; so soon after twelve we were well on the way to Rudleigh. Now and again I had to slow down and ease Florrie back into her corner. She stayed put most of the time, and once I'd got used to the idea of having her huddled up there beside me, it didn't seem quite as ghoulish as it had when I'd first thought of it.

We passed through Rudleigh market place just as the clock over the Exchange was striking half-past twelve. The clock tower stood out flat against the sky like a piece of painted scenery, and the moon was wrapped up in a shawl of cloud. But it was bright enough to see by, and as I started off up the hill—I took a good run at it across the empty square—I just caught sight of a figure in the lane that runs down between the Baptist Chapel and the Bucket snd Spade; it was someone on a motor bike.

I didn't have time to see him clearly, but unless my luck had changed he looked suspiciously like a copper. And before I'd got to the top of the hill I saw the beam of his headlamp in the mirror. It made an arc of light on the road as he wheeled round out of the shadow; and then I could see the glare of the beam as he started up the hill after me.

My instinct was to shove my foot down on the gas, shove it down hard and make a dash for it. I wasn't trusting my instincts, though, not for the moment. I wondered what the hell could have gone wrong; whether I had done something or left something undone that was going to lead to trouble. The immediate problem, a problem of seconds, was what I was to do and say. It'd got to be settled pretty quickly, too. The chap was gaining on me all the way. I didn't slow down, though, and I didn't accelerate either. I just kept on as if I didn't know he was there.

We were out on the road leading over Rudleigh Heath towards St. Vitus by this time, and as he drew level with the car he signalled to me to stop. So I stopped; and so did the workings of my inside. If you've ever wondered what happens when the tongue cleaves to the palate, I can tell you: mine seemed to have cloven for good—or possibly for bad; I couldn't tell yet.

The cop got off and walked back towards the car. I just had the presence of mind to get out as he came up to the door. He glanced inside at Florrie, but I still wasn't going to give up. I said to him quietly:

'Sorry. Don't want to wake my wife. She's tired out.'

He looked me over for a second or two; then he moved away towards the front of the car. I followed him. He was obviously a college-fed copper; he had a moustache like a pair of antlers and a Cavalry Club accent.

'Happen to notice a town back there?' he said.

'Rudleigh, you mean? Yes,' I said.

'Huh. Didn't give yourself much time to notice it, did you? Built-up area, Rudleigh, you know.'

I could see it was meant to cut like a knife, so I pretended I was bleeding. I said, very humbly:

'I know; but you know what it is at this time of night——'

'No excuse for diceing along at fifty, all the same.'

(I saw that I was wrong about the Cavalry Club.)

'Diceing?' I said. 'In this crate?'

A slightly human look came into his eyes. He paused, then he said:

'W'you in the R.A.F. by any chance?' He tried to make it as off-hand as he could.

'Not exactly. Mucked in with them a bit, though,' I said.

'Thought you sounded like it. Where 'bouts you stationed?' he said.

'Doncaster, first of all; then Cardington.'

'Cardington, were you? Ever run into a bloke called Bassett?' he said.

'Bassett? Bassett?' I said, very slowly, as if I was really trying. 'Rings a bell somewhere——'

'Toothy Bassett—Winco; 'member him?'

Couldn't do much harm just to remember him, I thought; so I let a life-like gleam of recognition flit over my face.

'Toothy Bassett?—oh, good Lord, yes! *Now* I remember him,' I said.

The ground still seemed to be shaking under my feet, but the tremors were less violent for the moment. Anyway, the cop seemed definitely cheered by the news.

'Good Lord!' he said, ' 'straordinary thing. Jolly good chap, old Toothy.'

'Wizard,' I said.

'God, you should have seen him on ops! Ever go on ops with him?' I shook my head. 'Got the guts of a cucumber, that feller.'

It wasn't a simile that I would have chosen; still, he knew Toothy Bassett and I didn't.

'Well imagine it,' I said. 'Great guy, Toothy, great guy.'

I was half-wondering if these warm, reminiscent tones could really be mine. The cop was stroking his moustache with the back of his glove. In the light reflected off the road I watched his expression; he was gaping wistfully, rather abstractedly, at the front bumpers, and there was a glazed look in his eye. I could see the poor devil was re-living the only part of his life that had really had any meaning for him.

We stood there for a minute or two, and he drooled on about various people I'd never heard of and had to claim as bosom pals. Then I struck in with the 'small world' note, and we both came back to it—for different reasons, reluctantly.

'Keep an eye on that clock of yours, old man, won't you?' he said.

'You bet. Sorry I let it over-run,' I said. 'Won't occur again.'

'Good show!' he said. He went back to his bike and got on it; and then he turned round towards Rudleigh again. I got back into the car. As he went past, he waved his glove, and the night air was sullied with his parting shot:

'Cheerho!'

I drove on, and in about ten minutes we got to St. Vitus. I

went straight through the village, past the turning that leads off to Uncle Arthur's house, and I kept on till I got to the wood which is on the boundary of his place. It runs along beside the road for half a mile or more; on the other side of the road there's just Rudleigh Heath. There aren't any houses for a good long way in either direction.

All the way past the wood the road runs very gently down hill, and when I came in sight of the trees I cut the engine and put the car out of gear, so that it just rolled on quietly by itself. About a hundred yards before the wood ends, there's a rough ride which leads straight out on to the road. When we got to this ride I swung the car round, and it bumped over the top of the ditch into the wood, and there was just enough momentum to take it on behind a big bank of rhododendrons between the trees and the road.

I turned off the lights and sat still listening. Presently I got out, and I stood and listened again. I waited a long while; but the only sounds I could hear were the noises of the wood. A tree creaked as the wind lifted its boughs a little; a cone dropped on to the ground; a rabbit, or perhaps it was a fox, rustled along in the ditch close by; I could even hear the frogs far off in the pond near the middle of the wood; and birds that must have been woken by the car were fluttering and shifting among the trees.

I went round to the near side of the car and opened the door carefully, because Florrie's full weight was against it. She slid stiffly, slowly down off the seat, and she lay there with the back of her head on the step looking up at me.

I lifted her out and got her up across my shoulder with a fireman's lift, so as to leave my right hand free. Then I started off through the wood.

The moon was still behind the clouds; there was just enough light for me to see my way, but that was about all. I knew every inch of the wood, though. Time was when I used to play red-skins over the whole place, and there wasn't a track or a ditch that I didn't know. The ground was pretty soft from the rain, and it was thick with wet leaves, so I could move along fairly quietly.

It's surprising how much heavier a dead body seems than a live one; don't ask me why. I only know that after about ten minutes, going fairly gingerly and stopping every now and then to listen—I suppose for the sake of listening, really: I don't know what I expected to hear—Florrie seemed to weigh about half as much again.

I was moving through the wood diagonally, and every so often I came on to a ride, where the trees had been cut back on either side for the guns to stand—a sort of rough path two or three yards wide.

After a little while it seemed to be getting a bit lighter, and when I came to the next ride I stopped and looked up at the sky. There was still a lot of cloud about, but the moon was shining bright and clear for the moment, and it was throwing a sort of silvery light through the trees.

As I went across the ride, something—what it was I haven't any idea—something, anyway, made me suddenly turn my head. In the middle of the ride, about a hundred yards further down, a man was standing quite still in the moonlight.

As I watched him, he moved his hands slowly to and fro in front of him, as if he might have been conducting some musicians hidden under the trees. That hardly seemed likely, so I thought again; and I realized then what was going on. It was Geary, the keeper, and he was setting a snare. I couldn't see the wire in the darkness; I could just see that he was drawing out the noose, that was all. Then he stooped down and pegged the snare into the ground; and when he'd got it set, he kicked some leaves over to hide it.

Florrie seemed to weigh more every second. She had slipped down a bit off my shoulder while I was walking, and now it took all I'd got to hold on to her so that she didn't slip right down on to the ground. I didn't dare move a muscle.

Geary stood in the ride and lit his pipe. He didn't seem to be in any hurry, and by the time he'd decided to move on I was pretty well dropping in my tracks. His gun was leaning against a tree and he picked it up and put it under his arm; then he gave a little soft whistle, and suddenly old Bruce rustled out from the shadows and went nosing off along the ride. Geary stumped away after him, and a few seconds later I took the first full-sized breath I'd drawn for quite a time.

I let them both get well away, of course, before I made a move. Then, when I couldn't hear anything more, I heaved Florrie up and got her back across my shoulder properly; and I started off again.

The noises you hear in a wood at night always seem to sound twice as loud as they sound in daylight. Just after I'd crossed the ride I trod on a twig, and it went off like a mortar-bomb. I stood stock still—a second too late. I knew Bruce had pretty sharp ears, and I guessed he had heard me. A minute later he came chasing back along the ride, giving little yelps and whining with excitement, and I could hear Geary in the distance, cursing after him. The old dog went bounding on into the wood, though, by himself. I listened for a while to see if there was any sign of Geary following; but there didn't seem to be, so I started up again.

It was too dark to go quickly. The best I could do was to try and get along without making too much noise. I kept on, making for the north side of the wood; and in a minute or two the sound of Bruce had almost died away. But he must have changed his tack all of a sudden, because one minute he seemed to be thrashing about over towards the left, getting fainter and fainter; and then suddenly it sounded as if he was coming back towards us.

I did begin to go a little quicker then; but I started knocking into things and stumbling over. The ground was full of holes and there were fallen branches and roots and brambles trailing all over the place. With only one hand free, and Florrie's full weight on my back, it was almost impossible to get along in some places. I seemed to have landed in a sort of thicket. My legs kept getting caught in the brambles and tearing my skin through my trousers, and sapling stems came whipping across my face.

There was sweat—or it might have been blood, I couldn't tell, but I could feel it—running down into the corner of my eye. Still, I knew I couldn't go back, I should have to go on; so I did. Then a bough brushed my hat off, and I had to stop and stoop down as well as I could and fumble about till I could find it—unless I left it there. I was tempted to leave it for a second, only I knew it would be too much of a risk.

Then Bruce began to bark. Whatever he thought he'd come across, he could tell now that it wasn't a rabbit—not the sort he was after, anyway—and I knew that Geary would guess he had got hold of something. Whether it was a fox or a poacher he was pretty certain to come after it, and he'd be just as liable to let off at one as he would at the other.

I stood still and let Bruce get close enough to hear me. Then I called him, very softly. He stopped barking—but only for a moment; then he suddenly let out again, more excited than ever. I called to him softly once more. I could hear him bounding and bashing about in the thicket until he got quite close. Then he was suddenly on top of us, leaping up and licking me and whimpering with pleasure, as soon as he recognized who I was.

But he was puzzled and excited about Florrie; he couldn't understand. He kept nosing round her and whining and jumping up. I let him lick her hands and her face, anything to quieten him down; but he knew something was wrong and he couldn't make out what it was. All I cared about was that he shouldn't start barking again; and after a bit he calmed down and just sat there making little whining noises.

Then I heard Geary, some way away, whistling for him. He pricked up his ears at that, and started whimpering again. Eventually I got him to leave us and he slipped off into the bushes, wagging his tail.

I stood there in the darkness and I waited. I could hear Geary moving slowly through the wood, slowly coming nearer and nearer. He seemed to be moving about the thicket in a circle. Presently I heard him talking to Bruce again.

'Goo' dawg! . . . Git in 'ere, goo' dawg! . . . Git in 'ere, 'man . . . goo' dawg . . .'

And Bruce went thrashing about in the undergrowth. He came back once to where we were and stayed a minute or two, panting and whining. I patted him—I didn't dare to whisper this time—and then I pushed him off again, and he went back to Geary.

If I'd had room in my mind for anything but prayer perhaps I would have remembered how often I'd been thankful to Geary for his patience in searching out a pheasant that I'd winged or a rabbit which I *knew* I'd hit. Not that it would have given me much comfort to remember that at the moment. He must have spent at least ten minutes though, just beating round the thicket, sometimes not more than a few yards away, with Bruce rustling in and out of the bushes all the time.

Then, by the grace of God, a rabbit got up somewhere and the old dog was after it straight away. Geary called and cussed after him for a little; then I heard him lighting his pipe again, and presently he went off the way Bruce had gone.

I waited this time till there was no sound anywhere; then I pulled my way slowly out of the scrub and I went on.

After a while I came out on the edge of the wood, with Pyke's Field on the other side of the ditch, and I moved along, slowly, till I got to a gate.

This was the field with the pit in it where I had lost that hare the day I was out shooting with Herrick. Man and boy, I suppose I had known the pit for more than twenty years, though I'd spent more time there as boy than I had as man. I'd played pirates there and smugglers; I'd been shipwrecked there and marooned; I'd even found Doctor Livingstone there, rather surprisingly one afternoon, in the person of Gerald, the farmer's boy; I had been Stanley for the occasion.

There wasn't an inch of the place, a foothold or a ledge or a tree stump that I didn't know. And except for Gerald, who lived in Canada now, and who claimed to have made the discovery, I doubt whether there was another living soul who knew about the cave. You couldn't have known about it, in fact, unless you'd been shown where it was, because until you climbed right up into it you couldn't tell there was a cave there at all. The entrance to it was hidden completely by an overhanging ledge of ground, and there were bushes growing across the front of it.

I knew that if only I could get Florrie's corpse up into the cave it would be safe—and so would I. But the most difficult part of the job was still ahead. The pit was only about thirty yards or so from the hedge; but those thirty yards gave no cover of any sort. Still, the possibility of anyone else besides Geary prowling around in the field or the wood at this time of night was pretty remote; and they'd have to be in one or the other to spot us crossing from the gateway to the pit. Even then, unless we struck the skyline by accident there wouldn't be much chance of our being seen in the dark—not that that really gave me much feeling of security. I knew I'd got to make the journey somehow, though; so I decided to wait for another patch of cloud to slide over the moon, and then to make a run for it.

The first time I had been dropped, *une bonne bouche pour le maquis*, it was very much like this; the same sort of sporadic cloud cover; landing in an open field and having to race across it, not knowing whether anyone had spotted me or not, and expecting a yell or a shot every half-second. That night, though, at St. Jean-du-Gard, I had found myself among some of the best and most courageous friends I've ever met; and I'd thanked God for it, devoutly and completely breathless.

To-night my thanks would be for finding myself alone; that's what I hoped, anyway. Only just as I was going to lift Florrie over the gate into the field—the gate had been wired up, so I couldn't open it—I heard a sound over on the far side of the field; must have been about thirty yards or so beyond the pit. I wasn't sure what it was at first. Then I heard the sound again: it was Bruce; and I guessed Geary had worked his way round through the wood and had come out into the field.

It seemed as if he was coming slowly along beside the hedge. I waited and I listened: then I knew that in a few minutes he'd get to round where I was standing at this very moment.

There was only one way out, and I took it. I laid Florrie down in the ditch—I didn't make a sound—then I crept back a few yards into the wood till I got on to a ride; and I began to run.

The ground was soft and damp, so I got away without

making much noise. Every second, though, I was expecting to hear Bruce barking again; but nothing happened. So I stopped and listened again after a little while; still there was no sound. I couldn't make it out. It seemed against all the rules of bad luck that Bruce could have stayed on his own side of the hedge.

I went a little farther on till I came out almost on to the road; then I stopped again. If, by some miracle, Geary hadn't found anything, I guessed he'd probably be making tracks for home. I knew where his cottage was; it was back towards Rudleigh, about a quarter of a mile down the road. All I wanted to do now was to get away as fast and as far as possible; and yet some mysterious compulsion, some iron power of curiosity, made me stay.

God knows, I wasn't feeling exactly sentimental at that moment—or was I?—but the thought that I'd had to leave Florrie there, to dump her secretly and just let her lie unburied in a ditch, gave me a feeling that was so sordid, so unclean, I felt I should never wash it out of my mind.

I did, of course, in time, because time is a pretty powerful antiseptic. (I was glad, all the same, when they found her. It was a long while afterwards—so long, in fact, that there was nothing to connect either of us with what had happened). But that night, as I stood there in the bushes, heaving and sweating like a hunted hind, all I prayed for was that she should rest in peace for evermore.

The sky had cleared in the last ten minutes and the moon was bright enough to show the road quite clearly. Looking along the road past the end of the wood, I could see where Pyke's Field began. Further along still, though I couldn't see it, I knew there was a gate in the hedge, and presently I heard it give a creak as it was opened, and then as it was shut. I looked out along the road and I dimly caught sight of Geary trudging off towards his cottage; and there was Bruce with him, thank God.

As soon as the sound of his footsteps had died away, I pulled out of the wood and started off in the opposite direction. In about ten minutes I got to the open ride where I'd turned in with the car, and then I slowed down.

through, looking rather anæmic but strong enough to dry things up a bit, so I decided to walk.

It was a little after five o'clock. Dusk was dropping down already, and it was getting dark enough to suit my frame of mind. Still, by the time I got towards St. James's I had at least got something in the frame; so that things didn't seem quite as black or as bleak as they had looked up till then.

What I had decided to do was to go and see Herrick the moment he got back from Germany and tell him the whole tale. I knew that strictly speaking this would be breaking the letter of our agreement. But that agreement wasn't meant to cover a murder; not as I looked at the agreement, anyway. I knew that by going and telling Herrick all this I should deliberately be making him an accessory after the fact; and that was the part I didn't like. No man has a right to infect another man's conscience with his own guilt. Still, if he didn't believe me, no one else would. But if he did I knew that he would let absolutely nothing prevent him from lending me a hand out of the mess I had got into; and there was no hand that I would sooner borrow.

Even the idea of sharing what was on my mind with someone else, of being able to talk freely about it, seemed somehow to make the thing lighter. And by the time I got to Wirth's, though I wouldn't say tranquillity and inward joy beamed forth upon my face, I would say I probably looked a little less harassed than I had been feeling up till now.

Wirth was standing alone in the middle of the gallery when I came in. He was drinking a cup of tea and looking at a wash-drawing hanging on the wall. When he saw me he put down the cup without a word, just rolled his eyes, and made a motion for me to stay where I was. Then he flitted away up the little staircase into his office.

I waited. The office door was half open, and I saw him inside, propping the mounted Palmer up on a stand; then he stepped back and looked at it critically. Something seemed to be wrong; maybe it was the light. He pulled the stand round and had another look. This time it seemed to be all right. He gave a little gesture of perfection, then he turned round and fixed that unblinking glare on me, like an owl; and he crooked his white, fat finger for me to come up and see.

I went up into the office, and the next thing I knew was that someone I didn't even get a chance to look at had got their gun stuck in the back of my ribs; and then I heard the door shut quietly behind me.

Whoever it was with the gun frisked me quickly and thoroughly. I stood still and said nothing; the only things I could think of didn't seem likely to ease the situation.

I don't know whether you've ever been stuck up. I hadn't until this moment, and apart from being plumb scared by the suddenness of it, I realized what a fool it makes you feel. I put my hands up quite instinctively, and I turned to try and look over my shoulder. It was Earle who had got the gun; he pushed my face round violently, as if he didn't want me to get a look at him. That was no hardship to me; but Wirth was the only alternative—except for Palmer's picture, and somehow I had lost interest in that for the moment—so I had to look at Wirth.

I noticed I wasn't the only one whose breathing had increased with the tension of events. He was breathing audibly through his nose. He looked at me with that hard blank stare for a few seconds; then he pulled a big bandanna handkerchief out of his breast pocket, and he cocked up one knee to fold the handkerchief across it; but he was a bit off his balance.

'Careful,' I said.

He looked up sharply and fixed me again with that owl-like glare. All he said was, 'Shut up!' But he bit the words off with a venom that really was startling.

When he had folded the handkerchief into a strip he came and tied it over my eyes. I said to him, 'Is this really necessary?'

Apart from a dislike of not being able to see where I'm going—I've had it from birth—it seemed to me simply a way of dramatizing the situation; and from my point of view it was quite dramatic enough already.

What I didn't quite understand was this elaborate trap, if I was merely going to be bumped off. Dammit, they'd had plenty of opportunity to get me since they'd tried and failed outside the Minstrels—if they had wanted to, that is. So I comforted myself with the idea that now they had changed their tactics; maybe they had found that for some reason or other I could be more useful to 'em alive than dead.

In the cold light of reason, writing this long afterwards, I can see that as a line of argument this held about as much water as a butterfly net. But on the spur of the moment it was the best thing I could think of, and I hung on to it as though my life depended on it; which it did, in a way.

Nobody spoke; then Wirth pulled my arms down and clamped my hands together round the back of my neck. After that I heard him leave us and go back into the gallery. Earle just stood there with his gun pressed gently into my back. I heard Wirth pulling down the blinds; then I heard him locking up. Presently he called out softly, 'All right'; and Earle steered me out of the office and down the stairs.

Where we got to after that I don't quite know, except that we seemed to steer towards the back of the premises; then we stopped. There was an open door somewhere; I could feel the air coming in from outside. Then a car started up and I heard Wirth say, 'O.K.'

Earle jerked the gun into my side and I shuffled forward and out of the building; but only for a moment. I was pushed into the back of the car, and it started straight away. As we moved off someone slammed the door.

I was getting tired of clasping myself round the nape, but Earle still had his gun in my ribs, so I asked him whether I couldn't put my hands down.

'Put 'em in your lap,' he said, 'and see that they stay there.'

'I thought that was your job,' I said.

'You want me to smack your jaw with the butt of this thing, you're going the right way about it,' he said. I could see his sense of humour and mine were rather different; so I folded my hands demurely in my lap and I decided to keep quiet.

I wished that I knew which way we were going. But before we had left the gallery they had pushed me about in so many directions that I didn't know where we had started from. It seemed to me as if we had come out at the back of the place, but it might just as well have been at the side. And then, before we got going, we had twisted about in a mews—I took it to have been a mews, anyway; we had seemed to be bumping about over some cobbles, and I had heard someone washing a car.

I tried at first to work out a mental map of the way we were going, by spotting—as I thought—some particular turning or slope in the road, or the way the traffic lights seemed to come. Then we'd suddenly take another turning that I couldn't account for, and I'd be completely lost again.

For the first few minutes Earle kept the gun pressed hard against my side. Then he took it away, but he didn't say anything. I almost hoped that he was going to put it back again. It was somehow a more comfortable feeling to know definitely where it was than to have no idea what he was going to do with it.

I suppose if I had been bigger and braver—and possibly rasher—I would have started some sort of dog-fight in the gallery and tried to smash my way out. But taking the long view of the situation—and wherever firearms are involved, it's always my instinct to take the longest view I can get, preferably right out of range—a policy of appeasement seemed to me the most promising line to adopt. I rather wished I had brought my umbrella with me, just as a token of my inclinations. I guessed, in fact, that unless I was being carted off to some quiet little charnel house in the suburbs, I should probably be finding out quite a lot of things I wanted to know in the next few hours.

Neither Earle nor the chap who was driving seemed in the mood for talk. The only conversation they had was when the driver asked Earle for a light; and when he said, after we had been driving for about half an hour, that we should need some more gas. Earle said we should have to wait; and I was left wondering what for.

Presently the driver said to him, 'When do we eat?' He had a cold, sluggish way of speaking, as if he was the kind who hadn't much use for words.

Earle said: 'We'll see.'

'You bet we will,' the driver said.

Earle's reflexes seemed to be sagging; it took him thirty seconds to think what came next; and by that time its brilliance was fading.

'We'll eat when I say,' he said.

There certainly wasn't much in my situation to take comfort from, but I felt quite an inward glow at the amity that seemed to exist between them. For the rest of the trip their souls were so sweetly attuned that the spoken word obviously became unnecessary.

After we had driven for, I suppose, nearly an hour, we swung off the road in a sharp turn to the left; and then we stopped. The driver got out and opened the door, and Earle took the bandage off my eyes.

It was dark, of course, but there was already enough moonlight to show the shape of things, though it took a few moments for my eyes to get accustomed to being open. Earle stuck the gun in my back and pushed me out of the car into the driver's arms. The headlights of the car were shining on to a painted wall, and in the light reflected from it I saw the driver's face. It was a mean, impassive-looking mug and I didn't like it any better, seeing it at close quarters, than the last time I had seen it—in the coroner's court.

The place we had come to looked as if it had once been a petrol station. It seemed a sizeable sort of dump, though it looked pretty derelict. The windows were boarded up and the doorway was littered with leaves and rubbish. There was a row of petrol pumps in front of the building, and in the moonlight, with their odd-shaped globes, they looked like some kind of primitive totems.

The driver grabbed me by the arm as I got out of the car and pushed me ahead of him into the doorway. I noticed the handles of the doors were chained together and padlocked. Earle reached out from behind me and gave the chap a key. I could only see Earle's left hand, but I guessed he could still do business with the right if he wanted to, so I stayed still.

The fellow opened up and we went inside. He pulled out a torch, and I could see by the light of it that the place was wide and empty and rather eerie. The only sound was the sound of our footsteps, and they went echoing through the place as we walked across a concrete floor.

Overhead there was a skylight; it seemed to have been blacked-out once, but here and there the moonlight was coming through jagged holes. On the floor there were some odd bits of garage apparatus lying about. It occurred to me suddenly that perhaps this was the place Mrs. Knight had talked about—Earle's place on the Chertsey Road.

We crossed over to a door on the far side, and as we went through the fellow put out his torch and turned on a light.

Earle said sharply, 'Watch the black-out!' And he went to each of the windows in turn, and looked to see that the black-out frames which still covered them were properly fixed. I noticed now that he had put his gun away, and I remember feeling faintly thankful for it.

The room we were in had apparently been a sort of store-room. There were two or three bays of empty storage racks, some fitted with pigeon-holes, and a lot of sacking and crates and other gear lying about. Over in the corner there was a spiral staircase, and Earle started winding his way up it.

The sandy-haired mystery was still standing too close to me for my liking. I looked round at him.

'Get a move on,' he said; and he jerked his knee hard into my buttocks. I went on up, and left him foraging about among the racks.

The place upstairs might have been some sort of office at one time; there was an old-fashioned roll-top desk and a few odd bits of office equipment, but that was about all. It looked as if the only thing it was used for now was storing junk; everything was thick with dust, and there was all sorts of rubbish on the floor, spare parts and old tyres and a busted back seat of some car with all its innards trailing out of it. On the window ledge there was a collection of old empty bottles, and there were some out-of-date lubricating charts hanging on the wall.

Earle took one of the only two chairs and stuck it in the middle of the floor. He told me to sit; so I sat down, and I watched him light a cigarette. He saw me looking at him and he knew very well that I was getting desperate for a smoke.

Presently he went to the top of the stairs and called down: 'Dusty!' There wasn't any answer; so then he called again: 'Come on—what the devil are you doing? Can't you find anything down there?'

When Dusty did show up he had got a great ball of heavy binder twine under his arm and a piece of rope in his hand; and between them, in a matter of minutes, they had me appliquéd very neatly to the chair and gagged with Earle's handkerchief. First he had twisted it between my teeth, and then he had bound a scarf round my jaw to keep the thing in place.

I assumed these precautions meant that they were going to leave me alone; and I wasn't disappointed—or was I? When they had finished Dusty said, 'I'm getting hungry: when do we eat?'

Earle didn't answer. He went carefully over the whole of my harness, and when he had satisfied himself that the only way I could get out of it would either be by strangling myself or cutting my arteries on the twine, he turned out the light and they went away.

The beam of Dusty's torch shone for a few seconds as they went down the staircase; and then there was darkness.

I sat there listening to their footsteps growing fainter as they went back through the empty garage; then I heard them slam the outside door; and after a few moments there was the noise of the car starting off.

When that had died away all I had to listen to was my own breathing, and the sound that came from trying to turn my head or ease the position of my arms; not that that would really have done much good. It was the whole situation that needed easing; and as things were going it seemed to be getting more and more gummed up every minute.

CHAPTER

19

I DIDN'T HAVE TO TEST MY BONDS—IN ANY CASE, THEY HURT like fury if I didn't sit still—to know that between them my friends had made a pretty good job of trussing the goose. I could hardly move at all physically, but there was nothing to stop my mind from going round like a catherine wheel; though it didn't throw much light on my predicament, and such sparks of thought as flew off weren't at all pretty.

Both the past and the future looked to me equally dim. The only positive achievement I had to record was that in spite of all that had happened I hadn't entirely lost touch with the Opposition.

On the negative side, among a lot of other galling reflections, there was the fact that now it was through their initiative, not mine, that this contact was being kept up. It seemed rather a paradoxical situation, but I didn't think it very amusing at the moment.

Wherever it was, this little hidey-hole they had brought me to, it seemed to be fairly remote from human ken; the only ken that I got of any humans was now and again when I heard a car far away in the distance. Otherwise, for all that I could hear of the outside world, I might have been in a padded cell; I guessed I probably should be before this business was finished.

I had no idea what the time was; not that it mattered in the least. But the most irrelevant trifles seem to take on an extraordinary importance when you get really overwrought. And though I may be able to write about all this now as though I didn't take it very grimly at the time, what with the combined feeling of shock and suspense and impotence, my nerves felt as raw as an open wound.

I worked out that it must be somewhere about seven o'clock, judging by what I thought it to have been when I had got to Wirth's. I don't suppose there was twenty minutes in it either way; but I went on worrying and worrying about it. At any rate, it was something to take my mind off the immediate future.

The silence, as I sat there, was almost like something tangible. Perhaps the darkness made it seem more oppressive, I don't know; anyway, there was nothing I could do to relieve it. I'd already tried shouting, of course, as soon as I'd heard the car drive off. But I only sounded like somebody coughing with a mouthful of dumpling.

I imagine about an hour must have gone by before anything happened to break the silence; and then a telephone began to ring.

It couldn't have given me more of a start if someone had let off a cannon. I gave such a leap in the chair that the cord round my wrists and ankles cut into my skin like wire.

The telephone seemed to be somewhere near the bottom of the staircase, and it went on and on and on, so that I wanted more than ever to yell out loud. There was something most unpleasant, a kind of atavistic feeling, in my sitting there in the dark, as though I were some animal, listening to that insistent ringing, and knowing by instinct that whatever else it meant, it must mean danger for me.

Then it stopped.

During the next half hour or so the bell went again twice: and each time I leapt in my chair, and each time the cord cut savagely into my wrists and ankles. In the end, I found I was so keyed up waiting for it to start ringing again that I was almost counting the seconds. But it didn't ring any more.

The next thing that happened was that I heard a car stop outside; and then I heard footsteps crossing the bare floor of the garage. A light went on down below, then there were feet on the iron staircase, and Earle's head and shoulders twined up cautiously out of the spiral.

He stopped so that he was silhouetted against the light downstairs, and he looked over into the darkness to see if I was still safe and sound. Then he came on up with Dusty behind him, and they turned on the light.

They had been away, I suppose, for the best part of two hours—two of the most uncomfortable hours, physically as well as mentally, that I think I've ever spent. I had a feeling, though, that this kind of discomfort might be preferable to what would happen now that they had come back.

Neither of them said anything. Earle stood and looked at me as if he was trying to weigh up my feelings; then, thank God, he took the gag out of my mouth. I almost felt grateful to him, and I pulled a few faces, just to relieve my muscles as well as my temper.

He sat down in front of me astride the other chair with his arms folded over the back of it. There was nowhere for Dusty to sit except the desk; so he shoved up the roll-top and lounged against the inside.

Earle and I just looked steadily and unmoved at each other for a few moments. Looking unmoved was easier for him; he knew what was coming; and it was now that I really began to sense the unpleasantness of the situation. I imagine poor Pepys waiting to be cut for the stone must have felt rather like I was feeling; only I hadn't got anyone praying for me outside the door. Perhaps that might have made things worse, though—if anything can be worse than apprehension of the unknown.

Dusty took out a penknife, and he began slowly whittling away a bit of wood which he had picked up off the desk. Still nobody spoke. Earle looked up at the light; then he got on to the chair, and he fixed his scarf over the shade so that the bulb glared down on to my face and left the rest of the room in shadow. And there the three of us sat, Earle and I just looking at each other, and Dusty working quietly away with his knife.

It was the first time I had seen Earle close to, except for the glimpse I had caught of him coming out of the grill at the Astoria. And my God, that seemed a good while ago. In point of fact, it was less than a week—one crowded week of glorious life. I wondered what the chances were of stretching it to last a fortnight. From the way Earle was looking at me I wasn't too sure about it. Not that there was anything particularly menacing about him—outwardly. Not, that is, if I could really have looked at him objectively, which wouldn't have been easy at this moment. He had a rather more hard-boiled, a more set expression than when I'd first seen him; it was a look that suggested there was a fairly uneven temper hidden away under the surface; not very deep down, either.

He took a cigarette and held the packet out behind him for Dusty, but he kept his eyes on my face. It must have pleased him to notice that I couldn't help watching the packet as he slipped it back inside his coat. He still sat looking at me with those large tawney-coloured eyes. Then suddenly he said:

'Now talk.'

I didn't answer for a moment because I hadn't decided exactly what line to take. He waited, and he spat a small fleck of tobacco off his lips: he spat it deliberately at me, and why, I don't know, but more than anything that he'd done up till then, that got under my skin; which, of course, was a good enough reason for hiding it. So I said, as calmly as I could:

'What is it you want me to talk about?'

'Don't mind,' he said; 'as long as you don't waste time trying to be funny.'

'That's all right,' I said. 'I've got the whole night ahead of me.'

I could see that I had one clear advantage—probably the only one—that he belonged to the lost tribe—he had no sense of humour at all; and like most people who haven't got a sense of humour, it made him uneasy when he came across it in someone else.

'Don't imagine you've got the whole night,' he said, 'or anything like it.' There was a slight edge on his voice this time. 'You've got five minutes and no more to make up your mind what you want to say.'

'I don't want to say anything,' I said.

He didn't answer for a second; he just sat there, keeping his finger on his temper. Then he said, 'In that case, we shall have to do a bit of persuading.'

I saw Dusty look up for a moment in the gloaming outside the radius of the light; then he went on with his whittling process.

'Might make things easier,' I said, 'if I had the faintest idea what all this was about.'

It wasn't a line I had much confidence in, but at the back of my mind I had a hazy kind of belief in time being on the side of the angels; and I hoped that, for practical purposes, the angels might count me in too on this occasion. Anyway, gaining time is always better than losing it.

'You must have a very short memory,' Earle said. He was standing up now and walking slowly round. 'This bring anything back to mind?'

As he said it there was a sudden burning flash of pain on the back of my hand, an agony that seemed almost intolerable . . . then he turned away; and I saw him drop the stub of his cigarette on the floor. Again, for a little while there was silence.

It wasn't a pleasant way of spending the night. Earle's powers of persuasion weren't very original, but he used them pretty thoroughly. There were short bouts of physical violence, not introduced tactically or for any reason that I could see, except to trim off the frayed edges of his temper; and he alternated these bouts with long, long spells of plugging the same set of questions at me over and over again.

What was I really after? . . . Who was I acting for? . . . How much did they know? . . . Naturally, he didn't put things quite as deliberately as that. In fact, he showed a good deal more subtlety and more ingenuity, besides being much quicker on the uptake, than I'd given him credit for. But that was more or less what his questions amounted to.

He was considerably hipped, of course, by having to put things in such a way that they wouldn't show how much—or how little—he really knew. And it was this more than anything else that helped to stiffen my upper lip and my backbone and all the other bits and pieces that began to need stiffening as the night went on.

Dusty took very little part in all this, except to lend a hand now and again in trying to break off some outstanding piece of my anatomy. Most of the time he just sat there on the desk and went on whittling away at the little figure that he was carving. Every now and again he looked up, if things seemed to be getting interesting, but he never once changed his expression; which was probably all to the good. I couldn't imagine it changing for the better.

My hunger to know the time had been satisfied by my being able to catch a look at Earle's watch now and again, when he sat with his arms crossed over the back of his chair. He kept coming back to this position, sitting straight in front of me most of the time, blowing the smoke of his cigarette into my face almost as if he was doing it accidentally.

Just about midnight—or that's what I guessed it to be—Dusty was doing some particularly unpleasant work with his knuckles on the back of my head where the hair grows short; and in the middle of this operation the telephone rang.

I hadn't said anything about it having rung before; after all, it was none of my business to look after theirs. They both looked over towards the stairs, as if they expected some sort of apparition to appear. Then they looked at each other: Earle jerked his head and Dusty went down to see what it was about.

Earle followed him to the head of the stairs and leant against the iron balustrade, listening. I could just hear one or two grunts coming from Dusty down below, but what he was saying I couldn't make out.

Presently I heard him coming up the stairs again. When his head came level with the floor, he stopped and he lit a cigarette. Earle was impatient, I could see that; but he let Dusty take his time; and Dusty waited till he got up into the room again; then he said:

' 'nother bible meeting,' and from the way he said it, the proposition sounded as if it might mean something he didn't welcome.

'When?' Earle asked him.

'Monday evening. And it's a "must" this time. Little Man's good-bye sermon—I hope.'

'Oh?' I saw Earle look at him sharply. 'When does he leave?'

'Day after.' Dusty paused for a second, and then he said quietly: 'You know something? I'm sick of these bloody meetings. Too much bloody talk, too little bloody action——'

Earle said, very sharply, 'Shut up!'

But Dusty apparently didn't feel like shutting up' he went on, still in the same dry voice: 'I don't need no bloody pep talks. We don't none of us need pep talks. Why the hell don't they get on with it?'

'Shut up!' Earle yelled at him good and loud this time. Dusty didn't turn a hair; all the same, he kept quiet; and he walked over and sat on the desk again, and went on carving his little figure.

Earle stood where he was for a few seconds, and when he came back and slumped down in front of me across the chair, I could see he was in a pretty good rage. He didn't say or do anything for a bit; then, when he did open up, he went out for results in a big way.

At the end of about a couple of hours, he had worked off the worst part of his temper. I hoped it was the worst part, anyway, because by that time its effects were showing a good deal more on me than on him. Between them he and Dusty made a pretty thorough job of beating me up; and though in the ordinary way you wouldn't take me for a girlish type—I hope—I just keeled over at the end of it like a Swinburnian maid, and I passed clean out of the picture.

How long I was out for, I don't know. But it was worth it just for the sheer pleasure of realizing, when I came round, that after six or seven hours of being lassoed to the chair, I was free from the waist up.

My head was down between my knees, and I felt as though every pin Paquin had ever held in his mouth was sticking into my arms and shoulders. It was a pleasurable kind of paralysis, all the same. And then Earle jerked me upright again and wiped a cold, sopping cloth round my head and face. It was so cold it made me catch my breath, and I sat there gasping for a little while and feeling faintly sick.

For a minute or two there was silence. Earle reached over

and filled his lighter from a bottle on the window-ledge, and Dusty went on quietly working away with his knife.

But I knew it couldn't be more than a temporary let-up; and presently Earle got to work again. His tactics were just the same—and they got him the same results; but only because now I was watching my tongue even more carefully than before.

There's a limit to what one's nerves will stand in the way of being filed down, and when you reach that limit, either they crack or they go dead. Mine were beginning to feel numb, partly, I suppose, because of the bashing I'd taken, and partly because I'd not had more than a couple of hours sleep in the last twenty-four, and so I was feeling pretty tired to start with.

Still, I knew I could rely on Earle to keep me awake; and he did.

He went on grilling me, on and off, till half-past four, on the evidence of his own watch—I still got a peek at every now and again. Long before this, though, at intervals of about ten minutes, Dusty had started slipping off into dreamland—and sometimes off the desk altogether. Each time Earle turned round and thumped him back into the cold world of reality. I didn't envy him his dreams, but I did envy him the chance to kip down, even with only a roll-top desk to snuggle into.

I was glad to see him getting sleepy, though, for other reasons—reasons which had only come to me in the last half hour. I didn't want him to be too alert the next time I felt faint—or looked as if I did.

I began to look it just about a quarter to five. Dusty had dropped off again, with the little figure he was carving lying in his lap and his knife resting in his hand. It must have been a fairly true-to-life performance that I gave, because Earle thumped Dusty back to earth again and slapped the wet cloth into his hand and told him to go quickly and get some more water.

This wasn't exactly as I'd planned things; it was going one better, in fact. I had my head stuck between my knees again, and I watched Dusty, upside down, twisting out of sight through the iron staircase. Then I lifted up a little.

Earle was standing straight above me, and I brought it all the way up from the floor, just like Carpentier used to bring it up—smash on the point of the chin . . .

Earle's head went back as if I'd broken his neck; and just in case I hadn't, I snatched a bottle off the window-ledge and as he went down in a half-turn, I helped him on his way.

I was still tied by the legs, so I toppled over on my knees and I reached out for Dusty's knife off the desk. Then I slashed through the cord round my legs and I stood up.

I guess in the excitement of the moment I didn't have a chance to notice how rocky I must have been feeling, because from then on I was working pretty fast.

I grabbed the bottle of lighter fuel and smacked it on the banisters. Then I poured the fuel all over the stuffing of the old car seat—it was stuffed with kapok—and when I jammed the thing in the top of the stairs and put my lighter to it, you'd have thought all the oil in Texas had gone up. There was a funny kind of waffling noise, and then a blanket of flame seemed to burst all over the room.

I just caught sight of Dusty glaring up through the spiral ironwork, but I didn't wait to see how he was going to take things. I ripped the black-out curtain down but I couldn't get the window open; it was stuck. So I bashed the glass out with a chair, and then slung myself out on to the window-sill.

In the few seconds before I let go I saw Earle beginning to stir. This was the second time I'd failed to hit him hard enough, and I made a mental note not to let it happen again.

The seat was blazing like a bonfire, and Dusty was butting away at it trying to get it unstuck. A lot of packing and stuff had caught fire as well by this time; it was very pretty to watch, the whole thing, but I'd had enough of it.

I let go—and crashed three or four feet on to a corrugated roof; and then I went slithering and rolling over towards the edge. The gutter came away in my hand as if I was ripping rind off a cheese. I fell limp—it was only a one-storey drop—and I was up again and off the mark almost before I'd landed.

It was getting quite light, though it wasn't broad daylight yet, and there was a good deal of mist. I'd landed in a sort of yard, with a broken down wooden fence round it and refuse lying all over the place.

I got over the fence and I started running. The ground was glistening with frost and it was quite hard. All of a sudden I began to feel freezing cold, and as soon as I started off I realized that I was feeling pretty groggy too—not so bad, though, that I felt like taking it easy.

There seemed to be nothing but flat fields and hedges all round; but away over in the mist I could see something that looked like long rows of sheds; so I headed towards them. As I got nearer I could see it was a group of greenhouses, and on the far side of them I could see a road.

I slowed up when I got closer; then, as I didn't see anybody about, I got through a hedge, and lay down in a ditch on the other side. It was a dry ditch, thank God, and it gave me a bit of cover from both directions—from the greenhouses and the field.

I lay there panting, and shuddering because of the cold, and I looked back over the field towards the garage. The window was a square stab of flame, like a blazing lantern in the misty morning light; and smoke was rolling out at the top of the window and coiling straight up in the still air. Within about a couple of minutes fire and smoke seemed to be spreading all over the place, and a little trickling flame was beginning to creep along the roof towards the front of the building.

I looked at my watch. It was barely ten to five—barely five minutes since I'd given Earle his *paquet surprise* and the hubbub had started. As soon as I'd got my breath I moved cautiously out of the ditch, and I started up along an alleyway between two of the greenhouses.

Suddenly I heard something like the sound of a lorry. There wasn't time to go back, I was too near the road; so I lay down flat and listened.

The lorry stopped and someone jumped out.

It wasn't Earle and it wasn't Dusty either. I could tell that because whoever it was began whistling *Lily Marlene*, which didn't sound as if it would have featured in either of their repertoires at the moment. Then he broke off whistling and

I heard him light a cigarette; I was so close that I could hear him strike the match. Then I heard the tailboard of the lorry drop down, and presently the crack and smack of boxes being loaded up.

I didn't count them but there must have been about twenty or thirty; and all the time I was afraid the fellow would see the garage on fire—looking back down the alley between the greenhouses I could see a rolling column of smoke high over the hedge—and that he'd start off then to find out what was going on.

But he never spotted anything. Luckily there was a big signboard up in front of the greenhouses, and this must have blocked his view. Anyway, I heard him put the tailboard up presently, and then he started off.

He went past the top of the alley where I was lying, and as the lorry trundled away, I ducked out and chased after him. It was a near thing. I had to struggle like an eel on a hook to try and get my foot over the tailboard. The road was long and straight and in a few seconds we were beating along it at a pretty good pace, with a fifty-fifty chance of my being bounced back on to my skull at any moment. Gradually the odds shortened in my favour, though, and I managed finally to get in among the boxes and out of the wind.

It was pretty cold and pretty uncomfortable. I didn't know where we were or where we might be heading for. Still, I didn't much care as long as I was getting away from my night's lodging. I knew we must be somewhere on the outskirts of London, and presently I saw Brentford gasworks away over in the distance. From then on I knew the way, and in a little while we were at Hammersmith.

We stopped at the Broadway against the traffic lights, and I dropped off. It was a stone's throw from the place where I'd put Herrick down that morning I'd brought him up from St. Vitus. It reminded me how keen I'd felt then about the prospect he'd unfolded for me in the car. I couldn't help wishing now that I had had the sense to fold it up again and give it back to him.

CHAPTER

20

The arrangement was that Jackson and I were to meet at St. Guthric-under-the-Wardrobe, or whatever it was called, where they were giving the *Requiem*, at about three o'clock. By that time I had managed to get a bit of sleep, and I'd shaved and bathed, and dealt with the worst of my afflictions; luckily, though, these didn't show too badly. And I had dealt also with one simple problem of deduction which you'd think anybody but a blind man would have spotted straight away.

While I was lying in the scented waters of my bath—that's the kind of sybarite I am; must have a drop of Rose Geranium—I began thinking back over my trip to Llandfrith, and about the talk I'd had with the Maxteds. And again, in my mind's eye, I saw that snapshot of Becker and the two girls.

Well, you know how it is when something keeps recurring in your memory but you can't place it where it belongs—then suddenly it comes to you? I suddenly remembered something in that snapshot which set me thinking of a whole lot of other things.

I remembered my first meeting with Jackson and our lunch at the Villa d'Este; I remembered her stopping a moment to look at Beethoven's *Briefe;* I remembered Maxted slicing his apple and wiping the blade on his trousers; and I knew that if Bob wasn't my uncle already he soon would be; would be, that is, if only I could manage to keep clear of last night's company. Not that I imagined that was going to be easy, even with my eyes and ears pinned wide open.

At five-to-three there was I, waiting at the church, waiting at the church . . . and then Jackson arrived. She looked as cool and collected as ever and just as pretty, with that yellow turban on that she'd worn at the concert. If I hadn't had good grounds for suggesting we might have a heart-to-heart talk later on, I certainly would have tried to concoct something.

The church was fairly full but we got seats. They were a bit towards the back but they weren't too bad; not that it matters very much where you sit to listen to something like Verdi's *Requiem*—if there is anything like it, which I doubt.

To me it's one of the most inspired and most inspiring of man's musical utterances. And St. Guthric's is an ideal place to hear it. I think it's one of the best of the few City churches that managed to escape the blitz. It's high and light inside and rather bare, but without being too severe. It's got a beautiful ceiling by Thornhill and a carved screen the colour of sandal wood. The only thing I don't care for is a rather heavy aroma of incense. Still, one forgets everything, even the surroundings, when you hear Verdi's *lux aeterna* floating up and soaring round those walls. It seemed like balm in Gilead, listening to such sounds, after the kind of things I had been hearing lately.

The *lux aeterna* comes towards the end of the *Requiem*. There's a passage in this part where the trio and the woodwinds all seem to be singing together like a choir of cherubim. That, at least, was the happy impression I got, as long as my glance didn't fall on the middle-aged *mezzo* with a fifty-inch bust.

For the moment, though, I wasn't really thinking about anything except these celestial sounds. I was looking up the gallery which runs round three sides of the church, and suddenly all my enjoyment came to a dead end.

Sitting up there, partly hidden by a pillar, I saw Dusty. I couldn't see much of him, but I could have told him a mile off after last night. I knew him by the turn of his head—he was looking away just when I caught sight of him—and by that sandy forelock of his, and his blue shirt-collar. Whether Jackson had seen him or whether she knew he was up there, I don't know. I didn't bat an eyelid—at least, I hope I didn't. I just slid my glance off on to something else and sat quite still.

It was a peculiar situation, if you come to think of it, with a contrast between appearances and reality which couldn't have been more far-fetched. Listening to that heavenly harmony in those surroundings you would have imagined that one's mind would have been as far removed as possible from any ideas of intrigue and brutality. And looking at the flowered-velvet matron sitting in front of me, and the innocent dome of her spouse—in fact, looking anywhere about the place, such thoughts wouldn't only have seemed improper—they'd have seemed almost indecent.

I suppose if I hadn't been as big a mug as nature's made me I might have been prepared for something like this. I was, in fact, but not for it happening quite so soon.

I didn't imagine for a moment that Earle would be likely to let things rest where they were; but I didn't expect to be dogged quite as openly and as persistently as this. Nor had I thought of associating Dusty with a liking for music; certainly not for anything ecclesiastical, anyway. Still, there he was; and I hoped he was being bored to death. For all I knew Earle might be up there as well, because from where we were I could only see the side of the gallery where Dusty was sitting.

I guessed there must be still about a quarter of an hour to go before the music ended. If we stayed till then I imagined that might be asking for trouble; and as I never know what to do with trouble when I get it, I began to try and think of some way to prevent it.

After a minute or two I pulled out my handkerchief and held it rather surreptitiously up to my mouth. At the same time I began to wilt a little, and I put on the sort of expression I imagine the early Christian martyrs must have worn, a look as if I were full of sweet reasonableness and feeling rather sick.

I knew after a moment that Jackson had noticed it, but I didn't pay any attention. I waited till she'd glanced at me a couple of times and then I caught her eye. She didn't exactly smile but it was something like it, and then she leant towards me and she whispered:

'You all right?'

I just nodded—to show I was past speech—and I started listening to the music at once with great concentration. I could tell she still kept glancing at me, and I let her see in a minute or two that the effort of listening was proving too much for me.

Presently she leant over again and she whispered:

'Shall we go?'

I protested, but only rather feebly; and so we slid out into the side aisle and tiptoed away.

As we went out through the inner door I glanced up at the gallery again, and I saw that Dusty's place was empty. I guessed it would take him thirty or forty seconds at least to reach the porch of the west door; and by that time we were not only outside but I had apologized for our having had to leave, and had excused myself on the grounds of being allergic to incense. Also, I'd dropped my glove on the step of the porch and had gone back for it.

It was dark by this time, and Jackson was in front of me looking for a taxi; so she missed seeing me lock the door on the outside.

At any other time I should have enjoyed waiting to see what would happen when the congregation broke up and tried to get out. But just now I wanted to go home, not only so that I should be shot of Dusty—for the time being, anyway—but because of the talk I wanted to have with Jackson.

As we got into the taxi I suggested we should go back to my place for a drink. I wouldn't have betted on her answer a week ago, but now I knew almost for certain that she'd say 'yes', and she did.

We could have gone anywhere, of course, for a drink; but it wasn't just that I was thirsty—I'm always thirsty. This time I was hungry too, and especially for information.

I was hoping the church would keep Dusty within its fold for some time—not that I imagined there was much chance of my being let out of his sight for long—and if it hadn't been that I had a special reason for our going back to the studio, I'd have suggested somewhere he might have been less likely to pick us up. Still, I hoped that by the time that happened, my talk with Jackson might have borne fruit; and unless her answers turned out to be lemons, it'd be fruit that Dusty wouldn't find very appetizing.

Time was short, though, and I'd got to work fast. If Dusty's telephone talk at the garage had meant what I thought it meant, Bruno Rankel would be out of the country by the day after to-morrow. And seeing what was now known about my inquisitive disposition, it seemed highly unlikely he'd come back again until something had been done to neutralize my capacity for making trouble.

When we got home I mixed a drink and I let Jackson do most of the talking, partly because I was thinking of other things and partly so that she wouldn't feel too much at ease—nothing like a one-sided conversation for producing an air of embarrassment; not that I imagined Jackson's poise would be cracked as easily as that. Still, it might help to break it down, and that was what I wanted.

I waited till she had put her drink on the table; then, when she was empty-handed, I opened a drawer and took out the Swedish knife Farmer Maxted had given me. I threw it over to her and she caught it—left-handed.

For about two seconds there was silence; and in those two seconds the atmosphere between us seemed to change completely, like a curtain going up and letting something very chilly into the room.

'Hullo, you're ambidextrous,' I said.

She was looking at the knife, but she hadn't turned a hair. The only thing I noticed was that she paused for a second before she answered; then she glanced up.

'Sometimes,' she said. She looked at the knife again. 'What's this for?'

'For you,' I said.

'For me?' She said it with such an ingenuous smile that if I hadn't had that snapshot from Llandfrith propped up in front of my memory she might have fooled me.

I could see that snapshot now, clear as daylight. Doreen was the girl on the left, so Mrs. Maxted had said, and Lena was the one on the right. The photograph had shown them facing each other as they stood pitching straw into the wagon—so Lena, of course, was pitching left-handed, only it had taken me about a week to realize it.

And when I did realize it, it reminded me of one or two other things. It reminded me first of all of that lunch with Jackson at the Villa d'Este. I remembered admiring the way she ate her spaghetti, like a professional—except that even professionals change the fork into the right hand for spaghetti; and her right hand had been fiddling with her glass; I remembered noticing that.

Another thing I'd realized was why the smaller blade of Lena's knife was the one that she had used most; that's to say, I tumbled to the reason as soon as I tried to use it. The way most people open a knife is to hold it in their right hand and pull the blade up with their left. But you can't do that if the nick for your nail is on the under side of the blade, as it usually is if you've got the knife in your right hand. The nick in the small blade could only be on the upper side if you've got the knife in your *left* hand. Sounds pretty confusing, I know, but you've only got to try and open a knife this way and you see at once how awkward it is.

Another thing I remembered was Jackson looking at my Beethoven's *Briefe*. I remembered seeing that ring of hers on her left hand when she took the book out of the shelf. I tried that too—pulling one out and opening it with my left hand—and it was just as awkward as trying to open the knife.

Thinking over these things, I'd thought back about others—the way she lit a cigarette or changed a record—and I remembered clearly that then she'd used her *right* hand. All the more reason, of course, why I should have noticed the other times, when she'd used her left. Still, I'd paid pretty heavily for my lack of observation, and this seemed a good chance to make up for it.

She stood there weighing the knife in her hand; and then said, 'Where did you find it, pray?'

'Place called Llandfrith,' I said. 'You know it?'

'Llandfrith? Yes, I know Llandfrith,' she said. 'I had a job there during the war.'

It happened that I was standing in front of the fire when she said this; but I had all the sensations of going to sit down on a chair and someone pulling it away from underneath me.

'I was working there in the Land Army,' she said.

I climbed back on to the level again, and I said, 'Under the name of Lena Bethell?'

She really did it beautifully; just opened those round, brown eyes of hers with something between a gape and a smile, and she said slowly:

'How . . . on . . . earth . . .?'

'Because I've just been up there,' I said, 'to Goronwy's Farm. That's where I found this.' I took the knife back from her. 'What made you into Jackson? Are you married or something?'

'No—not even "something." No, I just changed it—well, for purely personal reasons.'

'What were they?' I said.

The act was still perfect. She looked at me as if I'd said something I ought not to have said, but she could still smile about it. She said—and she hesitated a little over it——

'What I meant was . . . for private reasons.'

I said again, 'What were they? Was it the same reason you changed the colour of your hair?' She peeled the smile off this time, and she looked rather chilly all of a sudden. 'Had it anything to do with Carl Becker?' I said.

She turned round and looked at me with a fixed expression; then said slowly, 'What is this—some sort of third degree? Who's Carl Becker, anyway?'

'You really need to be reminded?' I said.

She pretended she did; I wasn't giving any help, though; so then she said:

'You mean the prisoner—that man on the farm, at Goronwy's?'

'That's who I mean,' I said. I saw I'd got to be patient if I wanted her to convict herself out of her own mouth. In fact, there wasn't any other way; so unless I could trip her into doing that it was going to be very difficult to put the screw on.

'I think you're behaving extremely strangely, aren't you?' she said; and there was definitely a hard frost on her manner now.

She began to get up, so I said to her, 'Sit down!' and I pushed her back on to the sofa again. 'We're both behaving strangely,' I said. 'Let's drop it, shall we, and start talking sense?'

She tried to get up again. 'Will you let go of me——!'

'Certainly,' I said.

I let go of her; but she didn't get up. I knew she wouldn't. She wouldn't go now without trying to get some idea of how much I knew. So she sat there, trying to look like an injured innocent. And such is the weakness of the flesh, or of mine at any rate, that I found myself almost feeling sorry for her. Oddly enough, if she'd been a plainer and more humble specimen, I think I probably would have felt more like relenting.

'Well, who's going to do the talking?' I said.

'Really! I should imagine you'd better, hadn't you? . . . Some sort of explanation, I should think . . .'

'Right. Let's get back to Carl Becker——'

'I never said more than two words to Becker in my life.'

'What were they?' I said. She didn't seem to have a very good memory, and I wondered if I could improve it with a fairly heavy piece of bluff. 'Rather more than two words according to the story Doreen tells, and she's fairly shrewd, I should say.'

'Doreen! Who, Doreen Shelley? Doreen knew absolutely nothing——'

'About what?' She'd stopped herself, but not quite quickly enough. 'What didn't Doreen know anything about?' I said.

'Me, of course. Why on earth should she have known anything special about me?'

'Who said she knew anything special? All I said was she seems fairly shrewd. And, after all, you shared a room together, didn't you, for quite a time?'

I wanted to keep her guessing, but I could see that if I was going to get her right off the line I should have to keep switching the points. So I said to her:

'Did you know anyone else up at the Camp there?—I mean besides Becker?'

She stalled; I thought she would.

'May I ask what right you think you've got,' she said, 'to cross-question me in this way?'

'I'm doing the asking,' I said. 'Did you know anyone else up there or not?'

She cut back at me impatiently: 'No, I did not. I knew a few of the girls up at the hostel and the people on the farm, that's all. And I really don't know why I should stay here just to allow you to pour out a lot of crazy questions at me.'

'Well, if all I'm going to get is a lot of crazy answers,' I said, 'perhaps you're right.'

She got up; so I opened the door for her.

I was praying on my metaphorical knees that she wouldn't have the nerve to go; and my prayer got a hearing. She turned away and flicked her cigarette into the fire, and she stood with her back towards me, looking at the burning logs for a few seconds. Then she said, quite casually, and with that faintly sardonic expression that I'd noticed once or twice before:

'I must say I should be amused beyond words to know how all this started.'

'It isn't as funny as all that,' I said; and I shut the door.

'Isn't it? Sounds utterly ridiculous to me, the whole thing.'

'Perhaps you don't know the whole thing.'

'I know all I want to know,' she said.

We were only talking like this, of course, because we were both playing for time, and neither of us could afford to lose. Jackson would have given her all to know exactly how much I knew. But it wasn't her all I wanted, not at this moment, anyway. I wanted something I could trip her up with; and in the end she gave it to me herself.

'That day I met you at the Villa d'Este,' I said, 'who were you really waiting for?'

She looked at me as if I might have been something unpleasant in a bottle, and she said, 'You seem to know all the answers, I should have thought you'd have known that one.'

'Perhaps I do,' I said.

'Well, then?'

'You were waiting for a man called Earle, weren't you?' I said.

She looked at me a long time; it must have seemed quite a good get-out—I meant it to, anyway, and she took it.

'You win,' she said quietly. 'I still don't see what it proves, though.'

Then I let her have it.

'It proves you were lying just now when you said you didn't know anyone at Llandfrith Camp. Earle was sacked from the Camp there after Becker got away. You knew that.' She tried to interrupt me but I didn't give her a chance; I let her have it all. 'And it proves you were lying again, because it wasn't Earle you were there to meet—it was Becker. Only Becker was dead, but you didn't know it then—or did you?'

She wasn't given to showing what she felt very plainly, but you could see for a second that she was frightened and that she was angry at being fooled.

'How should I have known it?' she said. And it was when she spoke she gave herself away, because everything was fairly well under control, except her voice; that had a kind of huskiness in it that wasn't like her.

'Maybe someone could have told you,' I said.

Again she didn't answer straight away; then she said—and you could see she was pulling herself together—'I haven't the faintest idea what you're driving at.'

'I'll explain, then,' I said. 'The person who killed Becker could have told you.'

'Are you suggesting that I know who killed Becker?'

'I'm not suggesting anything,' I said. 'I'm stating it as a fact——'

'You're mad,' she said.

'Oh no, I'm not. You know who killed him,' I said. 'You know perfectly well; and you know why, don't you?' (I was damn well going to find that out, if I couldn't find out anything else.) '*Don't* you?' I said.

She tried to move away from me, but I stopped her, and I made her look at me again. There seemed to be nothing but pupil in her eyes; she really was scared now, and she didn't want me to see it.

'You know why Jimmy Earle killed him, don't you?'

She looked up at me quickly with an expression I didn't understand at first; and she said, as if she was completely mystified:

'Jimmy Earle? You don't imagine Jimmy Earle was mixed up in it, do you?'

'Who killed Becker then?'

She turned away from me again, and I let her go this time.

'Well, it wasn't him,' she said, 'that I know.'

'How do you know?' She didn't answer. 'He told you so himself, I suppose?'

'Yes, he told me himself.' She said it with such flat conviction that I couldn't make sure whether to believe her or not.

'He'll have a job to prove it,' I said.

Suddenly, as I said this, she rounded on me, and the tension in her voice snapped.

'Will he? I just don't begin to understand you. What on earth is it you're trying to pretend?'

'I'm not pretending anything,' I said. 'If Earle didn't kill Becker, who did? Perhaps he told you that too?'

We stood there looking straight at each other like cats starting a fight. I could see she wasn't acting any more, for the simple reason—so simple that it hit me like a stone on the head—that she must have been in love with Earle all this time. Come to think of it, I don't know why I should have suspected such a thing. Anyway, I hadn't suspected it and I suppose that's why it came to me as such a surprise?

There was silence; some ash fell into the grate.

'I suppose you're going to say it wasn't Earle who tried to run me down outside the Minstrels' Club—or had you forgotten that?'

'Don't! Don't please talk about that,' she said, 'it was *horrible*!' She covered her eyes up with her hand, so I couldn't tell for a moment whether she was acting or not. I must say she gave every appearance of anguish; and I believed her when she spoke again. 'I swear—I swear I knew nothing about that——'

'Then how came Earle to know I was there?'

'Oh, I don't know, I honestly don't know,' she said, and it was pretty obvious this time that her distress wasn't put on. 'I may have said something, without thinking, about our going on there afterwards, after the concert; I may have done . . . I just don't remember . . .'

'And Earle may have told someone else without thinking, you mean?'

'He may have done. I don't know, I don't know . . .'

'Dusty, for instance?' She didn't answer. I let the idea sink in; then I said: 'So it was Dusty, was it, who killed Becker?'

From the way she looked, all of a sudden, I could see she had no feelings about Dusty at all.

'Of course it was him—and you know it,' she said savagely, although her voice now was almost a whisper.

'Why "of course"?' I said.

'Why do you imagine?' Then what she said sounded so trite, and yet was so unexpected, I could have laughed—'Every man has got his price, hasn't he?'

'Whatever that may mean. For Christ's sake!' I said, 'let's not talk in riddles any more. What was it Becker wanted?' It made her jump, the way I said it, and I meant it to. But I wanted hard facts, not double talk.

'He wanted too much,' she said, 'that's all I know.'

It was enough for me. At any rate, it gave a glimmer of daylight. Becker sounded as if he'd been a man of business. He had known, presumably, the value of the information he was carrying—its value, that is, to Wirth and company—and he had tried to cash in on it; only Earle wasn't playing.

I hoped I should be luckier than Becker, because now I was going to try and do the same thing—cash in on something that I knew and Jackson didn't.

And, all of a sudden, as it does sometimes, at the most crucial and inapposite moments of one's life, the telephone rang.

I answered it, and it was Herrick. I didn't know whether to plead a wrong number or whether to ring off or what the hell to do. Then I thought, well, he'll only ring again if I do that; so I took a chance.

'Hu*llo*, Cecily!' I said. 'How are you?'

There was just a second's pause, then he said: 'Do I gather you're not alone?'

'Far from it,' I said, 'of course, I'm not.'

'I see. Then p'raps I'd better ring later. I only wanted to find how things were going. All right, I hope?'

'Well, no, not exactly, darling,' I said.

Anyone else might have had some justification for thinking I was screwy. Herrick was a person of imagination, though.

'Sounds as if you're in a bit of trouble. Are you?'

'Oh yes,' I said airily, 'have been for ages.'

'Can you handle it?'

'D'you know, honestly I don't know. Isn't it silly of me?' I gave a gay little laugh with that one.

'You alarm me rather,' he said.

'But, of course! That's the whole idea,' I said.

'You mean you're in trouble actually at this moment?'

'You're a very discerning young woman, if I may say so,' I said.

' 'fraid I find this conversation more and more difficult to follow,' he said. 'I think I'd better ring you in the morning. You'll be there?'

'Well, I really don't know,' I said. 'I rather wish I did. It's awfully inconvenient.'

'I see. Well, I'll hope for the best then. Good-bye.'

'Good-bye, sweetie,' I said.

As I turned away from the telephone, Jackson took a cigarette out of her case, and I took out of my pocket the lighter I'd picked up on my short stay at the Hotel Excelsior. My own would have done—but not for this purpose. I gave her a light, and I held it so that she could see the initials on the lighter: J.Y.E. She recognized it all right, and she knew I was watching her.

'Know where I found it?' I said.

She still tried to cover up, but her voice gave her away again. 'Found what?' she said.

'This—I found it beside Becker's body. I know exactly what happened—and I know it wasn't Dusty who killed him.'

She was still looking at the lighter with a sort of glazed expression. Then she turned and looked at me piteously.

'No—no, it *was* Dusty. I tell you, it *was* Dusty. I don't know what's at the back of your mind, but whatever it is, there's a mistake——'

I still don't believe that at that moment she knew the truth. I believe Earle had told her it was Dusty, and that she had fallen for it. I hated to disillusion her; must have been that I was out of practice. Anyway, I stamped on my better feelings and I said as brusquely as I could:

'Certainly there was a mistake; but I didn't make it. Earle was the one who made it—should be more careful about letting people listen to his conversations,' I said. 'Perhaps you'd better tell him about it.

I don't think she understood what I was talking about, and I didn't care. I said to her:

'Listen, Jackson—Lena—whatever you call yourself, I'm not interested in your private affairs or Earle's. It doesn't mean a thing to me whether his misdeeds catch up on him or not. So I'm willing to do a deal. How about you?'

She looked about as near tears as I guessed she ever got—tears of impotence and fear, not real misery.

'Who's Bruno Rankel?' I said. 'D'you know him?' She nodded. 'Know where he lives?'

She hesitated this time; then she said, 'He lives in Hampstead.'

'Right. That's where we're going,' I said.

For a long time she didn't make any move; so long that I wondered what she was thinking about. But I knew now that I could afford to wait, so I said nothing. Presently she held out her hand for the lighter.

'Oh, no; not until we get there,' I said. She didn't like trusting me, and I don't blame her; but she knew the alternative; so we went out through the side door into the garage and got into the car.

At the top of the street, as we turned the corner, I pulled in sharply and stopped against the kerb. We sat and waited. She looked at me, wondering why. I didn't bother to tell her; but if anyone was trailing us it must have been with an invalid chair, because that was the only thing on wheels that turned out from the street behind us during the next couple of minutes.

We drove the first part of the way without saying much. There was one thing, though, I was still puzzled about; and that was what Jackson's friendship with Becker had amounted to, if anything. So I put it to her, as she had calmed down a bit by now.

She wasn't exactly forthcoming, but I gathered that she'd found him a change from the rest of Llandfrith society; he seemed to have been a moderately cultivated creature. And then, somehow or other, Earle must have got his claws into him—and into her, I imagined—and in the end, he had used her as a blind for Becker's escape.

She didn't say all this, of course, in so many words; it was largely a matter of putting two-and-two together. One thing which seemed pretty clear, though, and which accounted for a lot of others, was that she obviously was completely in Earle's grip. Whether this was a testimony to his strength or to her weakness I couldn't make out.

For the last part of the journey she was silent again, except to give me one or two directions. Rankel couldn't have chosen a better place for his hide-away. It was plumb in the middle of Hampstead's alien colony. His neighbours must have been mostly people who had come there to escape just the kind of beastliness it was his job to propagate. Certainly it was an ingenious form of camouflage.

I stopped where Jackson told me, in a long dark street in the Belsize district. The house was a big, old-fashioned semi-detached house with a tiled pavement leading up to the front-door steps.

'Well,' I said, 'what happens next?'

She was back on an even keel now; or she sounded as if she was.

'I've done my share,' she said.

'Not yet; you haven't finished yet,' I said. 'When we get safely out of here again, then we'll call it a day.'

I was thinking of my nice little Colt .25, the one I'd lost under Earle's car while I was wrestling with Paul. I'm not fond of firearms, but it would have been very comforting just now to have felt its little butt in my side-pocket. Still, a woman—especially a woman with a tender conscience—can be a very useful weapon in certain circumstances; and if it came to a question of choosing between Earle and Bruno Rankel as a sacrifice, I guessed there wouldn't be much hesitation on Jackson's part.

She sat in the car for a moment or two without saying anything, just looking along the empty street; then she opened the door and got out.

As we went up the steps I could hear someone's radio in the house next door—voices that sounded like Itma and gusts of laughter floating out through the window. It depressed me; I wasn't in the mood for Itma. The Thirty-seventh Psalm was more in my line at the moment—Fret Not Thyself Because of Evildoers.

Jackson rang a bell. There were three or four bells with cards tacked against them, but it was too dark to read the names. A light was shining through the frosted panels of the front door, and after a few moments a shadow showed against the glass; and then an elderly Jewish-looking woman in an overall opened up and peered round the door at us.

Jackson seemed to recognize her.

'Mr. Freedman in?' she said.

The woman nodded: 'Upstairce.'

I followed Jackson through a bare hall. There was a huge oval mirror on the wall, and a sideboard and some coats hanging on a rack; that was all.

The first flight of stairs had no carpet on it; it was made of marble and seemed to be a reminder of the house having seen better days.

When we got to the third floor, we stopped. I could hear a man's voice—it was a low, monotonous voice, as if he was reading to himself—coming from a room in front of us. We walked straight in.

The man with the low, monotonous voice stopped in the

middle of his reading, and he looked up. He was a small man, rather dark and thick-set, with round-rimmed glasses; and he had a soft curly beard.

He looked at me, considerably astonished; the feeling was mutual—because for one thing, there was the old firm, sitting round the room, Wirth and Earle and Dusty; and for another, because on the table in front of him, which was littered with papers, the beard had got a little old-fashioned musical-box with a stuffed canary on the top of it.

CHAPTER

21

DUSTY, WHO WAS NEAREST THE DOOR, SHUT IT BEHIND ME. IT began to look as if Jackson had brought off the neatest trick of the week; although from the way they sat there staring at me I could see I hadn't been expected.

The instant he saw me the man with the beard slid his hand into a drawer beside him, and I knew I was covered. He looked at Earle and Earle nodded.

'That's him,' he said.

Several of my more discreditable feelings were beginning to jostle each other for first place. I felt wild with myself—and with Jackson. I felt cheated, and fooled, and mystified, and extremely apprehensive; and yet, God knows why, I was excited too. Which of these feelings was the strongest I don't remember. I kept telling myself to look calm about it, whatever I may have felt. I never believe in admitting defeat—always best to leave that to your opponent. So I turned to Dusty and I said:

'I thought your bible meeting was to-morrow?'

It was the kind of inconsequent remark that only comes into one's head when what you really want is some epic phrase.

'Quite right, buddy, it was,' he said, '——only it isn't, not now. To-night it's to-night, see?' And he grinned, or at least he got as near to it as he could.

Earle had got up when we came in, and now he said to Jackson:

'Think you'd better wait downstairs.'

He looked over at the bearded chap as he said this, and the beard jerked his head for her to clear out. He had quite a masterful air about him, this little chap.

Jackson hesitated. First she looked at one, then at the other; she wouldn't even glance at me, though. Then she turned back and went to the door. As she went out I said to her:

'Nice work.'

And I meant it, though I rather wished she'd gone to work on someone else.

I should have liked it better if we could have had a more tender farewell, even after what she'd done to me. But that's how it is. The end of human relations, like the beginning of them, very seldom works out the way we'd plan these things if we had the chance.

Dusty shut the door when she had gone out, and after that there was silence—a long and heavy silence, and it was underlined by a clock that was ticking away on the mantelpiece. The sound reminded me of Poe's *Tell-Tale Heart*, and I hoped my own wasn't going to give the game away. To me it felt as if I'd got a diesel pump under my waistcoat.

I waited for someone to crack the silence. There was still a strong temptation in me to keep up the facetious line—I suppose because it seemed a way of hiding what I was really feeling. Deep down, I think I must have been just plumb scared; perhaps not so deep down either.

It says a good deal for the tension of the situation that although I'm usually pretty observant—from curiosity as much as training—I was more or less blind to what the room looked like. All my eyes were fixed on the company. I remember, though, that the writing-table where the beard was sitting had a lamp on it, which lit up his features in a rather dramatic way. Otherwise I think the room was only lit in one corner. I know there were some bookshelves somewhere, too, and a gas fire was burning; that's all I can remember.

I looked at the beard and the beard looked at me. He had a keen, purposeful face, but it was slightly chubby, and with his round glasses and his neat red mouth and his turned-up nose he looked a bit like a rather smug schoolboy.

I looked over at Wirth. He was smoking a cigar, and he gave me that glare again, like an owl. May have meant he had the beginnings of exophthalmic goitre; I don't know. It seemed to me, though, more like a deficiency in his sense of humour.

Earle just had his usual rather blank, sullen look; usual, that is, when I happened to be about, though I could see underneath it a definite hint of what it was that could have made two women as different as Jackson and Madame Toupet both fall for him.

Suddenly, without any warning, the beard began to make a sort of speech. He started off quietly enough, and then gradually, although he hardly raised his voice, he got so worked up you could almost hear him grinding his teeth to powder. It was all about the audacity of attempting to interfere with the appointed instruments of providence, upon whom the destiny of mankind relied for its blah-blah-blah . . .

Really, I'd never heard such a spiel of rubbish since the Nuremberg Rally; and it was all spat out with perfect seriousness. I thought at least it was going to lead to some startling peroration, but not a bit of it. Just as suddenly as he'd begun, he switched over and started trying to pump me.

He hadn't much more finesse than Earle though, for this kind of job; or perhaps it was that he had less patience. Anyway, it was gratifying to realize how little they had found out. It was the one bright spot, in fact, in a situation that seemed to be getting more and more livid every minute.

He sat at the table and he articulated his questions carefully, venomously; but he didn't get anywhere with them.

The others said nothing. It was a busman's holiday for them, sitting there watching the same sequence run through without having to act in it.

Then the beard got up, and he moved round and sat on a corner of the table. I backed away to give him more room, or rather, I started to, but he caught hold of my tie and he held me where I stood, right up close to him.

His expression never changed. He still looked like a smug, rather resolute schoolboy, but he had a grip like an orang-outang, and I could see the bicep standing out under his sleeve.

He kept on firing questions at me, and I kept on saying nothing. He still held on to my tie, and every time he asked a question he shook me. Now if there's one thing I dislike it's having my tie disarranged; and if there's another, it's anyone slapping my face—slapping it hard with both sides of the hand . . .

I knocked him clean across the room. That, of course, was a pleasure in itself, and on the rebound I up-ended the table, lamp and all, which was better still, because that jammed the drawer on the underside, the drawer where the beard had left his gun.

Then everything began to happen at once.

Wirth, seeing it was three to one, seemed to think it was a good chance to take a poke at me; maybe the price I'd got him down to for that Palmer was still rankling. I saw him coming at me with a chair, so I tore it away from him and I smashed him down with it, and as he fell he clutched the curtains in front of the window and dragged the whole set-up with him.

After that it was every man for himself.

I don't remember the sequence of events, but I remember Dusty coming at me with an open knife, and my swinging the chair at him, and the chair bouncing back and breaking through the bare window. I remember hearing the glass tinkling down into the street, and seeing Dusty bleeding—and then seeing Earle with his gun in his hand, and my tripping him up and the gun flying across the room. Who was up and who was down I don't know. I know the beard was back in the battle, though, and the lot of us were smashing our way all round the room, fighting mad.

How long it all lasted I've no idea—seconds, I suppose, but it seemed like a week-end to me.

Then someone was running up the stairs, a woman, and she was calling out, 'The police, the police!'

It was the woman who had let us in, Jackson and me. She came flying into the room, and as soon as she saw what was going on she let out a wail like a wounded emu. Then she grabbed the beard, and she shouted at him to run.

'Police, police here!' she kept saying.

The moment this sank in it was like something from the

Keystone Cops to see the way that room emptied. They left Wirth though; he was still out, lying under the broken window.

I ran after them on to the landing, but the woman fastened on to me like a crab. I yelled at her, I shouted:

'Get off, you cow, get away!'

But she still stuck, and by the time I was able to shake her off the others had disappeared upstairs.

In the end she fell back against the banisters, moaning, and just at that moment a squad of C.I.D. men—patrol men—and a couple of chaps in plain clothes, came pelting upstairs. Where they all came from or why on earth they were there, I didn't stop to think. I hadn't even time to feel astonished.

I pointed to Wirth.

'One in here!' I said, '—up there, the other lot—making for the roof.'

The bunch who were in the lead went streaking on up the next flight. Two chaps stayed to have a look at Wirth, and I tagged on behind the main body.

I shouted to the chap in front, 'Watch it—there's a gun up there somewhere!'

And then I heard a voice calling from downstairs. I looked down over the banisters, and of all people, there was Herrick, looking up at me from the hall. I must say that did surprise me—pleasantly for a change.

He saw me and he called out: 'Hullo—come on down.'

Sometimes my hearing isn't very good, especially for words of authority; so I shouted back to him:

'Just going up to watch the fireworks!'

I'd got half-way upstairs, and all of a sudden I heard a little tinkling tune, a tune I'd heard somewhere before. I stopped and I looked back into the room. One of the coppers had picked up the musical box, and he was listening to it; and I could see the little canary on top of it jerking slowly round in time with the music.

I didn't know whether to go or whether to stay. I love parties and I hated the thought of missing the one upstairs. But I'd forgotten about the musical box in this shemozzle. What it'd got to do with the affair I couldn't imagine. But it seemed to have been worth blackmail and murder, so I guessed it must be more important than I knew.

I went back into the room. The whole place was a shambles. Wirth was still lying on the floor by the window. He was looking rather green about the gills, but one of the policemen was ministering to him, and he was showing signs of coming round, which seemed a pity. The other copper, the one with the musical box, held it out for me to see.

'Just picked it up out of this mess,' he said, 'an' it started off playing; funny.'

'Thank you—that's just what I've been looking for,' I said.

He looked at me sideways, but he didn't say anything; and I took the box and I went down into the hall with it.

There was Herrick, and beside him there was the plainest plain-clothes man I'd ever seen. When he saw me at the top of the stairs looking, I imagine, pretty dishevelled, Herrick came up briskly to meet me. He looked, for him, almost eager, and he took me by the arm and led me down into the hall.

'You all right?' he said. 'Certainly seem to have given you a bit of a dusting, haven't they? How did you manage . . .?' He didn't wait to hear, he burbled on; most solicitous he was. I felt quite touched. 'You sure you're all right?' he said.

'Sure, I'm all right,' I said. 'This is what seems to be the cause of all the trouble.' I handed him the musical box; it was still playing. 'Look out for that bird,' I said, 'it's dangerous. It killed Becker and it damn nearly killed me as well.'

Herrick looked at it, and then he looked at me; what was in his mind I couldn't say. The dick looked at me too, but there was no doubt about what he was thinking. After a few seconds, the tune stopped, and so did the canary.

'What do you imagine it's for?' I said.

Herrick stroked the little bird with the back of his finger.

'Difficult to say,' he said. 'Some sort of musical code, I should think; almost certain to be. They're the devil to break, as a rule. Still, I daresay we'll manage it.'

'Fat lot of use it'll be now,' I said.

'Oh,' he said, 'it'll give the back-room boys some amusement, I expect.'

(As a matter of fact, it kept them in stitches for about six weeks. And by then, of course, the message was a little out of date; it merely gave the Beard a short list of instructions. I heard about these from Herrick later on. What they were I don't even remember now; but as the Beard never got a chance to carry them out, it doesn't much matter. It was pleasing to know that after all the pains that must have been taken to devise a new code, it was never the slightest use to anyone—except, as Herrick prophesied, to keep the back-room boys amused.)

'Well, if that's all I've been risking my neck for,' I said, 'I resign in a huff.'

Herrick handed the box over to the plain-clothes man, and he said to him:

'Look after this, will you, Collett—and for heaven's sake don't drop it.'

The man took the box and he carried it away as if it had got a piece of the true cross in it. We followed him down the steps.

'Lucky thing you started brawling upstairs,' Herrick said. 'We hadn't got a warrant, of course, so it just gave us the *entrée* we needed.'

'Well, I may be dumber than usual,' I said, 'but I'm damned if I know how you managed to get here at all.'

'How could you know?' he said. 'I came in a C.I.D. car. I got 'em to put a cover on you as soon as I'd spoken to you on the telephone. I guessed there was something odd going on.'

'Ah, you spotted the change in my manner, then?' I said. 'I never noticed anyone covering me, though.'

'Pretty poor job it would have been if you had,' he said.

It had just begun to drizzle as we got outside, and there was a greasy glimmer on the pavement. A policeman was standing about, and there were two or three C.I.D. cars drawn up along the kerb. Already a little group of inquisitive locals had got together, and they were standing there gaping up at the front of the house; and in one of the windows opposite they had pulled the curtains back and were looking out, waiting for something to happen.

'Who was that,' Herrick said—and I knew what was coming—'who came here with you in the car?'

To this day I've never decided what my true feelings for Jackson were—or what they might have been if I'd had a chance to develop them. I only know that my instinct at this moment was to try and cover up for her, to say as little as I knew.

'That was a girl called Jackson,' I said. 'It's a long story about her. It'll all come in my report.'

'Where's she got to now?' he said.

'Search me,' I said. 'P'raps she's still inside.'

Herrick turned to the chap in plain clothes. 'Collett,' he said, 'did you see anyone come out—before I arrived, I mean?'

'There was a woman come out, sir,' Collett said, 'just when we got here.'

'What was she wearing?' I said.

'Couldn't see, sir, really. A sort of yellow turban, it looked like——'

'You're keeping an eye on her?' Herrick said.

'Well, no sir. I didn't know then, sir . . .'

I heard Herrick take in a quick breath.

'Very well,' he said, quite quietly.

I knew that tone of voice, and I could imagine Collett blushing in the dark, poor devil. Suddenly he pointed up towards the roof:

'Look, sir——!'

There was a quick murmur from the little group beside us, and as I turned round, I just saw someone ducking along behind the parapet. Whoever it was, they dropped out of sight almost at once.

We stood there for I should think about two minutes, straining our eyes and ears for another sign of him; hardly anyone said a word. It was fairly dark, but the silhouette of the house-tops showed up quite plainly against the sky.

Presently we saw one of the C.I.D. men, just saw his cap, moving slowly along behind the parapet. Poor Collett kept gesturing and whispering to himself, as if he were right beside him.

'Get down, you bloody fool!' he kept saying, 'get down—keep down!'

A few more people had collected by this time, and one or two of them moved over now on to the opposite pavement to get a better view.

For a long while nothing happened. Occasionally you could see one of the patrol men moving cautiously about for a few seconds, and then he'd duck out of sight.

All of a sudden there was a shout and a great growl—it sounded like Dusty's voice—and then there was a scuffling noise. It all ended with another cry, a real cry of pain this time, and a woman who was standing near me clapped her hands over her ears.

There was an even longer pause after this. The tension had contracted suddenly. The crowd were dead still; they just stood there in the drizzle, gaping up at the roof.

Presently, a long while after, it seemed, there was a movement in the hall—the front door was still open—and then I saw Wirth being half-carried, half-dragged down the stairs; and behind him they were bringing Dusty down in handcuffs.

There was a little scurry on the pavement as soon as the crowd saw them being brought down the steps; but the coppers were too quick. They piled them both into a car and drove off straight away.

There was more to come, though. A few minutes after this they brought down Rankel. He was looking a bit the worse for wear, with blood on his face and running down into his beard. I couldn't feel very sorry about it myself, but at once there was a compassionate murmur from the crowd. Then he was pushed into a car and driven away too. They groaned again when they saw him go, but not out of sympathy this time, out of disappointment.

Herrick and Collett and I still stood there, waiting in the drizzle. And the locals went on waiting too, full of bovine curiosity. But the feeling of suspense had wilted for the moment. They began to talk and shift about. A man near me struck a light for his pipe, a woman laughed . . .

Personally, I was feeling more and more tense every minute.

Neither Herrick nor Collett said a word. Eventually I said to Herrick:

'I'm going up to see what's happening.'

Inside, in the hall, the Jewish lady was nattering distressfully to a detective; it was none of my business though; that was on the top floor.

When I got up there I saw an iron ladder leading to an open trap in the ceiling over the stairs. A pair of constabulary legs were dangling down through the trap, and the head belonging to them came through and looked fiercely at me as I started climbing up the ladder. I had to satisfy the chap of my *bona fides* before he'd let me go any further, and even then he wasn't very willing to let me come up.

'Bit of a rough 'ouse likely,' he said. 'Still, 's up to you. Better watch yourself.'

I promised to keep myself under strict observation, and he made way for me to climb through the trap. I got out on to the leads and I crawled cautiously forward in the direction he'd pointed out to me.

There was a chimney-stack standing at right-angles to the parapet, and as I crept along someone suddenly flashed a torch at me. I waited till my nervous system had settled down again, and then I crept on towards the stack.

There were three coppers there lying on their bellies, and one lying perilously against the gutter. Presently another one, an inspector, a big man, came crawling along the wet leads like an alligator.

The chap lying in the gutter could apparently see Earle but Earle couldn't see him. They seemed to have pushed him into a corner of the roof twenty or thirty feet away, and the problem now was how they were to work towards him without giving him too easy a target. They began a whispered discussion about strategy; and then suddenly a mild hubbub broke out down in the street. We could hear it quite plainly, and two or three people let out a shout.

The chap in the gutter raised himself up a little and peeped over the buttress of the stack.

'He's gone!' he said.

The inspector snapped at us:

'Stay where you are, everybody! Get down, off there, Phillips.'

And Phillips slid back into the gutter.

'Let's have a look-see,' the inspector said; and he changed places with Phillips, and looked out, very warily, over the top of the buttress.

He peered about for some time, but apparently there was nothing to see. Whatever it was that had set the crowd off down below, they were quiet again now. We all waited. Then the inspector came to earth again.

'Nip back and find out what they're on about down there,' he said. One of the men slipped away in the darkness. 'Mind how you go—don't get larking about.'

We crouched behind the chimney for a while. I could feel the heat of it through my jacket. I was beginning to get a bit damp by now, and it was rather pleasant. Then suddenly we heard the voices breaking out again down in the street, and again there was some shouting.

'What the hell's he having a game at, eh?' the inspector said irritably. He had a high brisk little voice which didn't seem to go at all with such a large man. In a few minutes, the man he'd sent away came back walking this time and out of breath. The inspector began to tick him off for not taking cover.

'It's O.K., sir,' the chap said.

I liked him; he seemed young and eager and he was trying to be very self-controlled, but he couldn't quite keep the excitement out of his voice. I couldn't have kept it out of mine either, so I said nothing.

'He's gone and got down on to that gangway like—you know, that kind o' bridge—goes over next door.'

'Anyone in there?'

'No, sir, the house is empty——'

'Right. Go back and get hold of Inspector Hamilton——'

'He's got in, sir, already. He's taking his men up the top. He's going to give us a light signal off the roof, two-and-two, soon as they've got the door blocked his side o' the bridge.'

'Good lad,' the inspector said. 'Now then, you men, listen—we're going forward up against the side parapet, see. No standing up and nobody taking no silly chances, get me? Soon as we get their signal over the way—well, we'll see. If he won't come back up here, we'll have to go and fetch him. Got the idea?'

The men nodded. I didn't need to; I was shaking already.

'Right. Phillips, you nip down there and tell Mr. Collett what we're going to do, see? Say I want Inspector Hamilton to give us cover from the roof over there, 'case this bird starts trying any tricks, get me?'

'O.K., sir,' Phillips said, and he slipped away in the darkness.

We crawled out from the shelter of the stack—I was sorry to lose its warmth—and lay down on the wet flats; and then we waited.

We all of us had our eyes glued on the black outline of the roof showing over the parapet next door. I could hear the man beside me whistling very softly to himself between his teeth. I envied him whatever it was, his cold courage, or maybe his obtuseness—or maybe it was just that his teeth didn't fit—anyway, whatever it was that gave it him his appearance of *sang-froid*, I envied him.

Still we waited.

Suddenly, in the blackness straight ahead of us, a light flashed out—one-two, one-two.

'There we are!' the inspector said.

We began to crawl forward towards the parapet. In the middle of it there was a gap with a handrail on either side—the place, presumably, where Earle had got down on to the gangway. We split up, so as to get on either side of this opening, and when we came close to the parapet the inspector knelt up behind it and he called out loudly to Earle:

'You, down there—you'd better come back up on to the roof, d'you hear? Come on.'

There was no answer.

He shouted out again:

'D'you hear what I say? Come back up here. No use you staying down there, you know.'

Still there was no answer.

'Now listen, you: I'm going to give you ten seconds. I'm going to count them. If you don't show up then, we'll have to come and get you. Now, be a sensible chap, will you, and come on up?'

There was dead silence. The inspector waited; then he began to count: 'One—two—three—four—'

He counted ten. Still there was no sign from Earle. Still the inspector waited. Then suddenly he shouted:

'Right! O.K. over there?'

There was a call from someone on the other roof:

'O.K.!'

The inspector moved along to the gap in the parapet, and the rest of us closed up on either side. And then, with no more hesitation than if he'd been getting over a stile in a country lane, he swung his legs briskly over the edge and slid down the ladder on to the gangway.

I heard Earle shout—twice he shouted, very loud:

'Keep back—keep back!'

I was on the ladder myself, and the others were just behind me when I saw the flash of a gun from the roof opposite, and in the same split second Earle fired too——

The inspector gave a fearful grunt and he sagged against the handrail. Earle's gun clattered down on the iron gangway and he flopped on his knees. The inspector shook his head like a boxer half-stunned, and he gave a sort of hiss.

'Grazed me leg,' he said, 'that's all—it's all right. Look out——!'

As the inspector shouted I saw Earle slump over on his side. One of the coppers jumped past me and tried to grab him as he twisted round. He missed him, though, and Earle rolled over underneath the handrail and fell away into the darkness.

A long shuddering breath came all the way up from the crowd. A woman shrieked. And someone, hearing the shots, I suppose, pushed up a window somewhere and a wireless started blaring out one of Sousa's marches.

PHILIP C. ALMOND is Emeritus Professor of Religion at the University of Queensland. His previous books include *The Witches of Warboys: An Extraordinary Story of Sorcery, Sadism and Satanic Possession* (2008), *England's First Demonologist: Reginald Scot and 'The Discoverie of Witchcraft'* (2011, paperback 2014), *The Lancashire Witches: A Chronicle of Sorcery and Death on Pendle Hill* (2012) and *The Devil: A New Biography* (2014, paperback 2016), all published by I.B.Tauris.

In this concise and accessible account of the afterlife in the imagination of the Christian West, Philip Almond takes the reader on a remarkable journey. As we progress through the centuries, wrestling with the conceptual problems of post-mortem life – will our bodies as well as our souls enjoy paradise? what exactly is the soul? and what is the relation between time and eternity? – we marvel at the tenacity that has compelled human beings in all cultures to insist on this seemingly impossible idea. As Almond argues from the outset, our quest for the afterlife is rooted in the conviction that our existence must have some ultimate significance and our ineradicable desire that the ubiquitous injustice that we witness in our earthly lives be righted in the hereafter.

KAREN ARMSTRONG, bestselling author of *The Case for God: What Religion Really Means* and *Fields of Blood: Religion and the History of Violence*

As is true of all his previous books, Philip Almond's *Afterlife* is thoughtful, perceptive, inquiring, accurate, wide-ranging, clear and engagingly written. It is a fine follow-up to his earlier biography of the Devil.

JEFFREY BURTON RUSSELL, Emeritus Professor of History, University of California, Santa Barbara, author of *A History of Heaven* and *Paradise Mislaid*

Philip Almond's cultural history of the afterlife is a fascinating – and frequently disturbing – journey through the Western imagination: its dreams, desires, fears and hopes. Erudite, lucid, the book draws us into an exhilarating current of eschatologies and final things that challenge any secular ideology because of their abiding relevance. Staring at death and finitude, humankind aspires to and tries to picture post-mortem conditions: a perennial occupation that cannot be erased. It is who we are. In his engaging book Almond offers us a roadmap to self-understanding.

GRAHAM WARD,
Regius Professor of Divinity, University of Oxford

Philip Almond's new book is a welcome and readable reminder that belief in life after death is not one simple set of convictions but a range of hopes and conceptions, including both the sophisticated and the simple, engaging in diverse ways with diverse models of what human life essentially is.

ROWAN WILLIAMS,
Master of Magdalene College, Cambridge, and former Archbishop of Canterbury

PHILIP C. ALMOND

AFTERLIFE

A HISTORY OF LIFE AFTER DEATH

I.B. TAURIS
LONDON · NEW YORK

Published in 2016 by
I.B.Tauris & Co. Ltd
London • New York
www.ibtauris.com

ISBN: 978 1 78453 496 7
eISBN: 978 0 85772 895 1
ePDF: 978 0 85772 806 7

A full CIP record for this book is available from the British Library

Text designed and typeset by Tetragon, London
Printed and bound in Great Britain by T.J. International, Padstow, Cornwall

To Winter

Contents

List of Plates

Each image appears in either the black-and-white plate section (BW) or the colour plate section (C).

Acknowledgements

This book was written in the Centre for the History of European Discourses, now part of the Institute for Advanced Studies in the Humanities at the University of Queensland in Australia. I have been privileged to have been a member of this centre for the past ten years. It has continued to provide a congenial, stimulating and, more often than one might hope to expect, exciting context in which to work. For this I am indebted in particular to my friends and colleagues Professor Peter Harrison, the director of the institute, Professor Fred D'Agostino and Emeritus Professor Peter Cryle. I am grateful also to the many postdoctoral fellows of the institute, especially Dr Leigh Penman, all of whose dedication to their work has provided so much encouragement to my own.

A wide-ranging book such as this is inevitably indebted to those scholars who have previously laboured in this intellectual domain. Without their often groundbreaking work, this book would not have been possible. In particular, I want to acknowledge the works of Alan Bernstein, Caroline Walker Bynum, Jacques Le Goff, D. P. Walker, Geoffrey Rowell, Colleen McDannell and Bernhard Lang, Michael Wheeler and John Casey. I take the opportunity once again to thank Alex Wright, my editor at I.B.Tauris, for his support and encouragement of this work. It is a matter of surprise to me that we have worked together on various book projects for over 20 years. I am grateful for it. I am grateful too to my partner Patricia Lee. Again, she has listened day by day to the text as it progressed, and has offered much helpful advice.

This book is dedicated to my fourth granddaughter, Winter Linde.

The present life of man upon earth, O king, seems to me, in comparison with that time which is unknown to us, like to the swift flight of a sparrow through the house wherein you sit at supper in winter, with your ealdormen and thegns, while the fire blazes in the midst, and the hall is warmed, but the wintry storms of rain or snow are raging abroad. The sparrow, flying in at one door and immediately out at another, whilst he is within, is safe from the wintry tempest; but after a short space of fair weather, he immediately vanishes out of your sight, passing from winter into winter again. So this life of man appears for a little while, but of what is to follow or what went before we know nothing at all.

Bede, *The Ecclesiastical History of England*

Death is not an event in life: we do not live to experience death. If we take eternity to mean not infinite temporal duration but timelessness, then eternal life belongs to those who live in the present. Our life has no end in just the way in which our visual field has no limits.

Ludwig Wittgenstein, *Tractatus Logico-philosophicus*

Jesus came into Galilee, preaching the gospel of the kingdom of God, and saying, 'The time is fulfilled, and the Kingdom of God is at hand; repent ye, and believe the gospel.'

Mark 1.14–15

Prologue

> When he awoke, he looked about with surprise. He couldn't believe what he saw. A startling change had come to his old body [...] The warmth of the sun soon dried the moisture from his new body [...] He had become a dragonfly! Swooping and dipping in great curves, he flew through the air. He felt exhilarated in the new atmosphere.
>
> Doris Stickney, *Waterbugs and Dragonflies: Explaining Death to Young Children* (2009)

The British television comedy series *Rev.* tells the story of an Anglican priest, Adam Smallbone, who has moved from a rural parish to St Saviour in the Marshes, a run-down parish in Hackney in the East End of London. There he has responsibility for the local parish primary school. When one of the school's favourite teachers is killed in an accident, Adam has the task of talking to the children about his death. He does so by telling the fable of the waterbugs and the dragonfly. He tells the children of a little colony of waterbugs at the bottom of a river. Every now and then, one of the bugs would crawl up a plant through the water into the light and never be seen again. One day, one special little waterbug decided that he too wanted to crawl up a plant. So he crawled up the plant, through the surface of the water and into the air. And he turned into a beautiful dragonfly. He flew around in the air and was as happy as he had ever been. But when he tried to go back down into the water to tell his bug friends how wonderful it was, he couldn't, because he wasn't a bug any more. He was a dragonfly. This upset him, until he remembered that all his friends would one day crawl up the plant too and join him in the sun.

Adam Smallbone's answer to the question of what happens to us when we die is, as we will see, a very modern one. But the questions with which he grapples are perennial. Do we survive death? Will we recognise ourselves? Will we be reunited with those we have left behind or those who have gone before? Will our actions in this life be punished or rewarded? Will we have an opportunity after death to make amends or change our ways? Will our lives continue immediately after death or do we have to wait for a final end to history? What kind of body might we have? For most of us, the thought of our ceasing to be is unbearable. On the other hand, the thought that we shall live forever is almost unthinkable.

This is a book about what follows death and what happens after life. More particularly, it is a history of the destiny of the dead, of what we might then be like and of what might happen to us after we die. It is also a history of the places that we might inhabit – heaven, hell and Purgatory, limbo and Abraham's Bosom, Hades and Sheol, Paradise, Tartarus and the Isles of the Blessed – and of the complicated history of the connections between them all.

We do not know what follows our deaths, any more than we know what preceded our lives. Hence, this book is about our imaginings of the afterlife from the ancient Greeks and Hebrews to the present. For all we know, one, some or none of these imaginings may be true. But whatever the case, the history of the afterlife is the history of our hopes that there will be something after death and of our fears that there will be nothing. And, granted that there is something rather than nothing, it speaks to our dreams of eternal happiness, to our nightmares of eternal punishment, and to the myriad ways in which these have been inflected over the centuries.

Weaving in and out of these imaginings are the two foundational narratives within Western thought about the afterlife. On the one hand, there is a narrative built around the anticipation that our lives will continue *immediately* after the death of each of us. At the point of death, the soul will be weighed in the balance, judged according to its vice or virtue and sent to the bliss of heaven or cast into the pit of hell. On the other hand, there is another narrative, one that is driven by the expectation that our eternal destinies will be finally determined not at the time of death, but at that time when history ends, when this world will be no more and when Christ returns to judge both the living and the dead. Then there will only be two possible destinations for our souls reunited with our bodies. For Christ will bid the blessed to enter an eternity of bliss or throw the damned into the everlasting fire.

With these narratives in place within the first few centuries of the Christian era, the history of the afterlife in the West became the history of a constantly fluid series of negotiations, contestations and compromises between two versions of our futures after death. The majority determinedly held to the necessity of both in an intellectual compromise that, as is often the way with such accommodations, was always on the verge of collapsing. This particular compromise disintegrated by, on the one hand, denying the ongoing conscious life of the individual immediately after death and passionately asserting the general judgement on the Last Day, often in the context of the expectation of the imminent return of Christ, while on the other asserting just as passionately the full delights of heaven for the righteous and the full horrors of hell for the damned immediately after death, generally in the expectation of a long continuation for the Church on earth together with a disregard for any immediate end to history.

Modern histories of the afterlife in the West have focused on one or other of these narratives. This book, by contrast, is shaped by the interplay, tensions and conflicts between them within a history that tells the story of each of them.

If the history of the afterlife in the West is one of a complicated and often messy tension between the destiny of the dead immediately after death and their destiny after the end of history, it is also the story of the conflict about the nature of the individual and what it is in the present that survives into the future. From the beginning of the third century, Christianity adopted the Greek tradition that individuals are composed of a mortal body and an immortal soul. This anthropology enabled sense to be made of the tension between the fate of the individual after death and after the Last Judgement. It was the soul that survived between death and the Last Day, and it was the body that was resurrected on the Last Day and reunited with the soul. Thus, the history of the afterlife is also the history of the conflict between the body and the soul as the essence of what it is to be human, sometimes the assertion of the necessity of both body and soul, occasionally the acknowledgement of the one to the exclusion of the other.

This opposition between body and soul was intellectually difficult to sustain. Thus, this book also traces the history of how the distinction between body and soul was sufficiently fragile for the one to be likely to collapse into the other and the difference between the two made effectually redundant. The soul was 'corporealised' and the body 'spiritualised'. On the one hand, it became necessary to accord to the soul the sort of quasi-corporeality that allowed it a geographical location after death either above or below the earth. As a result, it took on physical aspects – the soul was gendered, and had rank and status. On the other hand, it was crucial to 'spiritualise' the body – to resurrect it not as it was at the point of death but in an 'ideal' form most suited to its enjoyment of the delights of heaven or to its suffering of the pains of hell. This ambivalence around the natures of the body and the soul was also increased by tensions between different views of the purpose of the afterlife – between the passive contemplation of God on the one hand and the active life of community with one's heavenly companions, the saints, the angels and the martyrs, on the other; between progress towards happiness and perfection and the immediate attainment of these at death. Different heavenly needs meant different heavenly bodies.

And heavenly needs also changed. Thus, the history of the afterlife in the West is also that of a tension between an eternal life centred on the love and worship of God more or less to the exclusion of human relationships, one centred on human relationships as the exemplar of divine love, and one focused on human relationships to the virtual exclusion of God. The last two millennia have seen a transition through these three ideas, from a God-centred heaven to an array of secular heavens, both this-worldly and other-worldly.

At the same time, this book also gives a history of the human demand for justice. It tells of the belief that, on earth, the evil seem to prosper and the good to languish. It reflects on the recognition that, since virtue is not obviously its own reward, the best solution to the injustices on this side of the grave is to even them up on the other. Thus, it speaks of the creation of places after death where the righteous would receive their just recompense and the wicked their just deserts, and of punishments and rewards proportionate to vices and virtues.

The history of the human demand for justice in the afterlife is also a history of certain key attributes of God as he has been understood within the West during the past 2–2,500 years. It was God who would reward the good and punish the wicked, who would weigh up souls at the moment of their death and who would determine their eternal destiny. He did so, in different ways at different times in the history of the afterlife, according to various measures of his goodness, his justice and his righteous anger. More particularly, the issue around the nature of God went to the question of whether his goodness necessitated the ultimate salvation of all in spite of his justice and wrath, or whether his justice and wrath entailed the eternal punishment of the wicked, or at least their eventual annihilation, in spite of his will that all should be saved.

Be that as it may, and regardless of which divine attribute most determined the divine nature, it was accepted for the most part that God would save or damn in accordance with the virtues or vices of the dead. But it was sometimes also argued that he apportioned eternal happiness or everlasting torments merely as the arbitrary act of his own sovereign will, regardless of any person's virtues or vices. In short, God could do whatever he liked and, it was argued, he did just that. This was a view not conducive to encouraging the pursuit of virtue in this life in the hope of reward in the next.

Finally, amid all these tensions and complexities across the centuries, this book tells the story of what ultimately motivated all the variations in the two grand narratives of the afterlife in Western thought and what ultimately unifies them. Thus, this history of life after death speaks of our determination to find meaning and purpose in history from the perspective of that which ends history. It resonates with the conviction that the meaning and purpose of individual lives can be found from the perspective of the eternity that, it was believed and generally still is, follows death – that moment between time and timelessness, this life and the afterlife that threatens to render all of it just so much 'vanity and a chasing after wind' (Eccles. 2.11).

Chapter One

The Destiny of the Dead

> No one shall be found among you [...] who consults ghosts or spirits, or who seeks oracles from the dead. For whoever does these things is abhorrent to the Lord; it is because of such abhorrent practices that the Lord your God is driving them out before you.
>
> Deuteronomy 18.10–12

The spirits of the dead

According to the book of Deuteronomy (*c.*650 BCE) in the Hebrew Scriptures (the Old Testament), when the Israelites first entered the Promised Land, they encountered necromantic cults in which wisdom was sought from the dead. At least some of them adopted such practices for, as the above text makes clear, it became necessary to forbid them from doing so.

The biblical story of the Witch of Endor shows that such practices were not so easily extinguished. According to this, after the death of the prophet Samuel, King Saul had expelled all the mediums and wizards from the land. Terrified at the advance of the Philistines against him, and no longer able to seek advice from Samuel, Saul asked God what to do. However, neither from dreams, nor from divination, nor from other prophets did he receive an answer. So Saul broke his own ban on consulting with the dead by going in disguise to a woman of Endor who was a medium. He asked her to call up Samuel for him. When Saul asked her what she saw, she replied, 'I see a divine being coming up out of the ground.' Upon Saul asking her to describe him, she replied, 'An old man is coming up; he is wrapped in a robe.' Then Saul knew that it was Samuel, and he bowed with his face to the ground (see Plate 1 [BW]). The spirit told Saul of his disobedience to God and that God had therefore turned against him. The spirit could also see the future, and told Saul that God would give Israel into the hands of the Philistines. Saul and his sons would die: 'tomorrow you and your sons shall be with me' (1 Sam. 28.3–19). Samuel had been brought up from the world of the dead, and Saul and his sons would join him there.

It is clear from this story that, in ancient Judaism, the dead, whether good or evil, were to be gathered in one place. It is also clear that Samuel, capable still of appearing among the living, has retained some form of existence there. This place of the spirits of the dead was called 'Sheol'. And it was located below the earth. The first reference to Sheol occurs in the first book of the Bible, Genesis, when Jacob believed that his son Joseph, sold into slavery in Egypt by his brothers, was dead. When his sons and daughters tried to comfort him, he refused and said, 'No, I shall go down to Sheol to my son, mourning' (Gen. 37.35). For Jacob, Joseph is still someone who is somewhere and with whom he will be reunited after his death. But it is not a place of joy and, inevitable as it is, not a place of desire. Rather, it is a place of darkness, a shadowy place, a land of forgetfulness and, metaphorically at least, of destruction, beneath the earth or even in the lower parts of the earth. The dead have only a sort of 'half-life'. They become the *rephaim*, 'the shades': 'The dead [*methim*] do not live,' declared Isaiah, 'shades [*rephaim*] do not rise – because you have punished and destroyed them, and wiped out all memory of them' (Isa. 26.14).

It was not only a place to which all would inevitably go, but also one to which God sent his enemies *as* punishment if not *for* punishment and, if they crossed him, sooner rather than later. Thus, for example, during the many years that the Israelites wandered in the wilderness, Moses declared that only the descendants of Aaron would be priests. When this was opposed by Korah, Dathan and Abiram, Moses asked them to stand in front of their tents with their wives and families, and asked all the others to move away. Moses then demonstrated his authority:

> the ground under them was split apart. The earth swallowed them up, along with their households – everyone who belonged to Korah and all their goods. So they with all that belonged to them went down alive into Sheol; the earth closed over them, and they perished from the midst of the assembly. (Num. 16.31–3)

Two hundred and fifty of their supporters were also burnt alive by a fire sent from God, so that 'no outsider who is not of the descendants of Aaron shall approach to offer incense before the Lord, so as not to become like Korah and his company' (Num. 16.40). Moreover, God had power over those in Sheol. For as he could send people into Sheol, so also he could bring them back: 'The Lord kills and brings to life; he brings down to Sheol and raises up' (1 Sam. 2.6).

Sheol, however, was more than just a geographical location. The Old Testament's references to 'Sheol' also suggest a netherworld being, one who stands naked before God and has hands, womb, throat and a mouth to swallow the dead – 'an insatiate deity residing underneath, craving for human life but at the same time prone to negotiations and eager to receive ransom for the dead'.[1] Thus 'Sheol' refers to both a place and person.

We find the same ambiguity in the term 'Hades' in the underworld geography of classical Greece. There Hades (Haides, Aides, Aidoneus, Pluton) was king of the underworld and god of death and the dead. He was the son of Kronos and Rhea, and brother to Zeus and Poseidon. After the three brothers had vanquished the Titans and imprisoned them in Tartarus, they drew lots for the division of the cosmos. As Homer's *Iliad* (*c.* eighth century BCE) told it:

> For three brethren are we, begotten of Cronos, and born of Rhea, – Zeus, and myself, and the third is Hades, that is lord of the dead below. And in three-fold wise are all things divided, and unto each hath been apportioned his own domain. I [Poseidon] verily, when the lots were shaken, won for my portion the grey sea to be my habitation for ever, and Hades won the murky darkness, while Zeus won the broad heaven amid the air and the clouds; but the earth and high Olympus remain yet common to us all.[2]

Hades was married to Persephone, the daughter of Demeter (see Plate 3 [c]). They both reigned in a subterranean palace through the entrance to which – the gate of Hades – all had to pass, never to return.

As in the case of 'Sheol' in the Hebrew Bible, Hades was also the name of the place in which the god Hades ruled. And like Sheol, it was a dark and loathsome place to which all of us, with a few heroic exceptions, must go. As Walter Burkert eloquently put it:

> When the earth shakes during the battle of the gods, Hades leaps from his throne and roars in terror lest the earth break open and his realm be exposed to the light, ghastly, mouldering, and an abomination to the gods – as when a stone is overturned revealing putrefaction and teeming larvae.[3]

In the *Iliad*, the Trojan hero Hector had slain Patroclus, the much-loved friend of Achilles. Unable to give up the corpse of Patroclus, Achilles in his grief delayed his cremation. When sleep seized Achilles, the spirit or *psyche* (ψῡχή) of Patroclus, the ghostly image of Patroclus that survived his death, came to him in a dream:

> Thou sleepest, and hast forgotten me, Achilles. Not in my life wast thou unmindful of me, but now in my death! Bury me with all speed, that I pass within the gates of Hades. Afar do the spirits keep me aloof, the phantoms of men that have done with toils, neither suffer they me to join myself to them beyond the River, but vainly I wander through the wide-gated house of Hades. And give me thy hand, I pitifully entreat thee, for never more again shall I come back from out of Hades, when once ye have given me my due of fire. Never more in life shall we sit apart from our dear comrades and take counsel together, but for me hath loathly fate opened its maw, the fate that was appointed me even from my birth. Aye, and thou thyself also, Achilles like to the gods, art doomed to be brought low [...] Lay not my bones apart from thine, Achilles, but let them lie together.[4]

Achilles asked Patroclus to come closer so that they might embrace each other for a last time. So saying, 'he reached forth with his hands, yet clasped him not; but the spirit like a vapour was gone beneath the earth, gibbering faintly.' Thus were mighty warriors reduced to elusive shades in the murky darkness of Hades, like bats that flit about gibbering 'when one has fallen from off the rock from the chain in which they cling to one another'.[5]

This was the darkness that Odysseus also met when he journeyed to the underworld in the *Odyssey*, to the place where the four rivers of the underworld – the Styx, Cocytus, Pyriphlegethon and Acheron – met. In this case, it was a far-distant place to the west where 'baneful night is spread over wretched mortals.'[6] But it was also vertically 'beneath the depths of the earth,'[7] and the dead seemed to come up from below:

> Then there gathered from out of Erebus the spirits of those that are dead, brides, and unwedded youths, and toil-worn old men, and tender maidens with hearts yet new to sorrow, and many, too, that had been wounded with bronze-tipped spears, men slain in fight, wearing their blood-stained

> armour. These came thronging in crowds about the pit from every side, with a wondrous cry; and pale fear seized me.[8]

There Odysseus encountered his mother, Anticleia, who had died in his absence. When Odysseus tried to embrace her, she escaped from his arms like a shadow or a dream. 'This is the appointed way with mortals when one dies,' his mother told him, for 'the sinews no longer hold the flesh and bones together [...] and the spirit, like a dream, flits away, and hovers to and fro.'[9] Rather like the fate of Dante's virtuous pagans, it was a life after death as much pointless as punitive. So when Odysseus tried to console Achilles by suggesting that at least he ruled over the dead, Achilles replied:

> Nay, seek not to speak soothingly to me of death, glorious Odysseus. I should choose, so I might live on earth, to serve as the hireling of another, of some portionless man whose livelihood was but small, rather than to be lord over all the dead that have perished.[10]

Still, in the afterlife of Homer, while a shadowy half-life was the fate of most, there were hints of punishments for those who stood out from the common dead. These were most likely in murky Tartarus, the place of the Titans, 'where is the deepest gulf beneath the earth, the gates whereof are of iron and the threshold of bronze, as far beneath Hades as heaven is above earth.'[11] Odysseus saw Tityos, the attempted rapist of Leto, lying on the ground with two vultures upon him, tearing out his liver and plunging their beaks into his bowels. There too he saw Tantalus, standing in a pool with water up to his chin. As he reached down for the water, it dried up. As often as he stretched towards the fruit above him, the wind would blow the branches out of his reach. And Sisyphus too, Odysseus saw in torment, punished by Zeus for his hubris, forever condemned to push a boulder uphill until,

> as often as he was about to heave it over the top, the weight would turn it back, and then down again to the plain would come rolling the ruthless stone. But he would strain again and thrust it back, and the sweat flowed down from his limbs, and dust rose up from his head.[12]

Thus, for most, there was the shadowy half-life of Hades. For the greatest of the enemies of the gods, there were the torments of Tartarus. For a select few, however, there was no death. Rather, there was a transportation to the Elysian Fields, where life was 'easiest for men': 'No snow is there, nor heavy storm, nor ever rain, but ever does Ocean send up blasts of the shrill-blowing West Wind that they may give cooling to men.'[13] According to Hesiod, a contemporary of Homer, the destiny of the few was the Isles of the Blessed, 'along the shore of deep swirling Ocean' at the end of the earth. It was populated by the heroes who fell at Troy or Thebes. Untouched by sorrow, they lived there as 'happy heroes for whom the grain-giving earth bears honey-sweet fruit flourishing thrice a year'.[14]

In the third century BCE, the Hebrew Bible (the Old Testament) was translated into Greek for the Greek-speaking Jews of Egypt. Known as the Septuagint, this was the version of the text that the Greek-speaking composers of the New Testament made use of. Thus, granting the above analogies between the Greek Hades and the Hebrew Sheol, it is a matter of little surprise that the word 'Hades' (ἁδης) was used in the Septuagint for 'Sheol', and thence migrated into the Greek New Testament.

Rewards and punishments

Thus, with few exceptions, whether in Greece of the seventh century BCE or in the ancient Israel of the same period, the fate of the dead was the same – a half-life in the realm of the shades. As the same destiny for all, regardless of their behaviour, it provided no incentive for behaviour, good or evil, on this side of the grave. Later Old Testament texts began to note that, on this side of death also, there seemed to be little to be gained from a life of service and obedience to God. To put it simply, bad things happened to good people and vice versa. Thus, for example, the book of Malachi (mid-fifth century BCE), the final book of the Old Testament, reflected dissatisfaction with the outcomes of commitment to God:

> It is vain to serve God. What do we profit by keeping his command or by going about as mourners before the Lord of Hosts? Now we count the arrogant happy; evildoers not only prosper, but when they put God to the test they escape. (Mal. 3.14–15)

The writer of Ecclesiastes (third century BCE) believed that there was justice neither on this nor on the other side of death. 'There is a vanity that takes place on earth,' he declared, 'that there are righteous people who are treated according to the conduct of the wicked, and there are wicked people who are treated according to the conduct of the righteous' (Eccles. 8.14). And yet, 'the same fate comes to all, to the righteous and the wicked, to the good and the evil [...] This is an evil in all that happens under the sun, that the same fate comes to everyone' (Eccles. 9.2–3). It was a sentiment echoed in the book of Job (perhaps sixth century BCE), a work that took as its central theme the unmerited suffering of the virtuous: 'One dies in full prosperity, being wholly at ease and secure [...] Another dies in bitterness of soul, never having tasted of Good. They lie alike in the dust, and the worms cover them' (Job 21.23–6).

The best solution for injustice on this side of the grave was to even it up on the other. The earliest example of this is in the description of Sheol in the First Book of Enoch, a Jewish religious work that is not part of the Hebrew Bible, in a section of the text that can be dated to the third century BCE. Here, for the first time, there was a distinction made between the fate of the righteous and that of the wicked. Hades had now become segregated into four hollow places in which four different classes of the dead were located until the Day of Judgement (of which more anon). These were not merely waiting rooms for rewards and punishments yet to come. These rewards and punishments had already begun.

According to the text, the angel Raphael showed Enoch a high mountain in the west in which there were four deep 'hollow places'. Three of them were dark, while one was light and with a fountain of water in the middle of it. Raphael told Enoch that these 'hollow places [are intended] that the spirits of the souls of the dead might be gathered into them'. The dead were separated according to their ethical quality, and rewarded or punished accordingly. The first of these spaces, a place of light and life, was intended for the righteous. In the second compartment dwelt sinners whose wickedness had gone unpunished in their lifetimes and who were now experiencing 'this great torment'. It is less clear who resided in the next place. They were certainly the victims of murder, although their residence in a place of darkness suggests that they were not necessarily merely innocent ones. In the fourth and final place were another group of sinners, who, unlike those in the second compartment, did not seem to be suffering torment either after death or after the final judgement, probably because they received punishment during their lifetimes.[15]

It was inevitable that such nuances in the underworld would be simplified into two locations – one for the righteous and one for the wicked. As we will see later, it was a simplification that much subsequent theorising about the afterlife would try to avoid. However that may be, by the time of another non-biblical Jewish text known as the Second Apocalypse of Baruch (*c.*110 CE), the four locations of the First Book of Enoch have become two. Unlike in the First Book of Enoch, however, this time the two places in Hades are not so much places of rewards or punishment as waiting rooms for what is to come after the end of the world:

> [I]t will happen at that time that those treasuries will be opened in which the number of the souls of the righteous were kept [...] But the souls of the wicked will the more waste away when they shall see all these things. For they know that their torment has come and their perdition has arrived.[16]

The apocryphal Christian work the Fourth Book of Ezra (*c.*100 CE) has more historical importance because of its 'proofs' that the end of the world was at hand. Thus, when in 1726 a woman of Godalming in Surrey, Mary Toft, apparently gave birth to live rabbits, William Whiston (1667–1752), Isaac Newton's successor in the Lucasian Chair of Mathematics at the University of Cambridge, believed that she was the fulfilment of the prophecy in the Fourth Book of Ezra that 'menstruous women shall bring forth monsters'.[17] But this book also gave a long account of the fate of the dead immediately after death. In answer to Ezra's question whether the spirits of the dead would rest until the end of the world or whether there would be immediate torments, the angel told Ezra that the dead would have seven days of freedom during which the righteous would see the rewards awaiting them, and the wicked the torments yet to come. At the end of the seven days, the righteous anticipating with pleasure the joys yet to come would be gathered into chambers 'in profound quiet', guarded by angels. The wicked were doomed to continue wandering around 'ever grieving and sad' for what was to come.[18] After the final judgement, the wicked would go to the furnace of hell, the righteous to the Paradise of delight.[19] In an early version of what later came to be called 'the abominable fancy', the sufferings of the wicked would be increased by their knowing of the joys of the righteous – and the joys of the saved by their awareness of the wanderings of the ungodly and their ultimate punishments.

All of which brings us to Abraham's Bosom and the so-called *Josephus's Discourse to the Greeks Concerning Hades*. Traditionally ascribed to the Jewish historian Josephus (*c.*37–*c.*100 CE), this text is now thought to have been written by the Roman Christian Hippolytus (*c.*170–*c.*236 CE). According to Hippolytus, Hades was a place beneath the earth in which the sun did not shine and which was, as a result, completely in darkness. It was a guardhouse for souls, overseen by angels. Within Hades, there was also another place set apart, 'a lake of unquenchable fire', into which no one had as yet been thrown, although it was ready to receive the wicked on the Day of Judgement.[20] Both the righteous and the unrighteous were in Hades, although not in the same part of it.

At the time of death, all souls descended into Hades, at the entrance to which was a gate guarded by angels. Having passed through this gate, the dead were divided. The righteous were conducted in light to the right until they reached a place full of light, neither hot nor cold nor painful. There they enjoyed the contemplation of the blessings in their view, with expectations of the joys yet to come. There too, the righteous and the fathers were seen to be ever smiling 'as they wait for the rest and eternal revival in heaven which succeed this location'.[21] This place was known, we are told, 'by the name of *Abraham's bosom*'.[22]

The unrighteous, on the other hand, were dragged away unwillingly to the left as prisoners by angels who were ministers of punishment and forced down into the lower parts up to the edge of hell (γέεννα, Gehenna). There, 'they shudder in horror at the expectation of the future judgement, (as if they were) already feeling the power of their punishment'.[23] A deep and vast abyss lay between these two places in Hades, 'so that neither can any of the righteous in sympathy think to pass it, nor any of the unrighteous dare to cross it'.[24] There they all remained until the Day of Judgement. For Hippolytus, Hades remained the destination of *all* the dead, albeit divided into locations for the good and the wicked. It is clear too that Hippolytus made a further distinction within Hades, namely that it had within it a further and lower place, Gehenna, not yet populated but nevertheless the ultimate destination of the wicked after the final judgement.

Hippolytus may well have been influenced by his contemporary Tertullian (*c.*160–*c.*220 CE). Like Hippolytus, Tertullian also located all the dead (with the exception of the Christian martyrs), whether they lived before or after Christ, in Hades. There they remained until the Day of Judgement. Hades was 'a vast deep space in the interior of the earth, and a concealed recess in its very bowels [...] [on top of] the abysmal depths which lie still lower down'[25]. To those who complained of the unfairness in the good and the wicked going to the same place, Tertullian responded that both punishments and consolations were already experienced there, either in Abraham's Bosom or in the fire. The soul would be rewarded or punished immediately after death, 'without prejudice to the full process of the resurrection, when the recompense will be administered through the flesh besides.'[26] Still, even Tertullian was on occasion uncertain about the location of Abraham's Bosom within Hades. Nevertheless, he was driven to stress the great gulf between the two. Although he did not identify Abraham's Bosom with heaven or as part of heaven, he nevertheless wanted to designate it as higher than the underworld (*sublimiorem inferis*) and analogous to 'the Elysian Fields' (although presumably, unlike them, not located on the earth).[27]

This view that Hades was divided into two parts, in each of which the righteous and the unrighteous would receive anticipatory rewards or punishments was one that, as we will see in Chapter 2, St Augustine of Hippo (354–430 CE) finally came to. Augustine accepted the tradition that, between his death and resurrection, Christ had descended into Hades to preach to those who dwelt there. For Augustine, it was to the Bosom of Abraham that Christ descended in order to rescue the worthies who had preceded his coming. But unlike Tertullian and Hippolytus, Augustine believed that, on that day, Abraham's Bosom was emptied and that, from that point onwards, the righteous went into Paradise rather than Hades, a place opposed to it rather than part of it.

Go directly to Paradise

In their belief that, even after Christ, all, whether righteous or unrighteous, went to Hades immediately after death, Hippolytus and Tertullian were following the mainstream Jewish tradition. But among early Christian authors, they were in the minority. Generally, if it was believed that, as a result of Christ's preaching to the dead in Hades, those found worthy were translated elsewhere to a higher state, it was also presumed that the righteous who had died since Christ had risen from the dead had joined those worthies who had preceded them there. Again, generally, the most common view was that those who died in Christ went directly to Paradise.

The expectation that the righteous would go immediately to Paradise (or a Bosom of Abraham that was outside of Hades) was not only an apparent outcome of the emptying of Hades, but also a consequence of the words of Christ to the repentant thief: 'Truly I tell you, today you will be with me in Paradise [ἐν τῷ παραδείσῳ]' (Luke 23.43). However, granting the presence of Christ in Paradise on the day of his death, it was necessary to square this with the tradition of his descent into Hades on the same day. Clearly, even he was not able to be in two places at once.

Augustine, however, gave it his best shot to explain how Christ could be here, there and everywhere at the same time. If Christ was speaking as a man, declared Augustine, then since his soul went to the underworld, the repentant thief went with him there, and Paradise had to be conceived as part of Hades; if, however, he was speaking as God, then since God is everywhere, Christ was present with the blessed wherever they may be.[28] The Greek theologian Gregory of Nyssa (*c.*335–*c.*395 CE) had taken an alternative route by having Christ's body descend into Hades, while his soul escorted the thief to Paradise. The Alexandrian Neoplatonist theologian Origen (185–254 CE) had taken the simplest way by suggesting that, before he descended into Hades, Christ had dropped off the repentant thief in Paradise on his way.[29]

Paradise also bore an unclear connection to 'the third heaven'. In his Second Letter to the Corinthians, Paul had told his readers that he had been 'caught up' (or 'snatched away', ἁρπαγέντα) to 'the third heaven' (2 Cor. 12.2) and 'caught up into Paradise' (12.4), whether in body or not he was not sure. There he had heard things that were not to be told, 'that no mortal is permitted to repeat' (12.4). Paul was clearly referencing contemporary Jewish tradition that connected 'Paradise' and 'the third heaven' without necessarily equating them. Thus, for example, in the Second Book of Enoch, the product of a Jewish sect in the late first century CE, Enoch was taken up to the third heaven, whence he looked down upon Paradise, a place that was 'inconceivably pleasant' with trees in flower and ripe and pleasant-smelling fruits, in the middle of which was the tree of life, 'where the Lord takes a rest when he goes into Paradise'.[30] And within the Christian tradition, too, there remained uncertainty whether Paradise was to be equated with heaven as the final destination of the righteous or a penultimate destination.

If most were agreed that the righteous went to Paradise, where they were specifically located was a matter of much less certainty. This was, at least in part, because the relation of Paradise as a destination immediately after death to one after the final Day of Judgement was opaque. It was also in part because the relation of Paradise to heaven, whether after death or after the Last Judgement, was unclear. Finally, in part again, just to muddy the waters further, it was because Paradise could be construed as a 'physical' or 'spiritual' location or both, simultaneously or sequentially.

Be that as it may, it was generally accepted among early Christian thinkers that Paradise was the destination immediately after death for the saved. And all agreed, not surprisingly, that it was essentially like a garden (see Plate 5 [c]). This was because the term *paradeisos* (παράδεισος) derived from Old Persian and designated a 'garden' or 'park'. It had been used by the Greek translators of the Old Testament to refer to the garden in which God placed Adam at the time of Creation (Gen. 2.15). The Paradise upon which Enoch looked down from the third heaven was (or perhaps replicated) that garden in Eden out of which Adam and Eve had been driven and to which the saved would return after death. Thus, the last book of the New Testament, Revelation (2.7), spoke of 'the tree of life in the paradise of God' from which the righteous would be permitted to eat. That the destination of the saved was an Edenic garden meant not only that the painful mortality that resulted from Eden was replaced with the happy immortality originally intended by God. It also signalled that this had been brought about by the life, death and resurrection of Christ, who, as the second Adam, had restored humanity to its condition before the Fall of Man.

The most vivid description of the new Paradise occurs in the Apocalypse of Paul (mid-third century CE). This text is an extensive elaboration of the story of Paul's being caught up into the third heaven in 2 Corinthians 12.2–4. It is of significance not least because of its influence on Islamic accounts of the Mi'rāj, Muhammad's ascent into heaven. But also, as a result of its translations into a large number of European languages, it is the origin of many popular ideas about the delights of heaven and the horrors of hell in Western Christianity, not least because of its influence on Dante's *Divine Comedy*. In the Apocalypse of Paul, the destinations of the dead, both the righteous and the unrighteous, before and after the Last Judgement, are woven into a complex and often confusing narrative that combines Jewish, Christian and classical themes.

Paul's journey began with an overview of the destiny of souls at the time of death. From his position in heaven, Paul looked down upon the earth. From there he saw a just man who was about to die. Around him, both good and evil angels gathered. The evil angels found no place in him for them to inhabit. Thus, the holy angels took possession of his soul, guiding it until it departed his body. They told the soul to remember the body (*corpus*) that it was leaving, for it would return to that same body on the Day of Resurrection. The soul was then met by the guardian angel who had looked after it every day. The angel led the soul into the presence of God, who, knowing all that the man had done in his life, pronounced that his soul would be handed over to the angel Michael and led by him 'into the Paradise of joy, that it may become coheir with all the Saints.'[31]

Paul then saw the fate of an impious man. In his case, the good angels could find no place to inhabit. The evil angels took possession of his soul and drew it out of his body with the reminder: 'look upon your flesh [*caro*] from which you have come out; for it is necessary that you should return to your flesh in the day of resurrection.'[32] The impious soul was then led by its guardian angel to God, who, knowing of its misdeeds, pronounced his judgement:

> Let it therefore be handed over to the angel Tartaruchus [Tartarus], who is set over the punishments, and let him be cast into outer darkness, where there is weeping and gnashing of teeth, and let it be there till the great day of judgement.[33]

Although most souls were judged immediately, Paul saw one that had waited seven days to make an appeal, before his victims, who had been awaiting his arrival, also appeared before God to be judged. He too was eventually sent to Tartarus to be punished until the final Day of Judgement.

After Paul's vision of the divine court of justice, he was taken by his accompanying angel to the third heaven. There, at the entrance to the third heaven, he saw two golden pillars on which were written the names of the just even though they were still on earth. There he met Enoch and Elijah, the two Old Testament worthies who were believed never to have died but to have been translated straight to heaven (Gen. 5.24 and Heb. 11.5, 2 Kgs 2.11). The angel then led him over to the gates of heaven and showed him a land in which souls of the just dwelt for a short time after their death. This was a hidden Paradise on earth, Eden restored, where Christ would reign over the saints for a thousand years:

> And I looked around upon that land, and I saw a river flowing with milk and honey, and there were trees planted by the bank of that river, full

> of fruit; moreover, each single tree bore twelve fruits in the year, having various and diverse fruits; and I saw the created things which are in that place and all the work of God, and I saw there palms of twenty cubits, but others of ten cubits; and that land was seven times brighter than silver. And there were trees full of fruit from the roots to the highest branches, of ten thousand fruits of palms upon ten thousand fruits. The grape-vines had ten thousand plants.[34]

The angel then took him to a higher place in which the rewards of the just were seven times greater. They came to the Acherusian Lake, in which those who at death were repentant were baptised by the angel Michael prior to their entering the City of Christ.

Alongside the the garden, the city was perhaps the most common image of heaven. This was the result of the Old Testament imagining of a new Jerusalem that would be the capital of the final Messianic Kingdom (e.g. Ezek. 48.30–5), along with the book of Revelation's vision of a heavenly Jerusalem coming down from heaven to earth (Rev. 21–2). By the thirteenth century, the image of a heavenly city was beginning to overtake that of the heavenly garden, not least because of the dominance of Augustine's theology of the 'City of God' as opposed to the earthly city. It was an image that chimed with the developing dominance of urban life in the late medieval period (see Plate 6 [c]). The Apocalypse of Paul, however, like the book of Revelation, combined the imagery of the city with that of the Edenic garden. Thus, Paul's vision was that of a golden city surrounded by 12 walls and by the four rivers that formed from the one that flowed out of Eden. At the river of honey, Paul and his angelic guide met the Old Testament prophets; at the river of milk he saw all the infants that Herod slaughtered (among those who kept their chastity); at the river of wine he encountered the Old Testament patriarchs (among those who offered hospitality to strangers), while at the river of oil he saw all the faithful who had devoted themselves to God. He continued to the middle of the city, where he met those who, although unlettered, had goodness of heart and obeyed God. Having left the City of Christ, the angel took Paul westward across the ocean that encircled the earth, as in Homer, to the destination of the godless and sinful, a place of no light but of 'darkness and sorrow and sadness; and I sighed.'[35]

The punishments of the damned being far more interesting than the rewards of the righteous, then as now, here we find one of the earliest highly elaborated accounts of the multifarious suffering of the wicked allocated according to their vices. Thus, Paul first saw a river boiling with fire in which men and women who in their lives were found neither among the just nor among the godless – the lukewarm churchgoers – were variously immersed. The depth to which the bodies sank measured the weight of their vices – those who engaged in idle disputes up to their knees (academics beware), those who continued to fornicate up to their navels, those who slandered each other up to their lips, and those who hypocritically plotted against their neighbours up to their eyebrows.

This was just the beginning. To the north, Paul saw a fiery river running down into deep pits, with people groaning and wailing and crying out for mercy. Paul, worried that the pits would soon fill up were 30 or 40 generations of sinners piled up, was reassured about the depth of the Abyss: 'The Abyss has no measure, for beneath it there stretches down below that which is below it [...] For when the souls are thrown in there, they hardly reach the bottom in fifty years.'[36] The clergy especially were not exempt. By the fiery river, Paul saw a man being tortured by hell's angels, his bowels being pierced by an instrument with three hooks. He had been a hypocritical priest. Close by, there was a poorly performing bishop being stoned who failed to pity widows and orphans; and a fornicating deacon up to his knees in the fiery river, his bloodied hands outstretched, begging for mercy, with worms emerging from his mouth and nostrils.

Sins appear to be carefully matched to torments (although the modern reader is hard put to see how). Usurers were eaten by worms. Elsewhere, those who had disparaged the word of God were eating their own tongues. Magicians were immersed up to their lips in blood. Fornicators and adulterers paid their penalty in a pit of fire, while those who gave up their virginity before marriage, dressed in black, had burning chains placed on their necks by terrifying angels. Those who broke their fasts early were forever tempted (Tantalus-like) by fruit just out of reach. Users of prostitutes were hung by their hair and eyebrows; homosexuals, covered with dust, were to be found in a pit of tar and sulphur, running in a river of fire. Women who had had abortions, along with the fathers, were observed on a pillar of fire being torn to pieces by wild animals. And so on.

The angel then carried Paul to the north, where there was a well, guarded by an angel. At the request of Paul's angel, the well was opened so that Paul might see all the torments of the underworld. The angel of the well warned Paul to stand back, 'that you may be able to bear the stench of this place.'[37] The mouth of the well was so narrow it admitted only one person. Once anyone entered, 'no remembrance of him shall ever be made in the sight of the Father and his Son and the holy angels.'[38] Paul saw fiery masses burning on all sides. These were those who denied the incarnation of Christ, the virgin birth, and the miracle of the Mass when bread and wine were turned into the body and blood of Christ. To the west were those who denied the resurrection of Christ and the final resurrection of all the dead. In that place, there was nothing but cold and snow.

Still, there was the occasional ray of light in this unremitting gloom. The aborted 'infants' were 'handed over to the angels of Tartarus who were set over the punishments, that they might lead them to a spacious place of mercy; but their fathers and mothers were tortured in a perpetual punishment.'[39] When the damned saw Christ descending from heaven, they cried out to him for mercy. For the sake of Michael the archangel and Paul, Christ granted the damned one respite from punishment on that day on which he rose from the dead. God's justice was after all tempered with some mercy, although not as a favour to the damned.

Paul's journey in the underworld ended when the angel took him back to the Paradise on earth in which Adam and Eve had sinned. There he saw the tree of life and the tree of the knowledge of good and evil. While at the tree of life, he was visited by Mary the Mother of Christ, John the Baptist and his father, and the Old Testament worthies who wished to see him before he joined them permanently – Abraham, Isaac and Jacob, Joseph and his brothers, Moses, the prophets Isaiah, Jeremiah and Ezekiel, the righteous Lot from Sodom, Job, Noah, Elijah and Elisha, Enoch and Abel, and finally Adam, who declared, 'Take courage, Paul, beloved of God, you have brought a multitude to faith in God and to repentance. I myself have repented and received my praise from the compassionate and merciful one.'[40]

Paradise not quite regained yet

If it was generally accepted among early Christian thinkers that Paradise was the destination immediately after death for the saved, this was not the overarching view of the New Testament. On the contrary, in the New Testament, as in the Old, Hades was the destination of the dead. The Greek word for 'Hades' appears some ten times in the New Testament, twice each in the Gospels of Matthew and Luke, twice in the Acts of the Apostles, and four times in the book of Revelation.[41] In most of these cases, the New Testament use followed that of the Old Testament in indicating a shadowy place of neither pain nor pleasure to which all descended immediately after death. But there are several exceptions to this. The first occurs in the story of the rich man and Lazarus (Luke 16.19–31), in which (as we will see further in Chapter 2) Hades is at least a place where the wicked are punished (and may also be a place where the good are rewarded). The second exception occurs in the Gospel of Matthew (11.23) and in a parallel passage in the Gospel of Luke (10.13). Here the context indicates that Hades is a place opposed to heaven (ούρανος), to which the unrepentant people of Capernaum will go on the Day of Judgement. In a third case it means nothing more than death or the grave (1 Cor. 15.55).

That there is not a consistent account of Hades in the New Testament seldom worried early translators of the Greek New Testament. Most simply equated 'Hades' with 'hell', thus deeming it a place of punishment (which in the New Testament, with one exception, it isn't), and aligning the temporary place of all immediately after death with the eternal place of some after the Day of Judgement (which again in the New Testament it isn't). Thus, for example, Jerome's Latin translation of the Bible, the Vulgate (*c.*400 CE), used the Latin word for hell (*infernus* and variations) to translate Hades.[42] Martin Luther in his German New Testament (1522) generally used the German word for hell (*die Hölle*). The mid-sixteenth-century Protestant English Geneva Bible and the King James Bible of 1611 similarly opted for 'hell'. Luther also used the term *die Hölle* or a minor variant to translate the Greek word γέεννα (Gehenna). Similarly, the Geneva Bible and the King James Bible translated 'Gehenna' as 'hell' or 'hellfire'. In short, in these very important translations, no distinction was made between Hades and Gehenna. So it is little wonder that theorising about the afterlife using these translations could get messy. Moreover, to complicate matters further, Jerome's Vulgate retained the term 'Gehenna', thus maintaining a distinction between Gehenna and Hades. In so doing, Jerome was keeping the distinction that, as we will see further in the next chapter, Origen (*c.*185–*c.*254) had made. This was because Jerome accepted that Hades could contain the righteous and the wicked and thus was distinct from the place (Gehenna) that contained only the wicked.[43] Thus, both the rich man and Lazarus were in Hades. According to Origen, when Christ descended into Hades to preach to those dwelling there, those who were not converted descended further into Gehenna for punishment. For Origen, then, Hades and Gehenna were both places that existed and were populated on this side of the final Day of Judgement. Although Origen was drawing upon a distinction between Hades and Gehenna that was present within the New Testament, there the distinction is generally drawn in a quite different way. There they were primarily distinguished as places to be populated on either side of the time of the final judgement.

The Greek word for 'Gehenna' (γέεννα) was originally the name of a valley outside Jerusalem, the valley of Hinnom (in Jesus's language, Aramaic, 'Gehanna', in Hebrew 'Ge Hinnom'). This valley had been a site of pagan ritual activity in which children had been sacrificed by fire to the Canaanite gods Molech and Baal. In later parts of the Old Testament, it became more generally a place where all the wicked were eventually to receive their punishment on the Day of Judgement (Jer. 7.32). Subsequently, it was freed from its association with a *particular* place and designated as that more general subterranean space in which the unrighteous would be placed. Thus the Fourth Book of Ezra (*c.*100 CE) tells us that, on the Day of Judgement, 'the furnace of [Gehenna] shall be disclosed and opposite the Paradise of delight.'[44]

It is this understanding of Gehenna – as a place of punishment after the final Day of Judgement – that dominates its use in the New Testament. There, the term occurs 12 times: seven times in the Gospel of Matthew, three times in the Gospel of Mark, and once each in the Gospel of Luke and the Letter of James.[45] With two exceptions in Luke and James, it refers to the destination of the damned after the final judgement. Thus, for example, Jesus declared, 'Do not fear those who kill the body but cannot kill the soul; rather fear him who can destroy both the body and soul [ψυχήν] in hell [εν γεέννη]' (Matt. 10.28).

The important exception is Luke 12.4–5. The author of this Gospel rephrased Matthew 10.28 so that the saying of Jesus no longer referred to a final judgement of the body and the soul but to an immediate post-mortem judgement of the soul only: 'do not fear those who kill the body, and after that can do nothing more [...] Fear him who, after he has killed, has authority to cast into hell.' This is the first ever use of the term 'Gehenna' to refer to an immediate post-mortem destination of the dead. It is a usage that will also later occur in Rabbinic Judaism. This use of 'Gehenna' lines up with this same Gospel's story of the rich man and Lazarus, in which Hades is also the immediate destination of the dead. In short, in this Gospel, 'Hades' and 'Gehenna' do have the same meaning. This difference in understandings of 'Hades' and 'Gehenna' in the Gospels of Matthew and Luke also reflects the different understandings that they have about the destination of the dead more generally. The Gospel of Matthew suggests that, in the intermediate state immediately after death, there is neither pleasure nor pain. Rather, the dead await the Day of Judgement, when both rewards and punishments will be distributed. The wicked will then receive their punishments in Gehenna. By contrast, the Gospel of Luke has immediate punishment for the wicked in Hades or Gehenna, immediate rewards for the righteous in Abraham's Bosom, with a final judgement only of the righteous and no final judgement of the wicked followed by their being cast into Gehenna.[46]

Only once in the New Testament does the classical 'Tartarus' receive a mention: 'For if God did not spare the angels when they sinned, but cast them down into hell [*tartarosas*, ταρταρώσας] and committed them to chains of deepest darkness to be kept until the judgment' (2 Pet. 2.4). Here, the use of 'Tartarus' to indicate a place of punishment immediately after death aligns with the classical Greek understanding of it. Jerome's Vulgate retained the term 'Tartarus'. But Luther along with the Geneva and King James versions used the term 'hell', yet again lining up a classical place of punishment *immediately after death* with that place in which the wicked would be located *after the final judgement*.

Sufficient has been said to indicate that the understanding of the destination of the dead in the New Testament is complex. I have tried to make as coherent as possible what is anything but. Crucially, as we have seen, this instability of the New Testament texts was reflected in the vernacular translations of it, translations which themselves often reflected the different theological positions that the translators brought to their task. What is clear from the above discussion, however, is that the lines between the destinations of the dead immediately after death and their destinies after the final judgement were not only blurred within the original New Testament texts, but made more opaque by the various translations of those texts. It also demonstrates the crucial issue of the complex relations that exist between the supposed destiny of the dead immediately after death and their destination at the end of history. These relations were, as we will see in Chapter 3, crucially dependent on understandings of the nature of the human individual, more specifically on the matter (so to say) of bodies and souls. Before examining the issue of the relation of bodies and souls, however, there is another set of complex issues around the destiny of the dead, or at least some of them, that relates to the geography of the underworld generally, and to the place of limbo in particular within it.

Chapter Two

The Geography of the Underworld

There is a place down there not grim with pain
but only with sad shades whose deep laments
sound not as screams but melancholy sighs.
I take my place with children – innocents
in whom the bite of death set lethal teeth
before they'd been made free of human sin.

Dante, *Purgatorio*

Dante's limbo

In the early years of the fourteenth century, Dante Alighieri (1265–1321) was composing his *Divine Comedy* in three parts – the *Inferno*, the *Purgatorio* and the *Paradiso*. By that time, the fate of unbaptised infants had been determined within the Christian Church for the better part of the previous 900 years. At the time of their deaths, it was believed, they did not enter heaven. That they did not do so was because they died, as Dante put it, 'Before they'd been made free of human sin.'[1] Moreover, they never would go to paradise. Rather they would live forever on the edge of hell, 'suspended in that limbo.'[2]

Arguably, it was Dante's use of the term 'limbo' to refer to that place where dwelt the 'sad shades' of deceased children that popularised it in Western thought. He was not the first to use it, although it had only been coined shortly before his time. It was the Dominican monk Albert the Great (*c.*1200–80) who had first used the term *limbus* in the previous century to refer to a place in which at least some of the dead dwelt, and would do so eternally: 'Limbus signifies the hem of a garment,' he wrote, 'and can be applied to the place which is situated on the border of hell.'[3]

In Dante's architecture of the afterlife, there was a threefold vertical division between Paradise, Purgatory and, across the river called Acheron, hell (see Plate 8 [BW]). It was in the third canto of the *Inferno* that Virgil led Dante to the gate of hell, upon which was written the words 'Abandon hope, all you who enter here'. Upon entering through the gate, Dante heard sobbing, moans and plaintive crying in the darkness:

> Discordant tongues, harsh accents of horror,
> tormented words, the twang of rage, strident
> voices.[4]

These were the voices of those who lived their lives without having committed to either good or evil and consequently they were denied entry to heaven or hell. They would live eternally in the antechamber to hell, along with a choir of angels who, neither rebels against God nor true to him, lived only for themselves.

Virgil then led Dante to the river Acheron, on the other side of which hell began. There, on the bank of the river, a crowd of newly dead souls was waiting to be ferried across. A boat approached with an aged man, hair all white, at its helm. This was the ferryman who, in Greek and Latin sources, was paid for the journey across the river that separated the living from the dead with the coin that had been placed in the mouth of the dead for this purpose. The boatman, the demon Charon, 'with his hot-coal eyes', swept all the dead souls into the boat, striking at any dawdler with his oar (see Plate 2 [BW]). Virgil reassured Dante that Charon's reluctance to ferry him across boded well for his future. A sudden earthquake with wind and fire shook the earth, and Dante fainted, only to awaken on the other side in limbo, the first of the nine circles of hell beneath the earth.

Virgil and Dante, we are told, entered the darkness of the first circle, where

> no tears, no weeping, only sighs
> that caused a trembling in the eternal air

could be heard.[5] It was a place of melancholy sighs. These sighs were drawn from sorrow, not from pain, among the multitudes of speechless infants, women and men.[6] None of these had sinned; some had even gained merit. But none had been baptised and none could therefore gain entry to heaven. Virgil was among them:

They lived before the Christian age began.
They paid no reverence, as was due to God.
And in this number I myself am one.
For such deficiencies, no other crime,
we are all lost yet only suffer harm
through living in desire, but hopelessly.[7]

At one time in the past, Virgil told Dante, he had seen a power whose head was crowned with signs of victory. Dante's readers would have known that this was Jesus Christ, who, between his death and resurrection, had descended into hell, or at least into limbo. According to Virgil, he had led away to salvation those Old Testament worthies who had there been imprisoned – Adam, Abel and Noah, Moses and Abraham, David and Israel his father, together with many others. Until then, 'no human soul had ever been redeemed.'[8] The virtuous pagans, however, had not been redeemed. And Dante soon met some of those left behind, notably the great poets of antiquity – Homer, Horace, Ovid and Lucan.

Dante walked and talked with these virtuous pagans until they reached a fine castle surrounded by seven walls with a 'lovely stream' as its moat. Passing through seven gates, they came to a verdant lawn where other virtuous pagans were gathered – the philosophers Aristotle, Socrates and Plato, various characters from the *Aeneid*, the mathematician Euclid, the astronomer Ptolemy; and noble Muslims too – the philosophers Averroes and Avicenna, and the sultan Saladin. In hell they may have been, but this was benign enough. Although Dante had them in hell, his sympathy was nonetheless with these noble souls whose misfortune was to live before the time of Christ, and who were therefore predestined to spend eternity in a hopeless longing.

Among his contemporaries, Dante was seen as having broken with the orthodox Catholic theology of limbo in two ways: first, as we will see in more detail later, in his focusing not so much on those whom Christ freed from hell but on those who were left behind; and second, in his identifying the Limbo of the Infants or Children (*limbus infantum* or *puerorum*) with the limbo of the Old Testament worthies and ancient pagans (*limbus patrum*).

The orthodox position was that there were two limbos. According to the Franciscan theologian Bonaventure (1221–74), the underworld was divided into three places for the punishment of sins after this life. The first of these was Purgatory, reserved for the punishment of venial or forgivable sins. Next below was limbo, and below that was hell, for the punishment of mortal sins that had imperilled the soul. Limbo was further divided into two parts. In the lower part of limbo were those who had died in original sin (inherited from Adam), that is, unbaptised children (see Plate 12 [BW]). The upper limbo, also known as the Bosom of Abraham, was for those who dwelt there before the time of Christ but were delivered when Christ descended into hell. And consequently, since that time, the upper limbo had been empty.[9]

The idea of there being two limbos was made stronger by the Dominican theologian Thomas Aquinas (*c.*1225–74; Plate 7 [BW]) for, in his account of the netherworld, the two were separated by Purgatory. For Aquinas, hell had a fourfold division. One hell was the place of the damned, an abode in which the damned were both denied the vision of God and were physically tormented. Above that was another hell, a place of darkness without the vision of God but without physical torments. This hell, said Aquinas, is called 'the Limbo of the Children' (*limbus puerorum*). Above the Limbo of the Children was a further place of darkness without the vision of God but which did nonetheless include physical suffering (but from which release was possible). This place, said Aquinas, was called 'Purgatory'. Finally, above Purgatory, there was yet another hell. This too was a place of darkness without the vision of God, yet again without physical torments. This was the 'hell of the holy fathers' (*infernus sanctum patrum*). It was to this region of hell, he remarked, that Christ had descended between his death and his resurrection; he had gone no further.[10]

The Limbo of the Infants

Unbaptised deceased children were not located in a specific place, namely, limbo, until the thirteenth century. But Christian thinkers had been exercised about the fate of infants since the fourth. It was the Greek theologian Gregory of Nyssa (*c.*330–*c.*395 CE) who was the first to devote a work specifically to this issue.[11] About the point of such brief lives, he was deeply troubled: 'What wisdom, then, can we trace in the following?' he asked.

> A human being enters on the scene of life, draws in the air, beginning the process of living with a cry of pain, pays the tribute of a tear to Nature, just tastes life's sorrows, before any of its sweets have been his, before

> his feelings have gained any strength; still loose in all his joints, tender, pulpy, unset [...] such an one, with no advantage over the embryo in the womb except that he has seen the air, so short-lived, dies and goes to pieces again.[12]

How are we to feel about such deaths? he wondered.

> Will a soul such as that behold its Judge? Will it stand with the rest before the tribunal? Will it undergo its trial for deeds done in life? Will it receive the just recompense by being purged, according to the Gospel utterances, in fire, or refreshed with the dew of blessing.[13]

The key issue for Gregory was the nature of the afterlife of such infants. They did not deserve the punishments reserved for the wicked. Nor did they merit the rewards of the virtuous. If rewards or punishments after death were allocated according to principles of justice, 'in what class shall he be placed who has died in infancy without having laid in this life any foundation, good or bad, whereby any return according to his deserts may be given him?'[14] Gregory was quite certain that deceased infants, having done no evil, did not deserve punishment of any kind. That said, since reward was proportional to virtue acquired during this life, the participation of the deceased infant, whose soul 'has never felt the taste of virtue', in eternal happiness was minimal.[15] Of their post-mortem location, there was no indication. Although there is a hint in Gregory of Nyssa that their post-mortem happiness might develop, the state in which they existed immediately after death was a neutral one. How all this was to be squared with the justice and goodness of God was another question. Gregory's suggestion that God providentially cut infant lives short because he foresaw the immense evils that they would commit were they to become adults, thus demonstrating the divine kindness, was perhaps not the most persuasive of arguments – then or now.

Generally, within the theology of the Greek or Eastern Church, the fate of unbaptised children was rather underdetermined. All agreed with Gregory of Nyssa that deceased infants were worthy neither of reward nor punishment, not least because they lacked a moral identity. This was in keeping with the Greek theologians' general view of the consequences of the Fall of Man, that it entailed corruption and mortality but not a human nature despoiled by sin. So there is no sense in Greek theology that children were born in inherited sin and guilt as a consequence of the sin of Adam. On the contrary, for Gregory of Nyssa, children were born in a state of natural goodness.

However, the view that children were born sinless was significantly to change in the Latin or Western Church in the early part of the fifth century. It was then that the fate of infants became a core subject of dispute in the controversies surrounding the figures of Pelagius (*fl. c.*390–418 CE) and Augustine (354–430 CE). And it was on the battleground of the fate of infants who had died unbaptised that the question of original sin, the sin that was or wasn't inherited by all as a result of the sin of Adam, was fought out.

Pelagius was at the forefront of those who denied the doctrine of hereditary sin. Around 405 CE, before his controversy with Augustine broke out, Pelagius sided with those who declared it 'to be unjust that a soul which is born today, not from the lump of Adam, bears so ancient a sin belonging to another'.[16] It should not be countenanced, he continued, that the God who forgives human beings their own sins should impute to them those of another (i.e. of Adam). A child or a newborn baby, he declared elsewhere, cannot be held responsible for the sin of another. Evil is not born with us: 'Everything good, and everything evil, on account of which we are either laudable or blameworthy, is not born with us but done by us [...] and we are procreated as without virtue, so also without vice.'[17] As Pelagius's colleague Caelestius (*fl.* fifth century CE) had rather neatly put it, 'infants are at their birth in the same state in which Adam was before the transgression.'[18] They were born as a blank sheet upon which deeds of evil or good would only later be written. Still, as Augustine remarked, Pelagius and his followers were in agreement that, without baptism, deceased infants could not enter the Kingdom of Heaven. Moreover, Pelagius knew that infants, without the stain of original sin, did not go to hell. But just where such innocent infants did go, he knew not.[19] Augustine, as we will see, did know, and he had no doubts about it.

For Pelagius and others, having innocent deceased infants paying after death in hell for the sins they did not commit was in conflict with their understanding of divine justice. Augustine, by contrast, put his emphasis not on the sins of infants but on their suffering in this life. For Augustine, it was these postnatal sufferings that, if these children were innocent at the time of their birth, counted against the justice of God. 'Do you not realize,' he asked, 'that you make God unjust when you see the punishments to which babies are subject yet you continue to declare them innocent?'[20] So for Augustine, the sufferings of children in this life could only be explained as punishments justified by the sinful state inherited from Adam in which these children were born.

In his early work *De libero arbitrio* (On free choice of the will), Augustine had adopted a position on the fate of unbaptised infants not much different from that which he was later to oppose. If there is a life, he wrote, that is between sin and right action, 'have no fear that our Judge can pronounce a sentence that is intermediate between punishment and reward.'[21] Later, however, in the context of the debate about original sin with Pelagius, his views hardened. It is a fundamental truth of the Christian faith, he declared, that those who are born are damned unless redeemed through baptism.[22] This was simply the case regardless of age.

This was the inevitable consequence of his doctrine of original sin. Simply put, eternal damnation was the only possible outcome for those who died without the remission of original sin that baptism conferred. The unbaptised, he wrote, 'must be classed amongst those who do not believe on the Son, and therefore, if they shall depart this life without this grace, they [...] shall not have life, but the wrath of God abideth on them.'[23] In short, it was only possible to be with the Devil or with Christ. Still, there was some mitigation of this harsh outcome to be found. For Augustine, the punishments of hell were proportionate to the guilt of the sinner. Moreover, only original sin, not personal sin, could be attributed to deceased infants. Consequently, their punishment would be minimal: 'such infants as quit the body without being baptized will be involved in the mildest condemnation of all.'[24]

It was Augustine's view on the destiny of unbaptised infants that was to dominate the medieval period. Pope Gregory the Great (*c.*540–604), for example, took it as read: '[T]here be some that are withdrawn from the present light,' he declared, 'before they attain to shew forth the good or evil deserts of an active life [...] For they even receive everlasting torments, who never sinned by their own will.'[25] Anselm of Canterbury (*c.*1033–1109) is remembered in the modern world more for his ontological proof for the existence of God than for his view on the fate of unbaptised infants. Not surprisingly, perhaps, for it was Augustine's harsh view that he endorsed. Like Augustine, Anselm distinguished between personal sin and natural or original sin, between the personal sin that Adam committed and the sin that infected his nature as a result of this personal sin. It was this infection, natural or original sin, that he transmitted to all his descendants: 'the personal sin of Adam passes over to all who are naturally propagated from him; and in them it is natural, or original, sin.'[26] Again, like Augustine, Anselm did not think that all individuals deserved to be tormented in hell to the same degree; sins were unequal and punishments should be correspondingly the same. So the sin of infants was less than that of Adam. Nevertheless, damned they were: 'if what I have termed original sin is a sin, then it is necessary that every man who is born with it and does not have it forgiven is condemned.'[27]

There were others, however, who tried to mitigate the apparent harshness of the Augustinian position. Peter Abelard (1079–1142), for example, believed that while the justice of God in damning unbaptised infants to hellfire could not be denied, it needed to be balanced by divine goodness. Thus, he nuanced Augustine's 'mildest condemnation of all' by distinguishing the punishment of the soul from that of the body, and assigning to deceased children only the former. For those with only original and not personal sin in addition, he declared: 'I do not think that this punishment is anything other than to endure darkness, that is, to lack the vision of the divine majesty without any hope of recovery.'[28] In short, those who died unbaptised suffered the psychological punishment of the loss of the Beatific Vision, but not physical torments. It was a distinction that Thomas Aquinas was later to formalise in terms of *poena damni* (pain of loss) in contrast to *poena sensus* (pain of sense).

This view that deceased infants suffered only the loss of the Beatific Vision and not physical torments was endorsed by Bonaventure. Unbaptised children, he believed, existed somewhere *between* the blessed and those tormented in the eternal fires of hell. They shared with the blessed the absence of any exterior or physical pain. But with the damned, they shared the privation of the vision of God in darkness: 'and so they are both happy and sad.'[29] Like those in the limbo of Dante, their lament was deep, for they knew exactly what they had lost.

For his part, Aquinas agreed with Bonaventure that those who died unbaptised did not suffer physical torments, but only the loss of the Beatific Vision. But he disagreed about the nature of their fate. How deeply, he wondered, did they feel the pain of this loss? Initially Aquinas believed that they were not unhappy. For although they knew what they had lost, they did not grieve for that which they knew was beyond their capacity to obtain. No wise man, he wrote, 'grieves for being unable to fly like a bird, or for that he is not a king or an emperor, since these things are not due to him.'[30] However, in his later work *De malo* (On evil), Aquinas was to amend his position slightly. He now denied to children the knowledge of their loss, for the supernatural knowledge of the Beatific Vision was a consequence of faith that, lacking baptism, they did not have. In short, not only did they not lament that which was beyond their capacity to obtain, but also they could not lament the loss of that about which they could not know.[31] Moreover, he went on, they had a kind of happiness in general, the result of naturally knowing that souls were created for happiness.

The Limbo of the Fathers

Dante radically differed from his contemporaries in assigning both deceased infants and virtuous pagans to the one geographical space, namely the first circle of hell. In consigning virtuous pagans to limbo for eternity, he was also disagreeing with the mainstream theological orthodoxies which, up until that time, had consigned the virtuous pagans either downwards to hell or upwards to heaven. But Dante was at one with his contemporaries in his belief that the patriarchs and prophets of the Old Testament – Adam, Abraham, Moses, and so on – had gained salvation, and that they had done so through faith in Jesus Christ. Christ had harrowed Hades and delivered them from what was known, by the time of Thomas Aquinas, as 'the Limbo of the Fathers' (*limbus patrum*).

This doctrine of the harrowing of Hades (or hell) was that, between his death and resurrection, Christ descended into Hades and there preached to those already dead (see Plate 13 [c]). Then he led the righteous from there to Paradise or heaven, and in so doing defeated death and the powers of hell who had kept the dead imprisoned there.[32] The key New Testament texts were 1 Peter 3.19, according to which Christ went and preached to the spirits in prison, and 1 Peter 4.6, where the gospel is said to have been preached even to the dead.[33]

The most elaborate version of the harrowing of Hades is to be found in the mid-sixth-century Gospel of Nicodemus (in its earliest form after the year 555). Outside of the New Testament Gospels themselves, this was perhaps the most influential and authoritative of all early Christian writings.[34] The second part of the Gospel of Nicodemus, which dealt with Christ's descent into Hades, is extant in both Greek and two Latin versions, the latter of which were the parents of versions in every European language.[35]

According to the Greek version, prior to Christ's arrival in the underworld, John the Baptist had come proclaiming that Christ too was coming into Hades to offer salvation to all. This included not only the patriarchs and prophets but also the pagans who previously worshipped idols. The repetition in the underworld of John's earthly mission was a common theme in early Christian thought. Therefore, declared John,

> now only is the time of repentance for you, for that ye did worship idols in the vain world that is above, and for the sins which ye have committed: but at another time it is impossible that this should come to pass.[36]

And when Christ arrived at the gates of Hades soon afterwards, 'all the dead that were bound were loosed from their chains.'[37] After he had rescued Adam, Jesus said to all the dead:

> Come with me all ye, as many as have suffered death through the tree which this man [Adam] touched. For lo, I do raise you all up again through the tree of the cross. And with that he put them all forth.[38]

The underworld, we can only assume, was left empty.

Those whom Christ led into Paradise were delivered to Michael the archangel. There they met Enoch and Elijah, the only two figures in the Old Testament who never died, along with the repentant thief crucified with Jesus (named Dismas for the first time by the Gospel of Nicodemus). According to the Gospel of Luke, he was promised by Jesus, 'today you will be with me in Paradise' (Luke 23.43). Dismas reports that, when he arrived in heaven, Michael said, 'Tarry a little, for Adam the forefather of mankind cometh with the righteous, that they also may enter in.'[39]

The two Latin versions ('Latin A' and 'Latin B'), however, told a different story about whom Christ saved when he descended into Hades. Unlike in the Greek version, there is no mention of the preaching of John the Baptist to the idolaters in hell. Overall, the Latin versions appear to limit Christ's offer of salvation to the saints, and especially to the prophets and patriarchs, and (in Latin B) Eve. In Latin A, the fate of those left behind, as well as that of Satan, is unclear. By contrast, in Latin B, their fate is more certain. In the Latin A version, Jesus left Satan, and presumably also the dead not taken to Paradise, in Hades for all eternity. But in the Latin B version, there is a significant shift. There, Satan was not kept in Hades for eternity, but was cast into the fires of hell (Tartarus):

> And behold, the Lord Jesus Christ coming in the glory of the light, in meekness, great and yet humble, bearing a chain in his hands bound therewith the neck of Satan, and also, binding his hands behind his back, cast him backward into Tartarus, and set his holy foot upon his throat and said: Throughout all ages hast thou done much evil and hast never been quiet at any time. To-day I deliver thee unto eternal fire.[40]

Satan was confined to hell.[41] In addition, Christ only took *some* of those in Hades away with him to Paradise. The remainder were 'cast down [...] into Tartarus'.[42] For the Gospel of Nicodemus, then, whether Christ took all with him to Paradise (as in the Greek version), or only some (as in the Latin B version), Hades – the place to which all the dead were assigned from the time of Adam onwards – was *literally* emptied between Christ's death and his resurrection.

This matter of the salvation of the Old Testament worthies had been of crucial importance from the middle of the second century CE. For it was then that Marcion (d. *c.*160 CE) had drawn a sharp distinction between the New Testament God of love and goodness and the Old Testament God of law and evil. As a consequence, the worthies of the Old Testament were seen not as heroic precursors of Christ, but rather as villains. Thus it was not they who were saved when Christ descended into Hades. Rather, at least according to Marcion's orthodox opponent Irenaeus (*c.*130–200 CE), Marcion held that it was Cain, the Sodomites, the Egyptians, 'and all the nations who walked in all sorts of abominations' who 'were saved by the Lord, on his descending into Hades'.[43] The righteous men of the Old Testament – Abel, Enoch, Noah, Abraham, and the other patriarchs and prophets – 'remained in Hades'.[44]

By contrast, Irenaeus held that there was no discontinuity between the Old and New Testament Gods, and that the Old Testament worthies were forerunners of Christ. Thus there was salvation for all those righteous men of the Old Testament who, even though they were sinners, hoped for Christ:

> It was for this reason, too, that the Lord descended into the regions beneath the earth, preaching His advent there also, and [declaring] the remission of sins received by those who believe in Him. Now all those

> who believed in Him, who had hope towards Him, that is, those who proclaimed His advent, and submitted to His dispensation, the righteous men, the prophets, and the patriarchs [...] He remitted sins in the same way as He did to us.[45]

If the fate of the Old Testament worthies was a burning issue by the late second century CE, so too was the fate of the virtuous pagans as Christianity began intellectually to interact with Greek philosophy. Nowhere was there more of an engagement between theology and philosophy than in the Alexandria of the time of Clement (*c.*150–*c.*215 CE). According to Clement, philosophy was given to the Greeks, as was the law to the Jews, to prepare them to receive the gospel of Christ. Consequently, it was only just that those in Hades, both Jews and Gentiles, should be given the opportunity to be saved. For a righteous man, declared Clement, 'differs not, as righteous, from another righteous man, whether he be of the Law or a Greek'.[46] This did not mean that all would be saved, but it did mean that all would be given the opportunity to believe.

Clement was uncertain whether the offer of salvation made by Christ when he descended into Hades was made to all the Gentiles or only to those who were righteous. And he was unsure whether Christ descended into Hades to preach to all who were there or only to the Jews. If Christ did preach only to the Jews, Clement believed that, as here so also there, the Apostles also descended after *their* deaths to preach the gospel to those who remained and were ready to be converted. If the Lord had descended to preach the gospel to all,

> then all who believe shall be saved, although they may be of the Gentiles, on making their profession there; since God's punishments are saving and disciplinary, leading to conversion, and choosing rather the repentance than the death of a sinner.

Indeed, he suggested, souls there, 'although darkened by passions, when released from their bodies, are able to perceive more clearly, because of their being no longer obscured by the paltry flesh'.[47] In either case, both Jews and Gentiles were offered a chance at salvation.

Origen (*c.*185–*c.*254 CE), Clement's successor as head of the Christian Catechetical School in Alexandria, endorsed his approach to Christ's descent into Hades. Late in the second century, the pagan philosopher

Celsus had attacked the tradition that Christ had descended into Hades: 'You [Christians] will not, I suppose, say of him [Christ], that, after failing to gain over those who were in this world, he went to Hades to gain over those who were there.' Origen was one Christian who wanted to say precisely that. He not only rebuffed the suggestion that Christ's mission had been a failure on earth, but went on to defend Christ's descent into Hades:

> when He became a soul, without the covering of the body, He dwelt among those souls which were without bodily covering, converting such of them as were willing to Himself, or those whom He saw, for reasons known to Him alone, to be better adapted to such a course.[48]

Origen did not declare that all were converted. In fact, the implication of the passage above is that there remained some who were unwilling. This did not, however, mean that they remained in Hades. For Origen also made a clear distinction between Hades and Gehenna, that dark place of eternal and inextinguishable fire.[49] Thus, those who were not willing to be converted may have descended into Gehenna (hell) for punishment, and again Hades was permanently emptied. What we can conclude is that, among those who were converted, there were Gentiles as well as Jews.

'He descended into hell'

Such agonising over the fate of the dead before Christ was to converge in Augustine. In 414 CE, Augustine received a letter from an old friend, Bishop Evodius of Uzalis. He asked Augustine just who were the spirits in prison to whom Christ went and preached after his death (1 Pet. 3.19), such that they were all delivered from darkness and punishment and such that 'from the time of the resurrection of the Lord judgment is expected, Hell having then been completely emptied.'[50] It was a question that also perplexed Augustine, and his opinions were anything but fixed.

Still, of one thing Augustine was in no doubt. It is established beyond question, he wrote, that after his death, Christ descended into hell (*in infernum*).[51] That he had done so had been a commonplace in Christian thought since the first century CE. In 359, it was incorporated into a creed for the first time at the Council of Sirmium. In the so-called 'Dated Creed', it is said that Christ descended into the underworld and the gatekeepers of

Hades shuddered.[52] Augustine also understood Christ's descent as including the deliverance of those there. But he thought it presumptuous to say who these were. He was not unhappy to count Adam among them. This was agreed to, he wrote, 'by almost the entire Church'.[53] Some, he knew, wished to include the Old Testament worthies. And he was not unsympathetic to the idea that the virtuous pagans should be saved, for 'they may be justly held up as models in all the other virtues [except the worship of one God] of frugality, self-denial, chastity, sobriety', and so on.[54]

The stumbling block for Augustine, however, was the New Testament parable of the rich man and Lazarus (Luke 16.19–31). According to this, there was a rich man who was dressed in purple and fine linen and who ate sumptuously every day. At his gate lay a poor man called Lazarus, whose sores the dogs came and licked and who longed only to eat the scraps that fell from the rich man's table (see Plate 4 [BW]). When the poor man died, he was carried away to the Bosom of Abraham by the angels. The rich man also died, was buried and went down to Hades. There, while being tormented, he looked up and saw Abraham far away with Lazarus by his side. He called out, 'Father Abraham, have mercy on me, and send Lazarus to dip the tip of his finger in water and cool my tongue; for I am in agony in these flames.' But Abraham said:

> Remember that during your lifetime you received good things and Lazarus only evil things. Now he is comforted here and you are in agony. Besides all this, there is a great chasm fixed between you and us and no one can cross from Hades to us.

On the basis of this text, Augustine wanted to distinguish Abraham's Bosom and Hades. He could not see how both Abraham and Lazarus could be in a place of pain and suffering. Moreover, he thought it absurd that only Abraham and Lazarus were 'in that bosom of wondrous repose' before Christ descended into hell. In addition, he thought it likely that the prophets and patriarchs were there also, although he admitted to not understanding what benefit was conferred on *them* by Christ when he loosed the pains of hell. Thus, on the grounds that Abraham had said that a great gulf was fixed, he concluded that 'the bosom of that glorious infelicity was not any integral part of Hell'. He wished rather that Scripture had said that Christ had gone there: 'if sacred Scripture had said, without naming Hell and its pains, that Christ when He died went to that bosom of

Abraham, I wonder if anyone would have dared to say that He "descended into Hell".'[55] Still, as Augustine admits, Scripture *did* make mention of hell and its pains, and there was no reason to think that Christ went except to save its occupants. Even granting that Christ did descend into hell for that reason, Augustine was still uncertain whether 'He did save all whom He found [...] or some whom He judged worthy of that favour'.[56] On one point, however, Augustine did not waver. Those who had died since the resurrection of Christ and who had not embraced salvation in this life would have no opportunity to do so after their deaths. Their eternal destiny was fixed at the point of death.

Having said that, by 417 CE, in his letter to Dardanus, a high official in Gaul, Augustine had further refined his position. For now he believed that there was not a great chasm between Abraham's Bosom and Hades, but rather that there were two regions in hell, 'one for the suffering and one for the souls in repose'.[57] Abraham's Bosom had now become part of hell. And it was only to the Bosom of Abraham that Christ had descended in order 'to rescue those who were there to be rescued'.[58] Moreover, Augustine now equated the Bosom of Abraham with the Paradise into which the repentant thief was received on the same day that Christ died. Augustine also became much clearer now about who was saved as a result of Christ's descent into what had now become an upper region of hell. Among those there to be rescued were the Old Testament worthies. They 'were also to be saved by the same faith to be revealed in due time'.[59] So, by shifting Abraham's Bosom from being a place separated from Hades by a great gulf to being a part of Hades, Augustine now had a genuine reason for Christ's descent into hell, namely to rescue those who were in its 'upper part', the souls in repose, but not to assist those suffering in the lower region of hell. They were left to their fate. In his last work *De haeresibus* (On heresies), Augustine went as far as to declare it a heresy to believe that, on Christ's descending into hell (*ad inferos*), the unbelievers believed and all who dwelt there were freed (*liberatos*).[60] So it was only those in Abraham's Bosom, later to be the Limbo of the Fathers, that were saved when Christ descended into hell.

In spite of Augustine's position becoming the dominant one, the tradition that *all* were saved as a result of Christ's descent was still to be found at the end of the sixth century. Thus, Pope Gregory the Great wrote to two clergy of the Church at Constantinople about their preaching that Christ at his descent into hell had saved *all* those there who had acknowledged him as God and delivered them from the pains due to them. He repeated

Augustine's suggestion that it was heretical to think so, encouraging them to think differently. '[H]old ye nothing,' he declared,

> but what the true faith teaches through the Catholic Church: namely, that the Lord in descending into Hell rescued from infernal durance those only whom while living in the flesh He preserved through His grace in faith and good conduct.[61]

Unlike Augustine, Gregory did not distinguish regions of hell, nor did he explicitly exclude from salvation at least some of the virtuous pagans who did good works. In the middle of the eighth century, in spite of the authority of both Augustine and Gregory, Clement the Scot was condemned by a synod at Rome for flouting their authority by contending 'that Christ, descending to the lower world, set free all who were imprisoned there, believers and unbelievers, those who praised God and the worshippers of idols.'[62]

Still, if not *all* were saved, what of the salvation of at least *some* of the pagans, especially those who lived lives of great goodness? The tradition that virtuous pagans were saved by Christ's descent into hell remained alive in medieval theology, even if only held by a minority. Thus, for example, in the late seventh century, Anastasios of Sinai tells of a tradition that a scholar who disparaged Plato was visited by him in a dream. Plato asked him to cease his slighting of him for 'that I was a sinful man I do not deny, but when Christ descended to Hades, no one believed in Him before I did.'[63] However, with the increasing interest in classical traditions in the twelfth century, and the engagement of Christian theology once again with the traditions of Greek philosophy, the issue of the salvation of the virtuous pagans returned to the theological agenda. This was especially the result of the debate initiated by Peter Abelard.

It was in the early twelfth century that Peter Abelard, in his *Sic et non* (Yes and no), summed up the orthodox state of play on a number of issues around the fate of the pre-Christian worthies. In one chapter, he reviewed the question of the salvation of Adam. He found no sources that denied the salvation of the first man. On the question of whether Christ had liberated all the souls that he found in hell on his descent there, he cited a work of Origen to the effect that Christ had freed all. And he followed this with a similar claim from a late fourth-century commentary on Paul's epistle to the Romans that he attributed to Ambrose (*c.*339–97 CE): 'Indeed men sinned, Jews as much as Greeks, for which reason the death of Christ was an advantage to all; and at this time, this must be believed and observed, that he taught and freed all from hell [*et de inferno eripuit*].[64] Nevertheless, Abelard found that a strong majority of authorities were opposed to the view that Christ freed all from Hades and supported the view that Christ had rescued only those who hoped and believed that he would come to bring salvation.

But Abelard was not willing to leave it there. He had no doubt that the virtuous pagans had been saved. Thus, in his *Theologia Christiana* (Christian theology), he argued that the virtuous pagans, and particularly Plato and his successors in the third-century school of Neoplatonism, had come to the doctrine of the Trinity through the use of natural reason.[65] This was a step too far for Bernard of Clairvaux (1090–1153), for whom knowledge of the Trinity was a consequence of revelation and not reason. He ensured that Abelard's views were condemned at the Council of Sens in 1141.

Be that as it may, for his part, Thomas Aquinas agreed with Bernard against Abelard that the doctrine of the Trinity was a matter of revelation and not of reason. But, like Abelard, he was sympathetic to the plight of the virtuous pagans. Of Christ's descent into hell, he had no doubt. Thus, in his *Compendium theologiae* (Compendium of theology), he declared that, as Christ's body was interred in the earth, 'so also his soul descended into hell', although not to suffer punishment there. Christ descended into hell in order to free from punishment those who were kept there because of Adam, 'our first parent'. That is to say, he liberated only those who had inherited original sin. But he left there 'those who were obligated to punishments for their own sins'.[66]

In his earlier *Summa theologica* (Summary of theology), it is clear that those who were rescued and those left behind were in different parts of hell. According to Aquinas, before Christ's coming, the saints were at rest in Abraham's Bosom, where they were not punished. Nevertheless, it had a lack of rest attached to it, since the repose of those there was incomplete because they had not seen God. So in that sense it could also be called hell.[67] Before Christ's coming, Abraham's Bosom was also the Limbo of the Fathers. It was distinguished from the lower part of hell not only by its being a temporary rather than eternal place, but also by its not being a place of physical punishments:

> For those who are in hell receive diverse punishments according to the diversity of their guilt, so that those who are condemned are consigned

> to darker and deeper parts of hell according as they have been guilty of graver sins, and consequently the holy Fathers in whom there was the least amount of sin were consigned to a higher and less darksome part than all those who were condemned to punishment.[68]

However, after Christ's coming, the repose of the saints was completed through their then seeing God. This place of rest is still called Abraham's Bosom, declared Aquinas, although it could no longer be considered as part of hell or as the Limbo of the Fathers. Whereas the separate Limbo of the Infants remained after the death of Christ as the repository of those who died without baptism in original sin, the Limbo of the Fathers was emptied when Christ descended into it. But just who did Aquinas think was in the Limbo of the Fathers awaiting the redemption offered by Christ? To answer this, we need to turn to Aquinas's *De veritate* (On truth) and his distinction between *explicit* and *implicit* faith.

According to Aquinas, the faithful in every age must believe that God exists and that he exercises his providence over human affairs. But not all were bound to believe everything *explicitly* in every age, only those who were appointed teachers in those matters. Even the teachers were not bound to believe everything explicitly in every age, for there was a gradual progress in faith in the human race. Since the coming of Christ, leaders were bound to believe all matters of faith *explicitly*. However, before sin came into the world, it was not even necessary to believe in a redeemer yet to come, since at that time there was no need of such a figure. Before and after the Fall, it was necessary for the leaders to have explicit faith in the Trinity. But the ordinary people among the Jews needed only implicit faith contained either in their belief in the patriarchs and prophets or in their belief in divine providence. While the Old Testament worthies ranked among the teachers, there were no such teachers among the virtuous pagans. Thus, all the Gentiles counted only as ordinary people. Therefore, declared Aquinas, 'it was enough for them to have implicit faith in the Redeemer.'[69] Even so, perhaps there were instances of explicit faith for, he continued, 'it is likely that the mystery of our redemption was revealed to many Gentiles before Christ's coming.'[70] For Aquinas, on this account, Abraham's Bosom before the coming of Christ was pretty well populated, with Jews as well as Gentiles. And among the latter were the learned Greeks and virtuous pagans.

Unlike Dante, for whom the fathers and the children shared a limbo, Aquinas placed Purgatory between the Limbo of the Fathers above and the Limbo of the Children below. In spite of their virtues, Dante did not allow his virtuous pagans to escape limbo. They lacked what Aquinas would have called explicit belief. As Virgil declared, '[a]nd for no crime, save lack of faith, I lost the heavenly sky.'[71] In contrast, Aquinas's limbo was emptied. The *implicit* belief of those imprisoned there was sufficient for their salvation when Christ descended into that part of hell between his death and resurrection.

Thus, by the time of Aquinas, with the exception of Dante, there was general agreement on the fate of those who had lived before Christ. This was that all had been located in the Limbo of the Fathers and that this place beneath the earth had been emptied. This was either the consequence of *all* those who had been located there having been saved as a result of Christ's descent into hell, or it was the result of *some* of those located there having been saved, the remainder of them having left limbo and descended further into the lower region(s) of hell. In either case, there was a consensus that Adam and the Old Testament worthies had been saved.

About the fate of the virtuous pagans, however, there was much less clarity. All were agreed that, in terms of their virtuous works, they were more than worthy of salvation. But were good works sufficient, or was faith in Jesus Christ necessary for redemption? And if faith was necessary for salvation, was implicit rather than explicit faith sufficient to merit it? On this, opinions remained divided. Eventually, these became issues central to the Protestant Reformation in the sixteenth century. By that time the question had become focused not on the fate of those who had died without baptism or before Christ, but on the destiny of those who had lived since, both within and outside the Church, and on the means by which their salvation had been effected, whether by faith or by works. In the meantime, alongside the question of which persons are saved and which damned, there ran the question of what part of those persons is saved or damned – bodies, souls, both or neither?

Chapter Three

Souls and Bodies

> [B]ecause the man cannot be said to exist when the body is dissolved, and indeed entirely scattered abroad, even though the soul continue by itself – it is absolutely necessary that the end of a man's being should appear in some reconstitution of the two together, and of the same living being. And as this follows of necessity, there must by all means be a resurrection of the bodies which are dead, or even entirely dissolved, and the same men must be formed anew.
>
> Athenagoras, *De resurrectione mortuorum* (*c.*180 CE)

Composite creatures

Athenagoras, known as 'the Athenian philosopher', composed the earliest Christian philosophical work on the resurrection of the dead around 180 CE.[1] This work, *De resurrectione mortuorum* (On the resurrection of the dead), was directed at those among the cultured, both Christians and others, who thought the resurrection of the body at best unintelligible, at worst incredible. Its aim was to convince the doubters that it was both possible for God to raise the dissolved or dispersed bodies of the dead on the Day of Judgement, and that justice required that God should do so.

But this work was much more than that. It was also the first essay in the Christian doctrine of man. Athenagoras declared that man was a composite being consisting of a mortal body and an immortal soul: '[T]he whole nature of men in general is composed of an immortal soul and a body which was fitted to it in the creation.'[2] Athenagoras's key argument was to the effect that, since it was God's intention that human beings should live forever, his plan would be unfulfilled were it the case that only the soul lived forever. 'Man, therefore,' he wrote,

> who consists of the two parts, must continue for ever. But it is impossible for him to continue unless he rise again [...] The conclusion is unavoidable, that, along with the interminable duration of the soul, there will be a perpetual continuance of the body according to its proper nature.[3]

Importantly, unlike the resurrection of the body, the immortality of the soul did not have to be argued for. In spite of the absence of the idea of the immortality of the soul in the documents that made up the New Testament (*c.*50–100 CE), by the late second century this doctrine had been happily absorbed from the Greek Platonic tradition into the Christian understanding of man. Importantly, however, early Christianity defined itself against that same tradition by its passionate commitment to the doctrine of the resurrection of the body. In so doing, Christianity was able to line up its philosophical understanding of the nature of man as both body and soul with its commitment to a story of life both immediately after death and after the Day of Judgement. Christian anthropology (the doctrine of man) and Christian eschatology (the doctrine of the last things) coalesced. This was, as we will see, both a theological asset and a liability.

To argue for the resurrection of the body was no small thing. Plato (429–347 BCE) had, to all intents and purposes, opposed body and soul in terms of the mortality of the former and the immortality of the latter. 'So it appears,' he wrote in the *Phaedo*, 'that when death comes to a man, the mortal part of him dies, but the immortal part retires at the approach of death and escapes unharmed and indestructible.'[4] Thus, the soul will continue to exist in the next world, but the body will not. Plato argued for the immortality of the soul for philosophical reasons. But it was necessitated too by the demands of justice. For Plato, at least some souls were sufficiently evil to merit an eternity of punishment after death. So to Plato belongs the (perhaps dubious) privilege of being the first to argue for the eternal punishment of the wicked.

That said, the fate of the soul in the next world depended not only on vices acquired and virtues nurtured in this one. According to Plato's *Phaedo*, when a person died, his own guardian spirit led him to the place of judgement, whence, escorted by a spirit guide, he proceeded to the underworld. Wise and disciplined souls followed their guide, but the soul that was 'emotionally' attached to its body hovered around it for a long time, only to be finally led away by its guardian spirit after much resistance and suffering. When it reached the same place as the virtuous souls, it was shunned and avoided by all and wandered alone in utter desolation until, after a certain time, it was carried away to its 'proper habitation'.

There were many places set aside within the earth for the four categories of the souls of the dead. First, those who lived a neutral life set out for Lake Acheron, where they underwent purification from and absolution for the sins they had committed (a kind of Platonic Purgatory). Next, those who on account of their sins were judged to be incurable were thrown into Tartarus, from which they never emerged. There were others, thirdly, who were judged guilty of great sins but were nonetheless deemed curable. They too were cast into Tartarus, but were washed out after a year. Swept down the river of Cocytus (if they were murderers) or down Pyriphlegethon (if they had offended their parents), they came past Lake Acheron. There they cried out to their victims for permission to enter the lake. If those whom they had wronged rejected their pleas, they were swept away again into Tartarus. Finally, those who were adjudged to have spent lives of holiness were set free from confinement beneath the earth and travelled upwards to a pure abode on the earth's surface. Of these, 'such as have purified themselves sufficiently by philosophy live thereafter altogether without bodies, and reach habitations even more beautiful.'[5] Freedom from anxiety in this life about one's fate in the next can be obtained by forgoing bodily pleasure and adornment, and embracing the pursuit of knowledge, self-control, goodness, courage, liberality and truth.

For Plato, in spite of their immateriality, souls seemed nonetheless to have a quasi-materiality. After death, they were 'located' below, on or above the earth. In the *Gorgias*, for example, souls appeared at a crossroads from which two paths led, the one to the Isles of the Blessed, the other to Tartarus. The virtuous were sent straight to the Isles of the Blessed, the wicked to Tartarus, the incurable for eternal, the curable for temporary punishments. Those souls capable of cure were benefited on arrival in Tartarus by a Platonic 'abominable fancy'. There they saw the incurable souls

> suffering throughout eternity the greatest and most excruciating and terrifying tortures because of their misdeeds, literally suspended there as examples in the prison house in Hades, a spectacle and a warning to any evildoers who from time to time arrive.[6]

Similarly, in Plato's *Republic*, souls retained a form of corporeality. But there, the issue was further complicated by Plato's apparent endorsement of reincarnation. According to this, at the time of death, the soul left the body and travelled to a meadow where there were two openings in the earth and two in the heavens. The first two openings were for those entering or leaving heaven, the other two for those entering or leaving the underworld. Ascending from the underworld were souls 'full of dust and squalor', while descending from heaven were souls 'clean and pure'.[7] Each group spoke with the other about their experiences. Those from heaven spoke of the visions and delights of a beauty beyond words. Those from beneath the earth told of the dreadful things suffered and seen in their time there. Each group had spent at least a thousand years in heaven or the underworld. At the end of this time, some of those beneath the earth who were due for release were refused their freedom by the mouth of the underworld which 'bellowed when any one of the incurably wicked or of those who had not completed their punishment tried to come up'.[8] Savage men of fiery aspect carried some away to be further punished, others to be thrown into Tartarus.

Those who were allowed to ascend from beneath the earth joined those who had descended from the heavens in the meadow. They all then travelled to a pillar of light, brighter and purer than a rainbow. This was the spindle of the lady of Necessity, around which the spheres of the cosmos turned. There they took part in a lottery for priority in choosing their next life. The choice was theirs, but once made they were bound by the lady of Necessity to that life. Some switched from humans to animals, and vice versa.

When all the souls had chosen their next lives by the order of their lots, they were assigned a guardian spirit to help them through life. Passing under the throne of Necessity, they travelled (literally 'Lethe-wards') to the Plane of Oblivion, where the River of Forgetfulness (the Lethe) flowed. They were all required to drink a measure of the water. As each soul drank, it forgot all things. This explains why we don't remember our former lives. After they had fallen asleep, each soul was suddenly wafted this way or that, 'upwards to their birth like shooting stars'.[9]

In sum, in the Platonic tradition, the soul was immortal; it was assessed immediately after death for the moral state that it had attained in its embodied life, and it was accordingly rewarded or punished temporarily or (in some cases) permanently. These were all themes that were to be absorbed into the Christian tradition. Christianity also retained the Platonic ambivalence about the 'corporeal' nature of the soul. On the one hand, the Christian tradition accorded to the soul the sort of quasi-corporeality that allowed it a geographical location after death, either above or below the earth (and on occasion the possible post-mortem transition from the one to the other). Souls also bore, as it were, 'physical' signs. They took on bodily aspects. As Caroline Bynum has pointed out, 'Souls were gendered and ranked, bearing with them the marks of occupation, status, religious vocation, even martyrdom.'[10] This quasi-corporeality of the soul enabled Christianity often to underplay the necessity of body to personal identity, and thus to focus the afterlife on the destiny of the individual immediately after death rather than after the end of the world. It was also this quasi-corporeality that allowed the soul to be depicted as leaving the body (see Plate 14 [BW]), to be spatially located somewhere and to experience quasi-physical rewards and punishments after death. It could even be weighed on the Last Day (see Plate 15 [C]).

On the other hand, complicating matters again, Christianity also endorsed the idea of the 'incorporeal' nature of the soul that allowed only for 'psychological' rewards and punishments after death. On this account, the soul required a resurrected body on the Last Day to receive the necessary merited 'physical' rewards or punishments, in addition to the 'psychological' ones that the soul had already experienced.

Although Christianity was to adopt the Platonic doctrine of the immortality of the soul, it did so with two qualifications. The first of these went to the origin of the soul, the second to the conviction that, after the Last Day, the soul would be reunited with its body.

The origin of the soul

In the Platonic understanding of the soul, there was no point in time when the individual soul did not exist. That is, not only did the soul continue to exist into the infinite future, but it had done so from the infinite past. Moreover, it had done so and would forever do so in a successive myriad of reincarnations. In the Platonic tradition generally (Plato's view that some souls were sent to Hades forever being a notable exception), souls endlessly ascended from below or descended from above to be incarnated in new earthly bodies.

By contrast, Christianity did not endorse the doctrine of successive incarnations of the same soul. In part at least, that it did not do so was because, although it endorsed the existence of the soul into the eternal future, it could not do so into the eternal past. According to the Christian tradition, souls had not existed from eternity. Rather, there was a time when all individual souls were created, and before which they did not exist. It was also because, unlike the Platonic tradition that the world along with the souls in it had existed from and would continue until eternity, Christianity supported the belief that the world had had a beginning and would have an end. Thus, the Platonic doctrine of the eternity of the world and of the souls within it conflicted with a Christian doctrine of Creation to the effect that there was a point at which God created the world, prior to which nothing at all, including souls, existed. The Platonic tradition conflicted too with a Christian doctrine of the last things. According to this, there was a time to come in the future in which, while souls would continue to exist, the world would not. As a consequence, Christianity had to give an account of the origin of souls that squared itself both with its doctrine of creation out of nothing (*ex nihilo*) and with its doctrine of the end of history. In short, it needed an account of souls that was in accord with the view that there was a time when the world was not, and that there would be a time when the world was no longer.

The question of the origin of the soul was a complicated one. Even Augustine, never backward in being forward about most things, found it difficult to answer. 'Many are perplexed by questions concerning the soul,' he wrote in a letter to Jerome in 415 CE, 'and I confess that I am of this number.'[11] The question was not merely an 'academic' one and thus unimportant. It mattered theologically. For it went to the key theological issue of how the sin of Adam had been transmitted to his descendants. In this letter and in his work on the freedom of the will, written some 20 years earlier, Augustine had outlined the three possible options in the debate at that time, none of which he felt able to support. The first of these, known as traducianism, was the view that all souls originated from the first soul of Adam. Put simply, the soul, along with the body, in succeeding generations, was transmitted with the male seed to the woman during sexual intercourse. The second, creationism, was the view that God created new souls every time a foetus was formed in the womb and placed these souls into the developing bodies there. The third held that all souls were created at the time of Creation and these pre-existent souls were either sent by God into bodies or fell into them as a result of fault of their own.[12]

Those Christian theologians who were sympathetic to the Platonic tradition of the opposition between the material body and the immaterial soul were generally also sympathetic to the second and third of these options. Thus, they viewed traducianism (probably rightly) as having far too materialistic a conception of the soul. However that may be, in contrast to the Platonic tradition, all were in agreement that, although there would be no time in the future when the soul would not be, there was a time in the past when it was not. For reasons we will explore in more detail later, this was theologically and philosophically inelegant. In varying the Platonic notion of a soul that had no beginning and no end, it opened up a range of possibilities, all of which would be canvassed and all of which would complicate the Christian account of immortality: of a soul with a beginning at the time of the creation of the world, but no end; with a beginning at the time of conception, but no end; and, finally (among those unsympathetic to Platonism), with both a beginning and an end (at the time of death).

Supporters of the position that the soul pre-existed its time of conception in the womb were always in the minority. Its major proponent was Origen. He attempted not only to square the doctrine of the pre-existence of the soul with the Christian doctrine of Creation, but to read (very much against the grain) the Genesis story of the Creation and Fall of Man in the Garden of Eden in terms of it.[13] For him, it was a story not about Adam but about each of us. Thus, declared Origen, 'we must suppose, therefore, that in the beginning [before the Creation of the world] God made as large a number of rational and intelligent beings [...] as he foresaw would be sufficient.'[14] As a consequence of the misuse of free will, souls fell from eternity into time, from the intelligible into the ethereal, aerial or terrestrial realm. As Origen put it:

> Some sinned deeply and became daemons, others less and became angels; others still less and became archangels [...] But there remained some souls who had not sinned so greatly as to become daemons, nor on the other hand so lightly as to become angels. God therefore made the present world and bound the soul to the body as a punishment.[15]

Origen solved the problem of how incorporeal souls could be located in the world and move around in it by his theory of the vehicles of the soul. According to this, at the time of its fall, each soul was clothed in some form of matter – ethereal, aerial or terrestrial – fitted to and changing according to the changing nature of the soul inhabited by it. This body enabled the soul to move up or down, from heavenly to earthly to subterranean regions. In principle, according to Origen, all souls could eventually return to the communion with God that they had before the Fall. Then:

> the mind will no longer be conscious of anything besides or other than God, but will think God and see God and hold God and God will be the mode and measure of its every movement; and in this way God will be all to it.[16]

This was very much a Christian version of the Platonic soul's eternal contemplation of the Good, and was to become the Beatific Vision of later Christian tradition.

If Origen was successful in getting around the issue of the location of a disembodied soul, he was less successful in giving an account of the resurrection of the terrestrial body on the Day of Judgement. In fact, he couldn't do so; nor did he attempt to. Rather, he invoked Paul's distinction in his First Letter to the Corinthians (15.44) between the natural body that was sown and the spiritual body that would rise again. By Paul's spiritual body, Origen understood the heavenly or ethereal body, 'with corruption banished and mortality laid aside.'[17] So rather than define the Christian doctrine of the resurrection of the dead against Greek philosophy, Origen's account of the vehicles of the soul enabled him to align the two traditions. Origen was thus very much the Christianised Platonist, embedding Christianity in Platonism, rather than vice versa. More particularly, for Origen as for many Christianised Platonists, the resurrection of the physical body on the Last Day sat awkwardly with the Platonist view that embodiment was the consequence of a fall, something not to be united with for eternity but to be liberated from forever.

This Platonic distaste for embodiment flowed generally into those parts of Christianity that saw the flesh as a prime cause of sin and its physical mortification as a key moment in Christian spirituality. Only by the subjugating of the flesh could the soul spiritually flourish. But more particularly, it also generated eschatologies that, as in the case of Origen, significantly reframed the doctrine of the resurrection of the body in spiritual terms. In so doing, these eschatologies generated accounts of life after death that paid scant attention to the resurrection of the body on the

Day of Judgement. Moreover, with his view that those souls not sufficiently pure to ascend to God would be reborn in another age to continue the process of purification, Origen came as close as was possible to a Christian doctrine of reincarnation.

Origen's account of the pre-existence of the soul gained little purchase within the Christian tradition. It was declared a heresy at the Second Council of Constantinople in 553. There was the occasional resurgence of support in the medieval period, and a minor flowering among Platonists in the seventeenth century.[18] But that century also saw the beginnings of a European scepticism more inclined to argue for the mortality of the soul after death than for its immortality before birth. It was only late in the nineteenth century that intellectual interest was again taken in the pre-existence and reincarnation of the soul. As we will see in Chapter 7, this was the consequence not of a resurgent Platonism, but of the arrival in the West of analogous ideas from the Hindu and Buddhist traditions.[19]

If Augustine was uncertain about the doctrine of the pre-existence of the soul in spite of his own Platonic inclinations, he was less so about traducianism, the theory that souls were transmitted in or along with the male seed. This was not least because it lined up better than the other alternatives with his belief that original sin was similarly transmitted with the male seed from Adam to all his descendants.[20] If Jerome is to be believed, traducianism had no shortage of supporters at the beginning of the fifth century: 'This is the view of Tertullian, Apollinaris and most Western writers [*maxima pars Occidentalium*],' he declared.[21] According to Tertullian, who was its main proponent in the West, the seed of the soul breathed first into Adam by God amalgamated with Adam's bodily seed, 'so that even now the two substances, although diverse from each other, flow forth simultaneously in a united channel.'[22] Thus, all human souls come from the first man, Adam, along with original sin. Do we not, asked Tertullian, 'in that very heat of extreme gratification when the generative fluid is ejected, feel that somewhat of our soul has gone from us?'[23] This makes a little more sense (although perhaps not much more) when we know that for Tertullian the soul is made up of tiny material particles (although not divisible into them).

Jerome's claim about the dominance of traducianism was probably an exaggeration. For we know that many more supported the view that the soul was created by God at the very moment of conception than supported traducianism. Creationism dominated Eastern Christianity and, in spite of the lack of clear endorsement from Augustine, it was to become the dominant Catholic understanding of the origin of souls within the medieval scholastic tradition. Aquinas, in the mistaken belief that he was quoting Augustine, laid out an agreed Catholic position in the thirteenth century:

> We do not believe in the fiction of Origen that human souls were created at the beginning with other intellectual natures, nor that they are procreated together with their bodies by coition, as the Luciferians with Cyril, and certain Latin writers have presumed to maintain. But we affirm that the body alone is begotten by sexual procreation, and that after the formation of the body the soul is created and infused.[24]

Still, this was by no means the end of the matter. The debate between traducianists, creationists and others was reignited during the Reformation period. Thus, for example, in 1601 the English natural philosopher Nicholas Hill reported on some 23 theories of the soul's origin.[25] Lutherans generally adhered to traducianism, while Calvinists drifted towards creationism. Both were more concerned with the origin of sin in the soul than the origin of the soul itself. And all – Catholics, Calvinists, Lutherans and Anglicans – felt the need for 'soulidarity' against those who doubted its immortality or even its very existence. This was the cutting edge of the debate then. The number of works in the sixteenth and seventeenth centuries arguing for the soul's immortality into eternity far outnumbered those devoted to the specifics of its beginnings. Of these, *The Immortality of the Soul* by the English Platonist Henry More (who, incidentally, supported the pre-existence of the soul) in 1659 was the most convincing example. At 459 pages, More's work was both exhaustive and exhausting. As Don Allen remarks, 'When an atheist or melancholy Christian had digested More's mathematical analysis of the soul's nature and immortality, he undoubtedly regarded all previous rhetorical, philosophical, or biblical demonstrations as futile and hopelessly unconvincing.'[26] Or he was perhaps beyond caring.

Time and eternity

The issue of the immortality of the soul was dependent too on the issue of the relationship between time and eternity. Indeed, however we conceive of the afterlife, this relationship is an absolutely crucial one. It will play out into modern times, transformed into the issue of whether moral and spiritual progress is possible in the afterlife. To begin, we need to distinguish two forms of eternity, each of which has a different relationship to time, as suggested by Augustine and elaborated by Aquinas. The everyday experience of time is of a present moment receding into the past and being replaced by the future. In this case, eternity is a never-ending succession of such moments extending into infinity. By contrast, the second form of eternity is outside of time and consequently non-successive. God's experience of eternity is of this kind.[27] And it belongs only to God. But angels and the souls that are saved share in it, to the extent that they share in the divine immutability (from which God's eternity derives) and enjoy the Beatific Vision (see Plate 19 [BW]).[28] Still, even so, the blessed can continue to participate in successive time if they desire. Thus the blessed live in what Aquinas called an 'aeviternity', occupying a state between time and eternity, or, perhaps better, they partake of both time and eternity.[29] 'Aeviternity' applies however only to the saved and not to the damned. In contrast to the blessed, the damned in hell have no share in the divine eternity but only a share in successive eternity. They will continue to suffer eternal punishments in hell into the infinite future. 'The fire of hell', declared Aquinas, is called eternal 'only because it never ends.'[30]

Thus, we can now add to our earlier discussion of the immortality of souls their relation to eternity. First the souls of the blessed will participate in the non-successive and still eternity of God. This is the eternity to which the Christian mystics aspire in the here and now, finding in their present experience of the divine a foretaste of the timeless eternity yet to come. Second, the souls of the blessed will also participate in the successive eternity of heaven. Like souls, therefore, heaven had a beginning but will have no end. In contrast to the blessed, the damned will dwell only in the successive eternity of hell, which, like heaven, also had a beginning but will have no end.[31] The world, along with the souls within it, had a beginning. But there will be a Last Day when Christ returns to judge the living and the dead. Then, the world, if not the souls within it, will end. Thus, the destiny of the dead is not only embedded within a story about the fate of the soul immediately after death, but in a cosmic history that, unlike the Platonic tradition of infinite world cycles, sees the world not only as having a divinely created beginning but also a divinely designated ending.

All of which leads us to the second qualification that Christianity made to the Platonic doctrine of the immortality of the soul. This was that, after the Last Day, the soul would be reunited with its body. It was this resurrected earthly body that would go forward into eternity, and that would partake of both time and eternity. Here, Christianity was the inheritor of a Jewish tradition that, unlike Platonism, viewed the human individual as a psycho-physical unity and, far from viewing embodiment as a misfortune, valued it as the result of divine intention. Embodiment, like the Creation itself, was viewed as a good. More philosophically, this meant that embodiment (in some form) was a crucial part of personal identity, and resurrected bodies a theological necessity.

Resurrected bodies

Within the early Christian tradition, the resurrection of the body was part of a larger apocalyptic story. This was a cosmic narrative to the effect that Christ was the expected Messiah who would usher in the end times, that he had been raised from the dead and had ascended into heaven, that he would come again and complete the establishment of God's Kingdom, that he would judge the living and the resurrected dead, and that some would receive eternal happiness and others eternal misery. Until towards the end of the first century CE, the expectation within early Christianity was that these events were imminent. With the exception of Christ's role in all this, Christian expectations of the future were in accord with those of most other Jewish groups of the time. This was a context in which the continuing existence of the individual immediately after death had little purchase.

Two New Testament texts set the pattern for later elaborations of the last things. The first of these was the 'Little Apocalypse' in the Gospels of Mark, Luke and Matthew. The last of these (Matt. 24.1–25.46) describes the final events of world history as they were foreshadowed in the Old Testament book of Daniel. First among these events will be the rise of a series of false prophets pretending to be the Messiah. The abomination of desolation, spoken of by Daniel (11.31), will then be set up in the holy place. Then will follow the Second Coming:

> all the tribes of the earth [...] will see 'the Son of Man coming on the clouds of heaven' [Dan. 7.13] with power and great glory. And he will send out his angels with a loud trumpet call, and they will gather his elect from the four winds. (Matt. 24.30–1)

All the nations will then be gathered before him and, on the basis of their love for others, 'he will separate people one from another as a shepherd separates the sheep from the goats, and he will put the sheep at his right hand and the goats at his left' (Matt. 25.31–3). To those on his right, he will say:

> Come [...] inherit the Kingdom prepared for you from the foundation of the world; for I was hungry and you gave me food, I was thirsty and you gave me something to drink, I was a stranger and you welcomed me. (Matt. 25.34–5)

But to those who, in rejecting others, rejected Christ, he will say: 'You that are accursed, depart from me into the eternal fire prepared for the devil and his angels' (Matt. 25.41).

The second exemplary text for the final judgement was the last book in the New Testament, the book of Revelation. In the nineteenth chapter, John described the war between Christ (the rider on the white horse) and the armies of heaven against the beast (the Antichrist) and the kings of the earth with their armies. The armies of the wicked would be destroyed, and the beast, along with the false prophet, would be thrown into 'that lake of fire that burns with sulfur' (19.20). All the rest would be slaughtered by the rider on the white horse with his sword, and the birds would eat their flesh. Satan would be bound and confined to the pit for a thousand years. The souls of the just who had been beheaded for their testimony for Jesus would then be brought back to life and reign 'with Christ a thousand years' (20.4). The rest of the dead would not come to life until the thousand years were ended.

At the end of this millennium, Satan would be released from his prison and join with the nations of Gog and Magog to make war against the saints. Fire from heaven would consume them, and the Devil would be thrown into the lake of fire and sulphur to join the beast and the false prophet in eternal torments. The final resurrection and the Last Judgement would then follow:

> Then I saw a great white throne and the one who sat on it; the earth and the heaven fled from his presence, and no place was found for them. And I saw the dead, great and small, standing before the throne, and the books were opened. Also another book was opened, the book of life. And the dead were judged according to their works, as recorded in the books. And the sea gave up the dead that were in it. Death and Hades gave up

> the dead that were in them, and all were judged according to what they had done [...] anyone whose name was not found written in the book of life was thrown into the lake of fire. (Rev. 20.11–15)

Christianity was established within just this kind of apocalyptic Jewish milieu. At the top of almost everyone's expectations was the resurrection of the dead. Among Jesus's contemporaries, only the Sadducees rejected it. They inaugurated a sceptical tradition of attempts to reduce it to nonsense. Thus, the Gospels depict them trying unsuccessfully to trap a Jesus who believed in the resurrection of the dead into an admission of its absurdity.[32]

The centrality within early Christianity of the resurrection of the dead on the Last Day was reinforced not only by its origin in such an apocalyptic milieu, but also by the belief that Jesus himself had risen from the dead. His resurrection foreshadowed and thus guaranteed the future resurrection of all the dead. Thus, to sceptical Corinthian Christians who were doubting the future resurrection of the dead, Paul declared:

> But in fact Christ has been raised from the dead, the first fruits of those who have died. For since death came through a human being, the resurrection of the dead has also come through a human being; for as all die in Adam, so all will be made alive in Christ. (1 Cor. 15.20–2)

Still, just as there was uncertainty within some Christian communities over whether Christ had really risen from the dead, there was also uncertainty about the nature of his risen body among those who believed in his resurrection. The Gospel accounts of the risen Christ reflect this. On the one hand, they stress the physical nature of the risen Jesus: the tomb was empty; Jesus ate broiled fish in the disciples' presence; he breathed on them; he invited them to touch him to see that he was not a ghost but had flesh and bones; and the women at the empty tomb held on to his feet. On the other hand, the Gospel accounts hint at the spiritual nature of the risen Christ: he appeared suddenly among the disciples; he was able to pass through locked doors; he was sometimes not recognisable to his disciples; and he instructed Mary Magdalene not to touch him (see Plate 16 [c]). In general, they vary in their depiction between a 'heavenly' Jesus who materialises on earth (primarily in Matthew) and an 'earthly' Jesus who has as yet to ascend to heaven (primarily in Luke and John).[33] It is an ambiguity about the nature of the body of the resurrected Jesus that flowed directly into uncertainty about the nature of resurrected bodies on the Last Day.

Thus, the New Testament generally had an expectation that the dead would rise on the Last Day. But it was remarkably silent about the nature of the bodies that would then be resurrected. The most elaborate exception to this was Paul's First Letter to the Corinthians, in which he responded specifically to the questions, 'How are the dead raised? With what kind of body do they come?' (1 Cor. 15.35). His answer was quite unequivocal: 'flesh and blood cannot inherit the kingdom of God, nor does the perishable inherit the imperishable' (15.50). Thus, there was no resurrection of the flesh in Paul. What was sown as a physical or natural body (σῶμα ψυχικόν) would be raised a spiritual body (σῶμα πνευματικόν): 'we will all be changed, in a moment, in the twinkling of an eye, at the last trumpet. For the trumpet will sound, and the dead will be raised imperishable, and we will be changed' (15.52; see Plate 18 [c]). There is no doctrine of the immortality of the soul in Paul, nor anywhere else in the New Testament for that matter. But crucially, and perhaps a little surprisingly, there is also no doctrine of the resurrection of the physical body (that is, the same one that was buried). Rather, as the metaphor of 'the sowing of seed' suggests, there was both a continuity (for it is we who are raised) and a radical difference (for we are changed).[34] This will be the case whether we are alive or dead when the last trumpet sounds.

While the New Testament was either silent about the nature of our resurrected bodies, or opted for a non-physical version like Paul, the established view from the second century CE onwards was in favour of the resurrection of the physical body (although perhaps 'qualitatively' different). This was formally endorsed by the fourth Lateran Council of the Western Church in its first canon in 1215:

> But He descended [to hell] in soul, arose in flesh, and ascended equally in both; He will come at the end of the world to judge the living and the dead and will render to the reprobate and to the elect according to their works. Who all shall rise with their own bodies *which they now have* that they may receive according to their merits, whether good or bad, the latter eternal punishment with the devil, the former eternal glory with Christ.[35]

Skeletal remains would be 'refleshed' (see Plate 17 [BW]). To all intents and purposes, this was the view endorsed in the sixteenth-century Reformation in the Lutheran, Calvinist and Anglican traditions.[36]

Why was it that early Christianity so overwhelmingly opted for the resurrection of the physical body in spite of Paul's clear preference for a spiritual body and in the face of doubts about a physical resurrection within the Christian community? In part, it referenced the apparently physical resurrection of Christ; in part, it referred to the necessity of a restoration through Christ of that which had been lost through Adam, that is, the immortality of the physical body; in part too, it wanted to assert the virtue of embodiment against those who viewed the flesh as evil. But it was particularly a reaction to a shift within Christian anthropology from understanding man as a psycho-physical unity to understanding him as a dual being comprised of body and soul. A *spiritual* body was too easily assimilated to a physicalised soul. Thus, with the absorption of the Platonic doctrine of the immortality of the immaterial soul into the Christian tradition, it was necessary for Christianity to define itself against the Platonic tradition not by the resurrection of a *spiritual* body, but by the resurrection of the *physical* body, and one moreover that was in material continuity with the one that had died. All of which brings us back to where we began this chapter, namely, with the assertion of Athenagoras in *De resurrectione mortuorum* that 'along with the interminable duration of the soul, there will be a perpetual continuance of the body according to its proper nature'.[37]

For Athenagoras, arguments for the resurrection of the body turned on four main considerations. The first of these was God's ability to raise the dead and depended on the evidence of his power already apparent in creation. Who could believe, he wrote, that out of a drop of semen there could arise 'bones, and nerves, and cartilages [...] muscles too, and flesh, and intestines, and the other parts of the body'?[38] That same power will be evident in the resurrection of the flesh, even

> to separate that which has been broken up and distributed among a multitude of animals of all kinds which are wont to have recourse to such bodies, and glut their appetite upon them [...] and unite it again with the proper members and parts of members, whether it has passed into some one of those animals, or into many, or thence into others.[39]

The second and third arguments concerned the requirements of justice. Since justice is not found in this life, there needs to be a resurrection of the dead to apportion justice on the other side of the grave. Moreover, since God must judge the entire human being, it is necessary that body and soul both survive in order that the being who practised either righteousness or lawlessness be appropriately rewarded or punished.[40] Finally, and fourth, justice requires that the same person be punished or rewarded as is vicious or virtuous. This is only possible by the resurrection of the same bodies being 'restored to the same souls'.[41]

That it is the resurrection of the physical body that distinguishes Christians was the key argument in Tertullian's *De resurrectione carnis* (On the resurrection of the flesh), a work written against those who denied the materiality of the resurrection body. Thus, he began this work: 'The resurrection of the dead is the Christian's trust. By it we are believers.'[42] As for Athenagoras, so also for Tertullian, the resurrection of the flesh arose as a consequence of the nature of man as both body and soul. It was also a requirement of justice that there be recompense on the other side of the grave for the righteous and the wicked, and that the whole person, body and soul – both active agents in virtue and vice – receive appropriate rewards and punishments. God would be unjust were he 'to exclude from reward the flesh which is associated in good works' and idle were he to 'exempt it from punishment, when it has been an accomplice in evil deeds'.[43]

All this is not to suggest that, for Tertullian, rewards and punishments occurred only after the final judgement. Body–soul dualism enabled Christianity both to have immediate post-mortem pains and pleasures inflicted upon the soul, and to have the same inflicted on the reunited body and soul on the Last Day. But Tertullian was perhaps the first to apply 'physical' rewards and punishments to the soul immediately after death and the same to the body reunited with its soul at the time of the Last Judgement. People are apt to suppose, he wrote, that the flesh will have to be present at the final judgement because otherwise the soul, being incorporeal, would be incapable of suffering pain or pleasure. On the contrary, he argued, as the case of the rich man and Lazarus demonstrated, souls are even now capable of torment and blessing even though disembodied. This is because the soul 'is corporeal, possessing a peculiar kind of solidity in its nature, such as enables it to perceive and suffer'.[44]

Tertullian recognised that, granting the soul was 'embodied' and therefore capable of pains and pleasures, critics would respond by declaring the final resurrection of the flesh unnecessary. Tertullian saw them coming. This 'physicalised' soul was capable only of receiving punishment for those misdeeds that it committed that did not require the flesh – sins of thought rather than deed. For sins of deed, the flesh was required. Thus, for punishment of these sins, the resurrection of the flesh was necessary. The soul, therefore, waits in Hades 'for the flesh, in order that it may through the flesh also compensate for its deeds, inasmuch as it laid upon the flesh the execution of its own thoughts'.[45] Still, if this was resurrection of the same body, it was with some qualifications. However mutilated our body in life, declared Tertullian, we will be restored to the integrity of our natural condition. Not all of our resurrected parts will, however, be needed for their original functions. There will be no more eating or drinking, no more sex, and no more child-bearing or breastfeeding. Although there will be no marriage in heaven, couples will be reunited.

Flesh and bones

With his emphasis on the resurrection of the physical body, Tertullian can do little with Paul's account of the spiritual body in his First Letter to the Corinthians except to read it against the grain (or in this case the seed).[46] But for a Platonised Christian like Augustine, the Pauline underplaying of the physical body was congenial. Thus, the early Augustine endorsed Paul's image of the resurrection body as a spiritual one. He did so by means of a distinction between the resurrection of the body (*corpus*) and the resurrection of the flesh (*caro*). The resurrection of the body did not entail the resurrection of the flesh because, while all flesh is also body, not all body is also flesh. Thus, in 393 CE, in his *De fide et symbolo* (On faith and the creed), Augustine declared that the resurrection body 'will no more be flesh and blood, but only body' (*non iam caro erit et sanguis, sed tantum corpus*). The spiritual body will be set free from time to enjoy 'eternal life in ineffable love and steadfastness without corruption'.[47]

However, by the time that he had completed *De civitate dei* (The city of God) in 426 CE, Augustine had moved away from his Platonic inclinations. The resurrection body has now become a much more 'fleshly' one. So the saints at the resurrection of the dead will 'inhabit *those very bodies* in which they have here toiled', but without the corruptions, griefs and troubles that are attached to the flesh on this side of the grave.[48] Thus the resurrected bodies will not only then be better than they are now in their best state of health, 'but will surpass the bodies of our first parents ere they sinned'.[49] So, unlike those of Adam and Eve, although they could do so, resurrected bodies will have no need to eat or drink, either to preserve them from disease or decay or to appease hunger and thirst. Then, we will have bodies that appear to be about 30 years of age, the age which Christ reached, of a height that we had or would have had at that time. Men shall rise in male bodies, women in female bodies. From those bodies, sexual desire will be withdrawn. Although the female members will remain, they will be 'adapted not to the old uses, but to a new beauty, which, so far from provoking lust, now extinct, shall excite praise to the wisdom and clemency of God'.[50] There will be, however, no marriages in heaven. Our thoughts will be visible to all, as others' thoughts will be to us. Then the flesh will serve the spirit (a spiritual body) and not the spirit the flesh (a carnal spirit) as is now the case. So they will be spiritual bodies, 'not because they shall cease to be bodies, but because they shall subsist by a quickening spirit'.[51] In this way, they replicate the risen body of Christ.

Augustine struggled with one of the key questions about the afterlife. If we are granted the vision of God, with what eyes do we see him? At one time he believed that God could not be seen through the bodily eye since that would suggest that God occupied a space at a distance from us and that he was corporeal and visible rather than present everywhere, incorporeal and invisible. Rather, he suggested, he will be seen through the eyes of the mind: 'The vision of God belongs to the inner man.'[52] On the other hand, later in his life, in *De civitate dei*, he suggested that, just as we can see now whether bodies are alive or dead just by looking at them, so the risen saints will be able to see God with their bodily eyes as he is in himself, in the bodies of those around them, in the new heavens and the new earth, and in everything that will then exist. But they will also see him when their eyes are shut, 'since they shall always see him with the spirit'.[53]

With Augustine's *De civitate dei*, the acceptance of body–soul dualism had enabled mid-fifth-century Christianity to clarify the nature of both life immediately after death and life after the resurrection. The notion of the immortal soul provided the philosophical underpinning for life immediately after death, and resurrected bodies reunited with their souls for eternal life after the end of history. In sum, therefore, the person consisted of an incorporeal soul, in existence since the time of its conception and immortal into the future and a mortal, physical body.[54] At death, the soul left the body and received rewards in Paradise or Abraham's Bosom (separate from or an upper part of Hades) or received punishments in Hades. The body decayed and corrupted in the grave. At the time of the resurrection, the power of God reconstituted the individual physical body from its remains (albeit transformed) and reunited it with its soul. The person would then be judged for an eternity of successive moments of punishments in hell, or an eternity of rewards in heaven that partook of both time and eternity. The greatest good of this would be the vision of God, physically and spiritually, in the inner spiritual and outer physical man.

However that may be, body–soul dualism not only clarified but also confused eschatology. It was difficult to speak cogently of the afterlife experience of the incorporeal soul without giving it physical characteristics. Thus, the soul was 'physicalised'. While it was not difficult to speak of a resurrected fleshly body being punished eternally in hell, it was not easy to speak cogently of a resurrected fleshly body in heaven without giving it the kind of 'idealised form' it merited as a reward and the sort of 'spiritual' attributes that made it possible to enjoy the vision of God. Thus, the body, in spite of its 'skin and bones', was spiritualised. In short, the clear distinction between body and soul was unable to bear the weight that the demands of eschatology put upon it. Moreover, as Augustine demonstrated, it was never easy for the Platonised Christian theologian to give the conceptual weight to the body that the Christian tradition required, and by which it distinguished itself from those contemporary philosophical traditions that valued the spiritual and strongly disparaged physical embodiment. In Augustine's case, a Platonised Christianity was messily interwoven with a Christianised Platonism.

Nevertheless, a Christianised Platonism continued to thrive as the theological underpinning of the Christian mystical tradition. It was a mysticism that looked back especially to the Neoplatonism of Plotinus (204–70 CE), which was transmitted to later generations through the writings of Origen, Augustine and the sixth-century mystical theologian Dionysius the Areopagite.[55] A spiritualised reading of the resurrection on the Last Day was to remain dominant within Eastern Orthodox Christianity.[56] This was a Platonist tradition that, in spite of the theological weight of the body, had an almost visceral distaste for it as an impediment to the experience of the divine. The vision of God that was pursued was of the soul and not of the body, of contemplation over action, of the cultivation of the spirit and the mortification of the flesh. Thus, the attainment of that 'spiritual vision' – the unity-in-difference between God and the soul now as a foretaste of that eternal unity after death – did not require embodiment either now or then. Certainly it had little interest in the reuniting of the body and soul for final judgement.

That a Platonised Christianity found it difficult to give the body its theological due was the result of the tendency within Platonism to think of the body as merely a container of the soul. This suggested that it was the soul that was the real person and that the body was dispensable. The matter was otherwise with Aristotelianism. Aristotle (384–322 BCE) had understood the soul to be the form of the body and the body to be the matter of the soul. Put simply, this meant that the soul was that which made inanimate things into living things. In turn, this meant that, as a living being, the real person consisted of both body and soul.

This Aristotelian understanding of personal identity was incorporated by Thomas Aquinas into his account of the nature of the person. For Aquinas, the soul could continue to exist without the body, although the body (without its animating principle – the soul) did not. Thus, Aquinas was able to give an account of life immediately after death in terms of the incorporeal, immaterial soul. The soul was therefore able to 'see' God immediately after death: '[A]s soon as the soul of the just man is separated from the body, it sees God.'[57] Having said which, we (and the Platonist) are left to wonder what the resurrected body could add to our post-mortem happiness granted we have immediate access to the Beatific Vision after death. But crucially, because on Aristotelian grounds personal identity consisted of both form (soul) and matter (body), the eternal life of the individual did nonetheless require the eventual reunion of body and soul. In order for us to enjoy eternal life, we needed both body and soul. Thus, Aquinas's Aristotelianised Christianity was better able to give the body its theological entitlement, even though (on his own terms) eternal happiness was not increased as a consequence.

Undoubtedly, an Aristotelianised Christianity did better suit the Christian view on the essential goodness of creation and matter. It also better framed the Christian view on personal identity. Consequently, it provided what a Platonised Christianity was unable to – a more coherent account of the necessity for the resurrection of the flesh on the Last Day. It also provided a better philosophical foundation for the apportioning of rewards and punishments to both souls and bodies. Thus, for example, Aquinas's distinction between *poena damni* (pain of loss) and *poena sensus* (pain of sense) enabled him to elaborate on the different modes of punishment to be apportioned to the souls and the bodies of the damned.[58] Unbaptised infants, we recall, suffered the psychological punishment of the loss of the Beatific Vision (*poena damni*) but not physical torments. After the resurrection, the reunited bodies of the damned would suffer both psychological and physical torment – *poena damni* and *sensus*. By contrast, the happiness of the souls of the blessed would not include 'physical' rewards. These were only to come into the mix in the nineteenth century. Rather, the happiness of the saints would consist exclusively of spiritual goods. This happiness would continue after they were reunited with bodies that would then be completely under the sway of their souls.

The punishment inflicted on the souls of the damned before the resurrection would also consist of spiritual evils. But surprisingly, Aquinas accorded to the soul a quasi-corporeality that enabled it also to be physically punished immediately after death. This was because the souls of the wicked, having set their affections on material things and having scorned divine and spiritual things, were punished 'not only by being deprived of spiritual goods, but by being subjected to the tyranny of material things'.[59] Thus, the soul separated from its body was in agony, not only because it perceived itself to be in fire (*poena damni*) but also because it actually experienced the fire (*poena sensus*).[60]

Sharks and cannibals

The more the emphasis upon the necessity of the body for eternity, the more necessary it was to defend the intellectual coherence of this idea. Thus, Thomas Aquinas also inherited from early Christianity a set of questions about the conceptual feasibility of the notion of the resurrection of the flesh. Athenagoras, for example, had agonised over the eventual fate of those eaten by fish whose bodies could not as a consequence be separated from the bodies of the fish that had consumed them; or, worse, those who had been eaten by fish that themselves were later eaten by men; or, worse still, those whose bodies could not be separated from those of the cannibals that had eaten them.[61] To get around this, Athenagoras came up with a genuinely original (if incredible) answer. This was to the effect that God had so created living beings that fish or human beings could not absorb 'non-natural' food (like human beings). Jonah, after all, was not digested in the whale. So non-natural food was either vomited or excreted. Thus, even if eaten, no skerrick of us was absorbed into that by which we were eaten. As a result, our bodily identity was assured on the Day of Resurrection. Moreover, at that time, and however widely dispersed the parts of our bodies might be, God could reassemble that which he once made.

Athenagoras was giving serious answers (or at least attempting to do so) to questions from 'cultured' critics of the resurrection that were only half-serious, if serious at all. Tertullian similarly took the questions seriously, although he knew that 'the mickey' was being taken. Heretics, he wrote,

> single out what parts of our bodies may suit them, handle them without delicacy, and [...] pour torrents of scorn upon the natural functions of our members, for the purpose of upsetting the resurrection, and making us blush over their cavils.[62]

Augustine too dealt seriously with a set of questions that he also believed were intended 'to cast ridicule on our faith':[63] whether aborted foetuses will rise; the sizes of resurrected foetuses and children; the bodies of resurrected monstrous births, the disfigured and the deformed; the fate of those devoured by beasts, consumed by fire, drowned or eaten by cannibals; and the gender of the resurrected. The short answer to all of these questions was, as noted above, that all would rise in the same bodies they had before death, but that they would spend eternity in the form that these bodies had had the potential to be rather than the bodies they had actually been.

By the middle of the twelfth century, these sorts of question about the materiality of the risen body were no longer the stuff of the opponents of Christianity. Rather, they had become a matter of genuine philosophical debate within scholarly circles. More specifically, they had become part of the overall medieval discussion about the resurrection of the dead by virtue of their inclusion in Distinction 44 of the fourth book of the *Sentences* of the bishop of Paris, Peter Lombard (*c.*1100–60). The four books of Lombard's *Sentences* were to become a standard textbook of theology for the remainder of the medieval period. His overall conclusion matched that of Augustine:

> Nor will anything perish of the substance of which the flesh of man is created but the natural substance of the body will be reintegrated by the collection of all the particles that were dispersed before. And the bodies of the saints will rise without any defect, shining like the sun, all deformities that are here being cut off.[64]

By the time of Thomas Aquinas in the thirteenth century, the discussion of these questions had become more and more elaborate and (for the modern reader) more and more obscure. Aquinas's discussion of cannibalism exemplifies this. By then it had generally been agreed, against Athenagoras, that what had been consumed was incorporated into the substance of the consumer. In the case of the flesh of one man absorbed by a cannibal into his own flesh, Aquinas concluded that the absorbed flesh would rise in him who had it first, the missing matter to be made up from other food consumed by the cannibal – or God would make up the difference. But, Aquinas wondered, if the cannibal had eaten *only* human flesh, then *all* the flesh that he produced would have a claim on it by those whom he had eaten. Thus, after all his victims had been given their 'share', there would be nothing of the cannibal to resurrect. In this case, wrote Aquinas, the embryonic material produced by his parents would have been retained by him. This would be sufficient for God to restore his body. But what if, Aquinas went on, his parents had only eaten human flesh? In this case, even his embryonic flesh derived from eating human flesh. Again, on the principle of original ownership, all the cannibal's flesh belonged to others and there was nothing of him left to be resurrected. However, in this situation, Aquinas concluded, the flesh will rise in him 'to whose perfection it belonged more intimately, and the cannibal himself would arise.'[65] The principle of original ownership was here overridden by the principle of greater importance or need: 'Accordingly, if something was in one man as the radical seed from which he was generated, and in another as the superfluity of nourishment, it will rise in him who was generated therefrom as from seed.'[66] Whatever the case, the miraculous activity of God would be central.

As to the nature of resurrected bodies, Aquinas's last work, the *Compendium theologiae*, summed up the state of play around the middle of the thirteenth century. On the Day of Resurrection, the soul will reunite with 'a human body made up of flesh and bones, and equipped with the same organs it now possesses.'[67] So bodies will be gendered. Nevertheless, having obtained immortality, the means that served to keep the body alive will no longer be needed. So there will be no need of food or drink, nor of clothing. There will also not be any use for the reproductive organs, nor (because surplus food produces semen) any possibility of reproduction. Still, the organs for these activities will be present: 'all the members of the body will have their place in the risen [body], for the preservation of nature *in its entirety* rather than for the exercise of their normal functions.'[68] All natural defects will be corrected and God will supply what is missing. Crucially, there will be a complete subjection of body to soul. So desire to eat, drink or have sex will be absent. Because of the influence emanating from the soul, the body will be subtle and spiritual. It will possess 'the radiant beauty of clarity'.[69] In addition, it will be unable to suffer and will be endowed with agility. With this kind of body, with no need for food, clothing, transportation or medicine, there will be no need for heavenly plants or (pet lovers read no further!) animals. The happiness of the blessed will consist solely of spiritual pleasures, notably the unobstructed vision of God.

The damned, like the blessed, will be complete in their kind, but having qualities opposite to the blessed. They remain gross and not subtle, and thus capable of suffering. Indeed, these defects will be heightened in them. They will not be agile but sluggish. They will not be radiant. Rather, they 'will be ugly in their swarthiness, so that the blackness of the soul may be mirrored in the body, as is intimated in Isaiah 13.8: "Their countenances shall be as faces burnt."'[70] Even though their bodies will be punished with flames, they will not be subject to corruption. The condemned person's soul, so far as it is the form and nature of such a body, will confer never-ending existence on the latter. But because of its imperfection, the soul will not be able to bestow on the body immunity from suffering. Consequently the bodies of the damned will suffer forever, but will not undergo dissolution.

These questions about the nature of the resurrection body were still live ones in the seventeenth century. The new empirical sciences provided fresh answers to old questions. Robert Boyle (1627–91), the father of modern chemistry, was convinced that the resurrection of bodies would happen, not in the course of nature but by the power of God. Nevertheless, in his 1675 work *Some Physico-theological Considerations about the Possibility of the Resurrection*, Boyle attempted to illuminate the biblical understanding of the resurrection by examples drawn from the natural world. It was not only the dispersal of the remains of the dead, but the corruption and change in bodily parts that Boyle saw as a genuine impediment to their reunion into the same body that once was alive. And the problem was made more complicated were parts of a person consumed by wild beasts or fish or, even worse, cannibals.

Boyle (like Aquinas but unlike Athenagoras) accepted that such bodily parts became a substantial part of the body that consumed them. Even then, he suggested, they may be retrievable by an intelligent, omnipotent God. That said (again, unlike Athenagoras), Boyle was not committed to an account of personal identity that involved a numerical identity of parts. Even in this life, he explained, the body is in a state of perpetual flux. Apart from skull and bones, 'in no very great compass of time, a great part of the human body must be changed.'[71] So the complete retrieval of all parts was unnecessary. Personal identity was retained if only a portion of the matter of the former body constituted the resurrection body. This, he believed, aligned with the biblical understanding of personal identity. Drawing on Ezekiel's vision of the resurrection of the valley of bones (Ezek. 37.1–14 – 'Dem bones, dem bones, dem dry bones') and his own chemical experiments on the stable and long-lasting texture of bones, he surmised that skeletal remains would ensure the identity of the post- and pre-resurrection bodies, God adding such other parts as he saw fit to restore the bodies.

The most substantial late seventeenth-century defence of the doctrine that post- and pre-resurrection bodies would be exactly identical in parts was that of the English scholar Humphrey Hody (1659–1707), chaplain to John Tillotson, the archbishop of Canterbury. Most of Hody's ingenuity was reserved for defending his account of the resurrection body by appeal to scientific and empirical evidence. To this end, he invoked the *De statica medicina* (On medical measurement) of Sanctorius of Padua, or Santorio Santorio (1561–1636), the founder of the modern study of metabolism. Sanctorius had constructed a large weighing chair upon which for some 30 years he periodically ate, worked and slept, weighing himself, everything he ate and drank, and everything he excreted. Hody had noticed his conclusion that the weight of his waste products was only a little less than what he had eaten and drunk. Thus, wrote Hody, should one man devour another,

> it appears from Sanctorius's Observation that not above the 50th part of the Flesh of the Person Devour'd would become the Flesh of him that ate it. And besides the other 49 parts of the Flesh, there would remain all the Bones untouched, which make up a great (the most substantial) part of the Body.[72]

It was necessary only that the most important parts be raised – bones, skin, nerves, tendons, ligaments, substance of vessels. Recognising that even one-fiftieth not being raised was sufficient to open his account to criticism, he added an unusual proviso: if God has decreed that *all* the parts should be raised up, he suggested, 'God will take care that no one shall die whilst his Body contains any Particles that belong to another.'[73]

He also dealt with the objection that, on the Last Day, there would not be sufficient matter on the whole surface of the earth to make up the necessary number of bodies for all those who would have lived and died by that time. A complicated set of arithmetical calculations was offered to avoid this dilemma. Thus, for example, on the ratio of the estimated square feet in England to an estimated number of persons in 10,000 years, he declared that the latter was only one-seventeenth of the former. And taking into account the ratio of the weight of men (with appropriate adjustments for women and children) to the weight of a solid cubic foot of common earth, he concluded:

> it will plainly appear that the weight of a Humane Body, taking one with another, is not so great as the weight of a Solid Foot of common Earth. It is manifest therefore, that in less than the Seventeenth Part of England, if you go but One Foot deep, there is as much Substance, as would make up all the Humane Bodies that ever were, are, and will be, tho' the World should last in all 10,000 years.[74]

For Hody, gravity posed a problem. Because resurrected bodies would have physical weight, they would be unable to be sustained in ethereal heavens. On the one hand, he suggested, their physical weight would not be a problem in such regions since there was no such thing as gravity in regions purely ethereal above the reach and activity of particular orbs. The more 'natural' solution was the one Hody preferred: 'Perhaps after all, our *Heaven* will be nothing but a *Heaven upon Earth*, or some glorious solid *Orb* created on purpose for us in those immense Regions which we call Heaven.'[75] Still, perhaps, this was not problematic after all. In accordance with the tradition, Hody believed that resurrection bodies would be incorruptible, powerful, spiritual, celestial, glorious, without wrinkle or blemish, beautiful and comely – just like Adam's, although not requiring food and drink. They would be physically perfect. So again, Hody's bodies may be 'earthy', but they are highly 'idealised', and far from recognisable in most cases as the ones we will possess at the time of our deaths. In short, for Hody as for many others, all the problems around the nature of resurrected 'earthly' bodies were 'spiritualised' away.

On the issue of the resurrection of the physical body, much theological ink had been spilt in the attempt rationally to defend the philosophically unintelligible. And in the end, if a 'spiritualised' resurrection body was not to be endorsed, the only recourse – from Tertullian to Aquinas to Hody – was to the miraculous. It is perhaps no surprise that as the feasibility of the miraculous disappeared in the eighteenth century, so rational defences of the resurrection of the physical body disappeared from intellectual history, relegated to a forgotten and unmarked theological grave.

Apocalypse soon

As we have noted above, resurrected bodies were one part of a larger apocalyptic story that related to the return of Christ to judge the living and the dead, some to receive eternal happiness and the remainder eternal punishment. The absence of any great concerns in the New Testament about life after death and before the Last Judgement was the consequence of early Christian expectations that the return of Christ and the Last Judgement were imminent: 'The end of all things is near; therefore be serious and discipline yourselves for the sake of your prayers' (1 Pet. 4.7). Yet even within the New Testament, we can detect signs that early Christians were worrying that the end times had not yet arrived. More particularly, they were concerned about the fate of those who would die before Christ returned. Thus, Paul had to write to assure Thessalonian Christians that those who had already died would be saved first:

> For this we declare to you by the word of the Lord, that we who are alive, who are left until the coming of the Lord, will by no means precede those who have died. For the Lord himself, with a cry of command, with the archangel's call and with the sound of God's trumpet, will descend from heaven, and the dead in Christ will rise first. Then we who are alive, who are left, will be caught up in the clouds together with them to meet the Lord in the air; and so we will be with the Lord forever. (1 Thess. 4.15–17)

Emphasis on the resurrection of the dead rather than the life immediately after death, or vice versa, was a consequence of different emphases upon the body and the soul within the dualism that Christianity inherited from Greek philosophy. But it was also the result of imminent expectations or otherwise about the end of history and the return of Christ in judgement. Such imminent expectations have waxed and waned from New Testament times to the present.[76] As they waxed, the destiny of the individual after the Apocalypse took precedence over destiny immediately after death. As they waned, the life of the soul immediately after death became dominant.

These expectations that the world was about to end arose among the poor, the dispossessed and the marginalised, looking forward in the next world to a reversal of their misfortunes in this one, and sooner rather than later.[77] But they were also present among the educated elite. More generally, they were part of the historical story within which Christian life was lived, a story that began with the creation of all things and proceeded through the Fall of Man and his redemption in Jesus Christ to a cataclysmic end. More particularly, expectations of the imminence of the end occurred both inside the ecclesiastical establishment and outside of it. Whether within or without the Church, these were expectations that arose among those who saw the return of Christ in the near future as an incentive to the reform of a corrupt Church in the present. They also flourished among those who, identifying the Church with Satan or the Antichrist, had given up any expectations of reform and looked forward in hope and fear to the salvation of the few and the destruction of the many.

The story of life after death in the West is that of a complicated, often messy, tension between post-mortem and post-apocalyptic life, between time and eternity, between incorporeal physicalised souls and corporeal spiritualised bodies. For its part, mainstream Christianity, whether in the Greek East or the Latin West, attempted to manage the tension between the two. This was a virtually impossible ask. On the one hand, as we have seen, the demands of eschatology required the distinction. On the other hand, as we will see, the requirements of anthropology enhanced the one to the exclusion of the other. And each, as we have seen, was liable to collapse into the other.

Chapter Four

Purgatory and Beyond

> Since the passion and death of the Lord Jesus Christ, these souls have seen and see the divine essence with an intuitive vision and even face to face, without the mediation of any creature by way of object of vision; rather the divine essence immediately manifests itself to them, plainly, clearly and openly, and in this vision they enjoy the divine essence. Moreover, by this vision and enjoyment the souls of those who have already died are truly blessed and have eternal life and rest. Also the souls of those who will die in the future will see the same divine essence and will enjoy it before the general judgment.
>
> Pope Benedict XII, *Benedictus Deus* (1336)

'Blessed be God'

On 29 January 1336, Benedict XII (pope from 1334–42) issued the papal bull *Benedictus Deus* (Blessed be God). To all intents and purposes, it ended the controversy that had raged in the 1330s over the Beatific Vision. This was a debate that engaged three popes, the king of France, the Holy Roman Emperor and any number of theologians. It was centred on the nature of the afterlife between death and the Last Judgement, specifically on whether the soul could fully enjoy the spiritual goods of eternity, namely the Beatific Vision, prior to its reunion with the body on the Last Day.[1]

The controversy had crystallised on All Saints' Day in 1331 when John XXII (pope from 1316–34), Benedict's predecessor, preached a sermon suggesting that the souls of the saints now contemplating Christ's humanity would, upon reunion with their bodies at the general resurrection, attain the full and final vision of God. As Paul would have put it, until they were reunited with the body, souls saw God only as if through a glass darkly. In the previous decade, John XXII had already suggested that the resurrected body was necessary to the complete Beatific Vision, since it was promised to the complete person – body and soul – and not just to the soul. In short, embodiment was necessary to the full joys of heaven. His view scandalised many and he received no support from any theologian of note. The universities of Paris and Oxford were against it. It caused such a stir that, by the summer of 1334, his papal position was in jeopardy.

It is probable that only his death saved him from having to face a General Council called to consider sacking him. On his deathbed, John XXII at least gave to the gathered cardinals the appearance of having slightly revised his opinion in the light of the controversy he had aroused: 'the holy souls see God and the divine essence face to face and as clearly as their condition as souls separated from their bodies allowed.'[2] This still left open the possibility that, after reunion with the body, the Beatific Vision of the soul might be even more intense. He might have received some comfort after his death from the knowledge that the Eastern Church supported his position, although we can only hope that he would have known personally by then whether he was right or wrong.

In response to the controversy, Pope Benedict XII left John XXII's final statement unanswered. But he did determine that all worthy souls (in some cases, after purification) would see God 'plainly, clearly and openly, and in this vision they enjoy the divine essence.'[3] Moreover, because such souls were truly blessed and had eternal life and rest, the virtues of faith and hope (being no longer necessary) would cease. After such intuitive and face-to-face vision and enjoyment have begun for these souls, the same vision and enjoyment 'will continue without any interruption and without end until the last Judgment and from then on forever'.[4] Those who were not found worthy of the vision of God would go to hell immediately after death. Nevertheless, on the Day of Judgement, they too would appear in their bodies before the judgement seat of Christ to give an account of their personal deeds.

On the face of it, this was a triumph of Platonism over Aristotelianism, of soul only rather than soul-plus-body as the criterion of human identity. For it did suggest that, to enjoy the Beatific Vision 'plainly, clearly and openly' (*nude, clare et aperte*), only the soul was essential in the afterlife. But there is one qualification that needs to be made. This is to the effect that soul was not *just* soul. That is to say, as we have noted earlier, the soul was highly physicalised and had quasi-physical experiences, not least because it was impossible to say anything about the soul without giving it body-like features. As Caroline Bynum concludes:

> It thus seems probable that the position of *Benedictus Deus* gained ground steadily in the thirteenth century and prevailed in the fourteenth, at least in part because theologians, poets, and visionaries imagined the soul that achieved beatitude as if it already in some way possessed, or expressed itself in, its body.[5]

If this was a triumph of Platonic anthropology over Aristotelian, it was also a triumph of one form of eschatology over another. For if the delights of the vision of God were available before the Last Judgement, there was no need for the soul to be reunited with its body on the Last Day, and thus no need for the resurrection of the body. Put simply, even if the resurrection of the flesh and the final judgement that followed remained on the theological books, they added no eschatological value. What mattered for our salvation was the destiny of the soul after death rather than its fate after its reunion with its body.

The *Benedictus Deus* of Benedict XII also left a number of other theological ideas high and dry, or, put more positively, solved the confusions and uncertainties around them that we noted in Chapter 1. If it were the case that souls enjoyed the complete joys of heaven or correspondingly suffered the full horrors of hell before the Last Judgement, then the earlier intermediate stages between death and the Last Judgement, like 'Abraham's Bosom' or 'Paradise' or 'Hades', lost their specific roles. They were now absorbed into heaven or hell, both of which now came into play directly after death rather than after the Last Judgement. From the time of Benedict XII, this was the official doctrine of the Catholic Church. Thus, whether after death or after the Last Judgement, the destination was simply heaven or hell, rather than some preliminary form of these.

There is, however, another doctrine embedded within the *Benedictus Deus* of 1336. This is the modification of heaven or the mitigation of hell known as Purgatory. According to this, souls remaining impure after death were purified before attaining the final vision of God (see Plate 9 [c]). Thus, Benedict XII declared the full vision of God for blessed souls immediately after death or, if not then, at least after a period of purging or purification. Aquinas provided a useful definition of this process:

> Although some souls may be admitted to eternal beatitude as soon as they are released from their bodies, others may be held back from this happiness for a time. For it sometimes happens that during their lives

> people have not done full penance for the sins they have committed, but for which they have been sorry in the end. Since the order of divine justice demands that punishment be undergone for sins, we must hold that souls pay after this life the penalty they have not paid while on earth. This does not mean that they are banished to the ultimate misery of the damned, since by their repentance they have been brought back to the state of charity, whereby they cleave to God as their last end, so that they have merited eternal life. Hence we conclude that there are certain purgatorial punishments [*purgatorias poenas*] after this life, by which the debt of penalty not previously paid is discharged.[6]

This meant that a soul could be deemed ready for the Beatific Vision at some time before, even well before, the Last Judgement. There seemed no good reason – theological, pastoral or devotional – to deny the purified soul its due reward at the time of its having been purged of the sin that remained at the time of its death. We can say that the doctrine of Purgatory, together with the possibility of souls sufficiently pure to merit the Beatific Vision on this side of the Day of Judgement, significantly drove the increasing emphasis on human destiny between death and the end of history and correspondingly decreased the importance of the Last Judgement.

Particular judgements

One important implication of the increasing emphasis on the destiny of the soul between death and the Last Judgement was that God made the decision on the individual's ultimate fate *at the time of his death*. Thus, the *general* judgement of all the resurrected dead on the Day of Judgement merely confirmed the *particular* judgement made when the soul departed its body. As Aquinas rather elegantly put it:

> Accordingly the soul will remain perpetually in whatever last end it is found to have set for itself at the time of death, desiring that state as the most suitable, whether it is good or evil. This is the meaning of Ecclesiastes 11:3: 'If the tree fall to the south or to the north, in what place soever it shall fall, there shall it be.' After this life, therefore, those who are found good at the instant of death will have their wills forever fixed in good. But those who are found evil at that moment will be forever obstinate in evil.[7]

New Testament support for the particular judgement was found in the key passage that dealt with life immediately after death, namely, the parable of the rich man and Lazarus (Luke 16.19–31). Not only were the rich man and Lazarus allocated to places of torment or comfort respectively, but it is clear that there was no possibility of transfer from the one to the other. Thus, Abraham told the rich man, '[B]etween you and us a great chasm has been fixed, so that those who might want to pass from here to you cannot do so, and no one can cross from there to us' (Luke 16.26).

That said, in spite of the implication in the parable of the rich man and Lazarus that there was a post-mortem particular judgement, it was only in the mid-second century that we find a clear statement of this, in an anonymous sermon known as the Second Epistle of Clement. In this case, the emphasis on judgement at the time of death was not motivated by the prospect of life immediately after death. Rather, it was determined by the imminence of the general judgement:

> But ye know that the day of judgment even now 'cometh as a burning oven,' and some 'of the heavens shall melt,' and all the earth shall be as lead melting on the fire, and then the hidden and open works of men shall appear.[8]

The Second Epistle of Clement was very much a theology of 'seize the day'. Death was the last chance. At the end of the day (or the end of the world, for that matter), repentance was crucial on this side of the grave, since there would be no opportunity for it on the other:

> As long therefore, as we are upon earth, let us practise repentance, for we are as clay in the hand of the artificer [...] So let us also, while we are in this world, repent with our whole heart of the evil deeds we have done in the flesh, that we may be saved by the Lord, while we have yet an opportunity of repentance. *For after we have gone out of the world, no further power of confessing or repenting will there belong to us.*[9]

Similarly, Cyprian, bishop of Carthage (*c.*200–58 CE), saw death as a final boundary for salvation, whether for those who persecuted Christians or those Christians who were persecuted. Thus, to the pagan proconsul of Africa, Demetrianus, who had blamed war, famine and pestilence on the impiety of the Christians, Cyprian wrote in 252 CE:

> Provide, therefore, while you may, for your safety and your life [...] Believe and live, and do ye who persecute us in tithe rejoice with us for eternity. When you have once departed there, there is no longer any place for repentance, and no possibility of making satisfaction. *Here* life is either lost or saved; *here* eternal safety is provided for by the worship of God and the fruits of faith.[10]

John Chrysostom, archbishop of Constantinople (*c.*347–407 CE), recognised that, were there the possibility of coming to belief after death, then no one would be damned and all would be saved: 'For all will then repent and adore.'[11] As we will see later, others were to believe that the eventual salvation of all would be no bad thing. For Chrysostom, however, it was a matter of justice. If goodness was not rewarded and evil punished in the next life, then not only was there no incentive to the moral life in this one, but also justice would be made a nonsense of, not least because in this world the righteous suffered and the wicked prospered.

By the year 400, there seems to be a general consensus on the 'particular judgement'. In 419, in his *De natura et origine animae* (On the soul and its origin), in a discussion of the parable of the rich man and Lazarus, Augustine agreed unquestioningly with the view that

> souls after quitting the body are judged, before they come to that final judgement to which they must submit when their bodies are restored to them, and are either tormented or glorified in the very same flesh wherein they once lived here on earth.[12]

It was an interpretation of this parable that he had adopted as early as 399. 'There is no room, you see,' he declared, 'for putting things right when life is over.'[13]

A fiery purging

At the time of writing the *Enchiridion* (Handbook) around 421, Augustine was still committed to the notion that death was the point beyond which *we* could no longer alter our destiny:

> Therefore, it is in this life that all the merit or demerit is acquired, which can either relieve or aggravate a man's sufferings after this life. No one, then, need hope that after he is dead he shall obtain merit with God which he has neglected to secure here.[14]

He also remained in no doubt that the unbaptised were damned, and that the damned were damned forever. Whatever men may conjecture as to the variety of punishments in hell or suggest about the mitigation or intermission of their woes, 'this perpetual death of the wicked, then, that is, their alienation from the life of God, shall abide for ever.'[15] Thus, he firmly rejected any suggestions that all would eventually be saved, even if after a period of punishment. But Augustine *had* nonetheless pondered the words of Paul to the Corinthians:

> The fire shall try every man's work, of what sort it is. If any man's work abide which he has built thereupon, he shall receive a reward. If any man's work shall be burned, he shall suffer loss; but he himself shall be saved, yet so as by fire. (1 Cor. 3.13–15)

Thus, he did come to believe that there was a distinction between those who, in this life, were willing to lose the worldly things rather than Christ and those who, in times of temptation, put their attachment to worldly things before Christ. The one who put his faith above all else in Christ did suffer pain at the loss of worldly things. But he was not consumed by his loss because, 'protected by his immoveable and incorruptible foundation', he was oriented above all to pleasing God.[16]

So it may perhaps also be, declared Augustine, after death. 'It is a matter that may be inquired into, and either ascertained or left doubtful,' he wrote, 'whether some believers shall pass through a kind of purgatorial fire, and in proportion as they have loved with more or less devotion the goods that perish, be less or more quickly delivered from it.'[17] Thus, for those of faith devoted to good works who had only sinned lightly on this side of death, there may be a period of temporary punishment after death to purify them in preparation for eternal life. Augustine put it slightly differently, albeit to the same effect, in *De civitate dei*. Temporary punishments, he there declared, may be suffered both in this life and the next before the Last Judgement. But those who suffer temporary punishments after death are not doomed to the eternal punishments that will follow that final judgement. To some,

1. The spirit of Samuel appearing to Saul at the house of the Witch of Endor.

2. Charon ferrying the dead across the River Acheron.

4. The sores of Lazarus licked by dogs in the house of the rich man.

7. Thomas Aquinas (1225–74), 'the angelic doctor'.

8. Miniature depicting Dante and Virgil in Purgatory.

12. The limbo of the children.

14. The soul leaving the body accompanied by an angel.

17. The dead rising from their graves on the Last Day.

19. God surrounded by the saints and angels.

22. Martin Luther writing on the church door at Wittenburg in 1517.

23. Elijah ascending into heaven without having first died.

28. The seer and visionary Emanuel Swedenborg (1688–1772).

29. *The Meeting of a Family in Heaven* by William Blake (1757–1827).

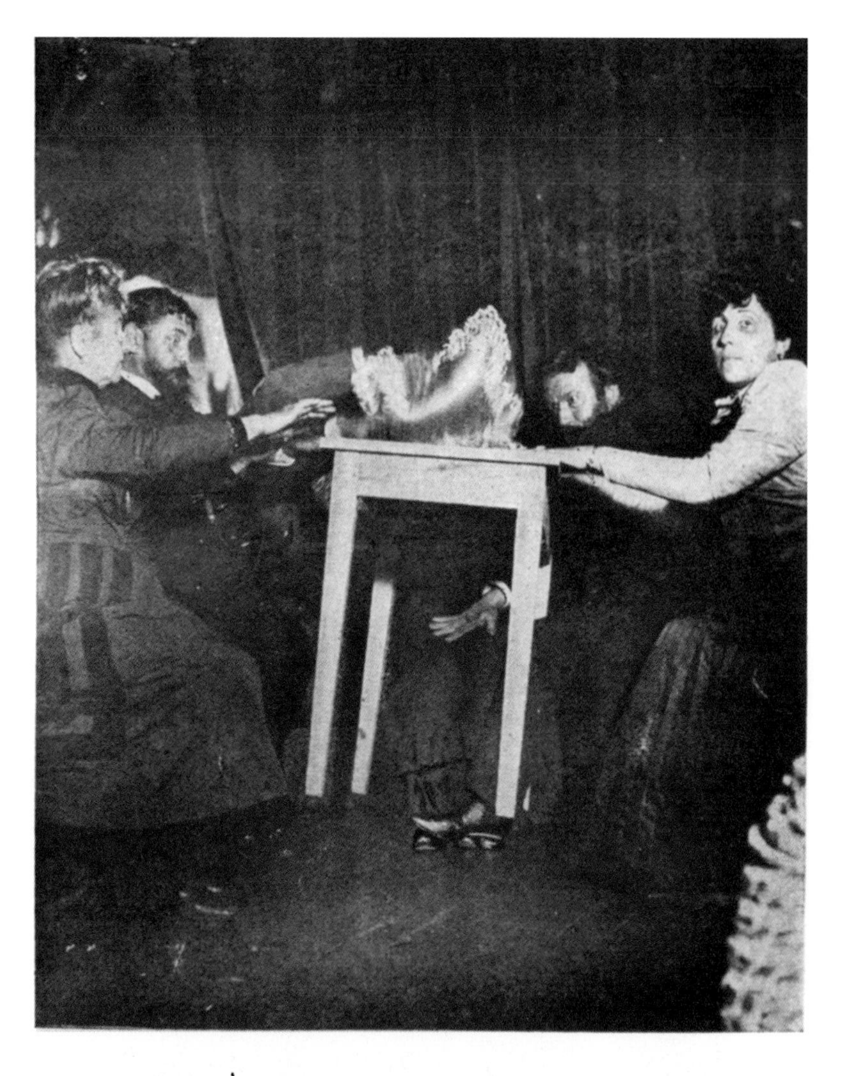

SOULÈVEMENT COMPLET D'UNE TABLE

Photographie prise dans le salon de M. FLAMMARION, le 12 Novembre 1898. (Le premier pied, à gauche, est à 18 centimètres au-dessus du parquet, le second à 13, celui de droite, au fond, à 8, et celui de droite en avant, à 14). Un assistant cache, à l'aide d'un coussin, les yeux du médium contre la lumière subite du magnésium. Ce médium (EUSAPIA) est mis dans l'impossibilité absolue de faire aucun mouvement suspect.

30. A table levitating during a seance with the medium Eusapia Palladino (1854–1918).

31. The biologist and spiritualist sceptic Thomas Henry Huxley (1825–95).

33. Elsie with a winged gnome (1917). The second of the five Cottingley fairy photographs.

34. The sceptical Charles Castle (Toby Stephens). From the film *Photographing Fairies* (1997).

'what is not remitted in this world is remitted in the next, that is, they are not punished with the eternal punishment of the world to come.'[18]

Augustine was not the first to contemplate the possibility of the purification of the soul after death. Clement of Alexandria (*c.*150–*c.*215 CE) had distinguished between those who would be punished eternally and those who would be punished temporarily. Thus there would be two kinds of fire, a consuming fire for the incorrigible and a discerning fire that purifies souls.[19] However, unlike Augustine, it is not clear that this 'purifying' takes place between death and the Last Judgement rather than after it.

The same can be said of Origen. His 'Hades', we recall, was not a place of purification but a place of waiting for the final judgement. Still, what we can say is that, at some time after death, according to Origen, there will eventually be a 'baptism of fire' for all souls, divided into three groups – saints, repentant sinners and unrepentant sinners. The first of these will pass painlessly, the second painfully, through the fire on their way to heaven. The third, the unrepentant, will be sent to the eternal fires of Gehenna.[20] Even for this last group, Origen (at least sometimes) seemed to admit that there was the possibility of salvation for souls. This was a result both of the mercy of God and of the souls' capacity to improve. However, in suggesting that hell might not be eternal, Origen was very much out on his own. As a result, he was transformed from hero to heretic.

Influenced by Origen, Ambrose (*c.*339–97 CE), bishop of Milan, had similar universalist tendencies. He seemed to have held too that souls could be divided into three groups, each of which had to go through a baptism of fire. For the righteous, who were like pure silver, the fire through which they passed was a refreshing one. For the wicked, who were like lead, it was punishment and torture. But for those sinners who were a mix of both silver and lead, the fire was purifying and lasted only as long as it took to melt away the lead.[21] Unlike Origen, however, Ambrose was certain that the purifying of such 'amalgamated' souls began immediately after death and could continue up to and beyond the Last Judgement.[22]

This period of purgation was to become fixed between death and the Last Judgement, and not go beyond it. But the key point had been established. This was the realisation that the division of people into two classes only at the time of death – the saved and the damned – was far too harsh. It was always clear that some (the saints, martyrs and confessors) merited heaven immediately after death. It was also clear that others deserved an eternity in hell. It now became just as clear, however, that there were among the baptised those who, although they died with unremitted sins, were neither sufficiently evil nor sufficiently incorrigible to merit eternal punishment. All of which suggested that the mercy and justice of God were best served if the class of the not so good but the not *too* bad (which is probably most of us) were both punished for and cleansed of their sins before admission to heaven.

Also embedded within this possibility of the purification of sins was the acceptance that sins differed in the degree of their seriousness. Augustine had distinguished between serious sins that he had called crimes that merited hell, and minor sins. But he had made no connection between slight sins and purgatorial fire. The first to make this connection was Caesarius of Arles (*c*.470–542). Caesarius too distinguished between serious sins (*capitalia peccata* – capital sins) and minor (*minuta*) sins. He warned against the sense of false security among those who believed that their capital crimes (*crimina capitalia*) would be purged by passing through fire (*per ignem transitorium*). It was not capital sins, he pointed out, that would be so purged, but only minor sins. Even then, Caesarius declared, minor sins were not to be ignored in the here and now on the assumption that the purifying fire to come was minimal. That fire of Purgatory, he wrote, 'will be more difficult than any punishment in this world can be seen or imagined or felt'. As for those who failed to repent of serious sins, they would hear the hard and irrevocable sentence, 'Depart from me, accursed ones, into the everlasting fire.'[23] From this time onwards, Paul's words in 1 Corinthians 3.15 on being saved 'but only as through fire' came more and more to be interpreted as the fire that purified in the time between death and the Last Judgement rather than after it.

Caesarius's link between purgatorial fire and minor sins was to be given the authority of the bishop of Rome, Pope Gregory the Great. Augustine had been tentative about the possibility of the purging of sins after death, not least because it acted as a disincentive to the pursuit of the virtuous life on this side of the grave. In the sixth century, however, Pope Gregory gave an emphatic 'Yes' to the question, 'Is there a purgatorial fire after death?' He had no doubt that God made his judgement on human destiny at the time of death. But nonetheless, he declared,

> we must believe that before the day of judgment there is a Purgatory fire for certain small sins [...] Yet we have here further to consider, that none can be there purged, no, not for the least sins that be, unless

in his lifetime he deserved by virtuous works to find such favour in that place.[24]

This distinction between major and minor sins was later to become formalised in terms of the difference between mortal and venial sins (*peccata mortalia et venialia*).[25] Penances for both kinds of sins in this life crossed over the border of death to the other side. All the more reason then to get right with God before death. For William of Auvergne (*c.*1180–1249), for example, the sufferings of Purgatory completed the sufferings of physical and spiritual penance in this life. The soul knows that no atonement in this life can satisfy the demands of divine justice:

> Interior penance is a spiritual judgement in which the sinning soul accuses itself, testifies against itself, judges itself guilty, that is, worthy of infernal torments and tortures for those things it has done wrong. Afterwards, it executes its own sentence upon itself, by torturing itself not only in spiritual ways [...] but even with corporeal afflictions such as fasts, works, lashings, and other things of this sort [...] And when it sees that all these do not suffice to satisfy the justice of the Creator fully, it applies with prayers and entreaties to the most clement Creator, imploring his mercy so that he might overlook the penalties due him.[26]

For William, no torments, spiritual or physical, that penitents can inflict upon themselves in this life could match the incomparably greater ones that will be inflicted in the hereafter. This provided an incentive, he found, to do all possible penance now in the hope of completing it before death, thus avoiding or at least minimising the pains of purgatorial fire.

Augustine too had recognised the desirability of a proportion between the seriousness of a sin and the time spent in punishment for it. As Jacques Le Goff notes, this was to lead in the later medieval period to the institution of 'a complex system of bookkeeping associated with the world to come'.[27] It was a bookkeeping that arose in keeping with progress in the mathematics of proportionality. Thus for Alexander of Hales (*c.*1170–1245), for example, the proportion between greater and lesser sins and their punishment in this world is the same as that between greater and lesser sins and their punishment in Purgatory. However, the punishments in Purgatory are not proportional to the punishments in this world, for the former are 'disproportionately bitter compared with the punishment endured in this world'.[28]

Again, there is no incentive to postpone repentance now, and no end of incentive to do penance both spiritual and physical in the here and now.

Most souls were realistic enough (or at least sufficiently humble) not to expect heaven immediately after death. Purgatory became, as a consequence, the default destination after death, granting hell could be avoided. The deathbed thus became a scene of high drama as the contrite embraced the last opportunity to avoid hell and ensure Purgatory. For the masses of people who were ill prepared for heaven, Purgatory provided a means by which the process of penitence could continue after death and salvation be gained before all hope ended on the Day of Judgement. And if all else failed, well, you could hopefully rely on those left behind to act on your behalf.

Praying for the dead

The accountancy of the hereafter was rendered significantly more complicated by the development of the notion of suffrages. According to this, prayers offered and good deeds done by those living could be of benefit both to those in Purgatory by mitigating their punishments and to those who performed them on the behalf of those being purified. It was a system that connected the living with the dead and ruptured the boundary between them. The Council of Florence gave 'suffrages' definitive expression in 1439:

> [We define] likewise, that if the truly penitent die in the love of God, before they have made satisfaction by worthy fruits of penance for their sins of commission and omission, their souls are purified by purgatorial fire after death; and that for relief from these pains they are benefited by the suffrages of the faithful in this life, that is, by Masses, prayers, and almsgiving, and by the other offices of piety performed by the faithful for one another according to the practice [*instituta*] of the Church.[29]

In fact, the Council of Florence was once again trying to manage a problem with which the Church had been wrestling for the better part of the previous millennium. Granted that God had determined the fate of individuals at the time of their death, could anything be done by those left behind to lessen the sufferings of those already dead? This was driven by the same motivation behind the possibility of a purifying fire after death, namely that the division of people into two classes only, the saved and the damned at the time of death, was far too harsh and that a more finely tuned division was required. Thus, in the *Enchiridion*, having made it clear that no one should hope that after he is dead he shall obtain merit with God that he has neglected to secure here, Augustine went on nonetheless to declare that it could not be denied that the souls of the dead were benefited 'by the piety of their living friends, who offer the sacrifice of the Mediator, or give alms in the church on their behalf'.[30] He recognised that there was a manner of living so good that such services were not required and one so bad that such acts would be of no help. But there was another manner of life, 'which is neither so good as not to require these services after death, nor so bad that such services are of no avail after death'.[31] Thus, when suffrages are offered for *all* the dead rather than *anyone in particular*, they act as thank-offerings for the lives of the very good, work as a form of consolation to the living when offered for the very bad, and are purgative for those in between.

Augustine was perhaps not as clear as he might have been on these classes of people. However, the ambiguities in Augustine aside, from the beginning of the fifth century the dead were more and more to be divided not merely into two groups, but into three – the entirely good, the entirely bad and the medium good/bad. Augustine recognised that there was one middle group of people who were purified of their sins. He also identified another middle group for whom prayers were worthwhile. But he did not identify these groups as one and the same. It is to the Englishman the Venerable Bede (*c*.673–735) that we owe the first identification of these two groups of the dead. As a consequence, the belief that suffrages on this side of the grave could lessen punishments for those in Purgatory entered Western Christianity. Thus in his fourth homily, written sometime in the early 730s, Bede declared:

> So the many righteous souls who are in the Church after the dissolution of the flesh are immediately received into the blessed repose of Paradise, where they wait in great joy, in vast choirs of joyous souls, for the moment when they will regain their bodies and appear before the face of God. But some who, because of their good works are destined to share the fate of the elect, but who, because of certain evil works have left the body in an unclean state, are taken after death by the flames of purgatorial fire [*flammis ignis purgatorii*] and severely punished. Either they are cleansed of the taint of their vices by a long trial [*longa examinatione*] in this fire, or thanks to the prayers, alms, fasting, tears, and Eucharistic offerings of

> their faithful friends, they are delivered from punishment and allowed to enjoy the repose of the blessed.[32]

By the end of the thirteenth century, these three groups of people – the good, the bad and the in-between – would be destined for three different places respectively: heaven, hell and Purgatory. At the time of the Last Judgement, Purgatory would be no more and only heaven and hell would remain. In terms of time, Purgatory had now superseded Abraham's Bosom and Hades as a location between death and the Last Judgement. In terms of space, it was now somewhere between heaven and hell. Originally part of hell, it had detached itself from there and moved upwards and closer to heaven, a place of hope, even though it remained a hell of temporary torments. Hell had been perceived as too awful a place to which to sentence those who were only moderately bad. Neither God's justice nor his mercy were served by that. The divine justice and mercy were better served by a place where souls, who, like most of us, were not really all that good at being really bad, could be both punished and perfected. Hell could then be preserved and reserved only for the most incorrigible.

This was the context within which Dante in 1319 was to create his own version of Purgatory. For Dante, Purgatory was not below the earth but on it. It was an island-mountain situated in the southern hemisphere, diametrically opposite Jerusalem (perhaps Australia on a very hot day?). Between the shoreline and the entrance to Purgatory dwelt those who had delayed their repentance until the end of their lives and had to wait various lengths of time before being allowed to enter the mountain of Purgatory proper through a golden gate. The mountain of Purgatory comprised seven ascending terraces, the circumference of each being smaller than the last as the summit was approached (see Plate 11 [c]). A steep passageway wound from one terrace to the next. On each of these terraces, souls were purged of their sins. These were not venial ones, but the seven capital sins in order: pride (the root of all sins), envy, wrath, sloth, avarice, gluttony and lust. These were the same sins that were punished in hell, although those souls in Purgatory had sinned less gravely than their counterparts in that place.[33] At the summit of the mountain lay the earthly Paradise, between the peak of purification and the entrance to heaven.

The progress of the soul through Purgatory could also be assisted by those on earth. Sapia of Siena was so wasted by envy that she relished the misfortunes of others more than her own good fortune. She left her repentance too late, but was helped by the prayers of the Franciscan hermit Peter Pettinaio. 'Then, coming to the utmost edge of life,' she told Dante,

> I sought my peace with God. And even now,
> my dues would not, in penance, have been paid
> had I not been remembered in the prayers
> that Peter Pettinaio so devoutly made
> in heartfelt charity on my behalf.[34]

Souls in Purgatory too sought help from the Virgin and the saints. The envious on the third terrace were heard to say, 'Mary, pray for us. / Michael! [...] Saint Peter! All the saints!'[35]

Souls who began the climb up the mountain towards purity had to want to embark on the journey. As they were progressively purged of each sin, they meditated upon its opposite virtue. Thus, the ascent to heaven was both a loss of vice and a gain in virtue. The climb itself was not an easy one:

> We scrambled through the bore of shattered rock.
> On every side its edges tightened round.
> The ground beneath us called for feet *and* hands.[36]

The punishments were severe. Thus, upon the envious,

> the light of heaven bestowed no generous ray.
> For all their eyelids, pierced by iron wires,
> were sewn up like an untamed sparrow hawk's
> when, restively, it won't keep calm and still.[37]

The fires of Purgatory replicated the fires of hell, but only temporarily and not eternally. Even at the summit, there was a wall of fire through which the penitent had to go in order to pass from Purgatory into the earthly Paradise. Once within the flame, Dante tells us,

> I could have flung myself –
> the heat that fire produced was measureless –
> for coolness, in a vat of boiling glass.[38]

Even so, the climb became easier and the punishments less severe as the soul ascended, lightened of its burden of sin:

> This mountain is by nature such
> that, down below, the start is always hard,
> yet hurts far less the more one rises up

until near the top the soul floats as lightly upwards in ascent 'as boats that travel down a flowing stream'.[39] The earthly Paradise at the summit provided the departure point for the soul's final journey to God.

Craving your indulgence

There were two further refinements to Purgatory, penances, suffrages and piety in the medieval period more generally. These were the 'Treasury of Merits' (*thesaurus meritorum*) and indulgences, or pardons. During their lifetimes, the Virgin Mary and the saints had accumulated a surplus of merits beyond those necessary for their own salvation (see Plate 26 [c]). The Treasury of Merits was the celestial bank in which these merits had been deposited. The merits of Christ were also included in it, so there was no chance of its ever running out of 'spiritual cash'. These surplus merits were available for transfer to the faithful to assist them in their salvation through the granting of indulgences (pardons, grants). In keeping with Christ's handing of the keys of the Kingdom of Heaven to the Apostle Peter such that 'whatever you bind on earth will be bound in heaven, and whatever you loose on earth will be loosed in heaven' (Matt. 16.19), the popes as the apostolic successors of Peter had final authority over this treasury.

Any bishops who granted indulgences did so only on authority from the pope. While he could not absolve souls in Purgatory of the punishments due to them, the pope could offer to God from the Treasury of Merits whatever was necessary for the cancelling of those punishments. Originally, for the granting of such pardons, pious Christians made financial thank-offerings to the Church. These were eventually to come before rather than after the receipt of indulgences, and thus came to function as payments for them. So payment for indulgences became a legitimate, if potentially dodgy, way of putting into practice the injunction of Jesus not to

> store up for yourselves treasures on earth, where moth and rust doth corrupt and where thieves break in and steal; but store up for yourselves treasures in heaven, where neither moth nor dust doth corrupt and where thieves do not break in and steal. (Matt. 6.19–20).[40]

Both Bonaventure and Aquinas had suggested that it was the Treasury of Merits that could be drawn upon to pay off the debts owed for sins. It was, however, Pope Clement VI (1291–1352) who formalised this connection in his bull *Unigenitus* (Only-begotten) in 1343. According to this, a great heap of treasure has been derived from the excess merits of Christ, the Virgin Mary and all of the martyrs and saints throughout history. Those who availed themselves of it were 'made partakers of God's friendship'. This treasury was not 'hidden in a napkin or buried in a field'. Rather, it was entrusted to be dispensed 'through blessed Peter, bearer of heaven's keys and his successors as vicars on earth'. It was to be applied to those that had confessed and were truly penitent 'now for total, now for partial remission of punishment due for temporal sins (or of temporal punishment for sins)'. There was no chance of its diminution or disappearance 'as well because of the infinite merits of Christ [...] as because the more men are drawn to righteousness as a result of its application by so much more does the heap of merits increase'.[41]

But were these indulgences able to be applied not only to the living but also to those already dead?[42] The tradition of indulgences for the dead can be found from the end of the eleventh century. Then it was often connected to zeal for the Crusades. In the middle of the thirteenth century, for example, Stephen of Bourbon (d.1261) heard the story of a crusading knight who, tiring of the adventure, wished to return home. After being told by a certain William of Paris that, as a papal legate, he had the authority to grant indulgences not only to Crusaders but also to their deceased relatives on condition they complete 40 days of service, the knight agreed to stay. When the Crusade was over, this knight had a dream in which his father appeared to thank him for having freed him from Purgatory.[43]

Among medieval scholars, virtually no one denied that the dead in Purgatory could benefit from indulgences. They were much divided, however, on whether such souls were under the jurisdictional authority of the Church as were those still alive on earth. In short, did God or the pope have authority over those in this intermediate state between heaven and hell? If the pope had such authority, then the indulgences granted by him to the dead were as guaranteed to reduce their time in Purgatory as those granted to the living. On the other hand, if the Church had no authority over the dead in Purgatory, then there was no certainty that indulgences would have any effect in reducing their time there or freeing them altogether. Such indulgences would then have only the same status as traditional suffrages. All were agreed that the effectiveness of *these* was in the hands of God and not in those of the pope. The majority opinion was probably that of Bonaventure (over against Aquinas), who argued that neither the pope nor the bishops had any jurisdiction in Purgatory:

> [I]n regard to the authority to judge, because the dead are outside the forum of the Church and of ecclesiastical judges, it seems that absolution [of penalty] is not possible for them, except as a *prayer for pardon* [that is, as a suffrage]; and so, to speak properly, *indulgence* is not granted to them. But if indulgence may be broadly called an outlay of someone's help, and a dispensation of the goods of the Church, thus is indulgence granted to them, but this dispensation is *not of a judge, but of a suppliant.*[44]

In short, indulgences were nothing more than suffrages.

This was a dispute that probably mattered little to those seeking to reduce the time in Purgatory of those they loved. It was much more about papal power – social, political and economic – than about the connection of this-worldly piety to an other-worldly Purgatory. In the end, it needed papal authority to attempt to bring it to some resolution. Pope Sixtus IV (1414–84) is mostly remembered as the pope who restored the Sistine Chapel, and after whom it was named. But in 1476, he also proclaimed the first papal indulgence for the dead in Purgatory. The indulgence sellers did not hesitate in suggesting that the older modes of suffrage were now redundant, and that no matter how long a soul had yet to suffer in Purgatory it would fly at once to heaven for the sum of six blancs. These were tickets in a medieval lottery that everybody won – well, everyone except the priests. They saw papal indulgences for the dead as a threat to one of their main sources of revenue. They 'promised to perform more effectually what for centuries had been their lucrative and exclusive privilege in celebrating masses for the dead'.[45] This forced the pope to point out that he had not been attempting to replace the traditional suffrages but rather to find a complementary way, in the mode of suffrage (*per modem suffrage*), to relieve souls in Purgatory.

Theoretically then, the question was settled in favour of the pope not having jurisdiction over the souls in Purgatory. But in practice it was otherwise, and perhaps inevitably so. The extension of indulgences to the dead administered by the pope from the Treasury of Merits entailed a vast increase in power – and wealth. As Jacques Le Goff writes:

> And for the Church, what a marvellous instrument of power! The souls in Purgatory were considered to be members of the church militant. Hence, the Church argued, it ought to have (partial) jurisdiction over them, even though God was nominally the sovereign judge in the other world. Purgatory brought to the Church not only new spiritual power but also, to put it bluntly, considerable profit [...] And finally, the 'infernal' system of indulgences found powerful support in the idea of Purgatory.[46]

Johann Tetzel (1465–1519) was a German Dominican friar and preacher, a grand inquisitor in Poland and later the grand commissioner for indulgences in Germany. In 1517, his task was to head up the campaign to raise funds from the German faithful on behalf of Pope Leo X (1475–1521) by selling indulgences in order to finish the rebuilding of St Peter's Cathedral in Rome and, incidentally, to assist in replenishing the financial resources of Albrecht, archbishop of Magdeburg and Mainz. (See Plate 21 [c] for a contemporary German satire against the sale of indulgences.) It is unlikely that he did so by using the jingle attributed to him: 'As soon as the coin in the coffer rings, the soul out of Purgatory springs' ('*Sobald das Geld im Kasten klingt, die Seele aus dem Fegfeuer springt*'). But it undoubtedly reflects the sentiments expressed within his indulgences sermons:

> You should know that all who confess and in penance put alms into the coffer according to the counsel of the confessor, will obtain complete remission of their sins [...] Why are you then standing there? Run for the salvation of your souls! [...] Don't you hear the voices of your wailing dead parents and others who say, 'Have mercy upon me, have mercy upon me, because we are in severe punishment and pain. From this you could redeem us with a small alms and yet you do not want to do so.' Open your ears as the father says to his son and the mother to the daughter [...] 'We have created you, fed you, cared for you, and left you our temporal goods. Why then are you so cruel and harsh that you do not want to save us, though it only takes so little?' [...] You may have

> letters [of indulgence] which let you have, once in life and in the hour of death [...] full remission of the punishment which belongs to sin.[47]

The implication of all this was that salvation was for sale by the Church and could be bought for a price. It led a young Augustinian priest, Martin Luther (1483–1546), to write a letter to his archbishop, Albrecht of Magdeburg and Mainz, on 31 October 1517, denouncing the sale of indulgences and proposing a disputation on 95 theses that he had drawn up and included in his letter (and, according to legend, nailed to the door of the Castle Church in Wittenberg – see Plate 22 [BW]). His tone was humble, but granting that Albrecht was to receive half of the funds raised in Leo X's campaign, he was unlikely to receive a sympathetic hearing. 'Spare me, Most Reverend Father in Christ and Most Illustrious Prince,' Luther wrote,

> that I, the dregs of humanity, have so much boldness that I have dared to think of a letter to the height of your Sublimity. The Lord Jesus is my witness that, conscious of my smallness and baseness, I have long deferred what I am now shameless enough to do, moved thereto most of all by the duty of fidelity which I acknowledge that I owe to your most Reverend Fatherhood in Christ. Meanwhile, therefore, may your Highness deign to cast an eye upon one speck of dust, and for the sake of your pontifical clemency to heed my prayer. Papal indulgences for the building of St Peter's are circulating under your most distinguished name, and as regards them, I do not bring accusation against the outcries of the preachers, which I have not heard, so much as I grieve over the wholly false impressions which the people have conceived from them; to wit, the unhappy souls believe that if they have purchased letters of indulgence they are sure of their salvation; again, that so soon as they cast their contributions into the money-box, souls fly out of purgatory; furthermore, that these graces [i.e. the graces conferred in the indulgences] are so great that there is no sin too great to be absolved, even, as they say – though the thing is impossible – if one had violated the Mother of God; again, that a man is free, through these indulgences, from all penalty and guilt.[48]

Rhetorically humble it may have been, but Albrecht would have heard the threat made by Luther at the end of his letter. For Luther went on to pray that the archbishop might do away with the treatise instructing the preachers of pardons and impose on them another way of preaching, lest, he wrote, there arise someone

> who will publish writings in which he will confute them and that treatise, to the shame of your Most Illustrious Sublimity. I shrink very much from thinking that this will be done, and yet I fear that it will come to pass, unless there is some speedy remedy.[49]

Albrecht would have been left in little doubt that Luther was about to cause trouble. And Luther duly did just that.

Thus, with a dispute over whether the pope could guarantee the eternal destiny of the living *and* the dead in Purgatory, the most important event in the history of Western Christendom – the Reformation – began. Human life on this side of the grave was radically changed as the consequence of a quarrel about life on the other side. Christianity was irrevocably divided into Catholic and Protestant. And all the issues around the afterlife that had seemed more or less settled were once again up for debate.

Chapter Five

The Sleep of Death

> About the same time others arose in Arabia, putting forward a doctrine foreign to the truth. They said that during the present time the human soul dies and perishes with the body, but that at the time of resurrection they will be renewed together.
>
> Eusebius, *Historia ecclesiastica*

The dying soul

The Catholic system of Purgatory, and the economy of the hereafter that had been built upon it, was dependent on two key ideas. The first was that of the immortality of the soul, at least in the sense that, although the body died, the soul continued on. By the time of the Reformation, that the soul was *naturally* immortal had become an integral part of the eschatology of the Catholic Church and the penitential and liturgical apparatus that went with it. The second idea was that, after death, the soul remained conscious. Only thus could the person be capable of experiencing the joys of heaven and the pains of hell or Purgatory between death and the Last Judgement.

By the early part of the sixteenth century, both ideas had been brought into question within the Catholic Church. And sufficiently so that Pope Leo X (1475–1521), in the first year of his pontificate in 1513, at the eighth session of the fifth Lateran Council, reasserted the natural immortality of the soul. He did so against both those who thought the soul naturally mortal and those who thought that the same (universal) soul animated all men. Thus, in his bull *Apostolici regiminis* (Of Apostolic government), he declared that

> we [...] condemn and reprobate all those who assert that the intellectual soul is mortal, or one and the same in all men, and those who call these things in question, seeing that the soul is not only truly, and of itself, and

> essentially the form of the human body [...] but likewise is immortal, and, according to the number of bodies into which it is infused, singularly multiplied, multiplied, and to be multiplied.[1]

Leo X was reacting to the development of such ideas within the Italian Renaissance, particularly in the universities of Padua, Ferrara and Bologna, where the natural immortality of the soul was being challenged by readings of Aristotle that argued on the one hand for the natural mortality of the soul and, on the other, for the existence of an eternal rational soul in which each individual participated only during his life time. In neither case was there a place for *individual* conscious existence immediately after death or into eternity.

In spite of Leo X, the challenge to the prevailing orthodoxy continued in the works of the Aristotelian Pietro Pomponazzi (1462–1524), successively professor at Padua, Ferrara and Bologna. In his *De immortalitate animae* (On the immortality of the soul) in 1516 and his *Apologia* (Apology) in 1517, he attempted to find a way between those Aristotelians supportive of there being only one eternal soul, those supportive of the mortality of the individual soul and the orthodox position on the natural immortality of the individual soul.

According to Pomponazzi, man is suspended between the animals and the angels. Like animals, and unlike angels, men are corporeal beings and mortal. But unlike animals, they are not completely defined by their bodies. The soul's capacity for knowing enables it to rise above the particular by grasping the universal and the immaterial. In this sense it participates in the life of pure intelligence and thus in immortality. However, although our souls can thus participate in immortality, they are inseparable from our mortal bodies and cannot survive our deaths. For souls, like bodies, are generated and not created by God. As Pomponazzi put it, the 'soul is essentially and truly mortal but relatively immortal'.[2]

With the mortality of the soul, the prospect of rewards and punishments immediately after death disappeared, along with the places in which it was located. The consequence of this was, on the face of it, that the main incentives for the virtuous life on this side of the grave – rewards for the righteous and punishments for the wicked – also disappeared. This might be true, declared Pomponazzi, for 'the greater part of men, if they do good, do it more from fear of eternal punishment than from hope of eternal good, since punishments are better known to us than that eternal good'.[3] Even the immortality of the soul, he suggested, was invented as a means to bring men to virtue by lawgivers 'not caring for truth but only for righteousness'.[4] For the philosopher who lives by truth, however, there is no need of post-mortem rewards and punishments. For virtue is its own reward and vice itself its own punishment (however difficult this might be to see for those of us of a less stoic and less virtuous disposition than Pomponazzi).[5]

'To sleep, perchance to dream?'

As we will see, the assertion of the mortality of the soul did not necessarily rule out the possibility of rewards and punishments after death. For those who saw human identity as essentially determined by its corporeality, the joys of heaven and the horrors of hell would not begin immediately after death but only after the bodily resurrection of the dead and the Last Judgement. However, it was not necessary to assert the *mortality* of the soul in order to subvert the doctrine of Purgatory. It was just as effectively undermined by the claim that, although the soul was immortal, it was *sleeping* between death and the Last Judgement and thus incapable of feeling anything, whether of rewards or punishments. This was Luther's tactic.

Luther was too much of a Platonist to undermine Purgatory by an Aristotelian argument for the mortality of the soul. And he rejected the Aristotelian position that the soul was the form of the body. Rather, between death and the reunion of the body and soul, the soul slept freed from the body. Luther knew that the idea of the unconscious sleep of the soul effectively destabilised the notion of Purgatory as much as the denial of the soul's post-mortem life. Thus, in his 1544 lectures on Genesis, he declared:

> The body is destroyed by putrefaction and worms. But what, it is asked, becomes of the soul before that Day of Judgement? [...] But the answer which Christ prescribes is simple when He says in Matt. 22.32: 'God is not God of the dead, but of the living.' This makes us sure that our souls are living and are sleeping in peace, and that they are not being racked by any tortures.[6]

Since the time of Christ, he went on, there has been no Bosom of Abraham in which the dead dwell. Rather, when we die, we are carried into the bosom of Christ, although Luther is uncertain just where this place might be. Like dreamless sleep in our present lives, in the sleep of the soul after death, there will be no consciousness of the passing of time: 'Salomon judgeth that the dead are a sleepe, and feele nothing at all. For the dead lye there accompting neyther dayes nor yeares, but when they are awaked, they shall seeme to have slept scarce one minute.'[7] The sleep of death will end on the day of the Last Judgement, when all the dead will awake reunited with their bodies. Thus,

> we shall censure ourselves that we were surprised or alarmed at such a sleep in the hour of death, and [we will] suddenly come alive out of the grave and from decomposition, and entirely well, meet our Lord and Savior Jesus Christ in the clouds.[8]

Luther was, however, sufficiently ambivalent about the sleep of the soul for later Lutheran reformers to tread quietly around this doctrine. And their reticence was reinforced by the uptake of mortalism in the radical wings of the European Reformation. All of these radicals were dissatisfied with Protestant emphasis on the objectivity of salvation, which underplayed the significance of personal religious experience. They insisted upon the baptism of 'believers', 'or on the possession of the gifts of the Spirit, or on the experience of regeneration'.[9] In short, they were less interested in the reformation of the existing order than in what they took to be a restitution of New Testament Christianity. Within such a biblically inspired Christianity, they found no place for the conscious existence of the soul between death and the Last Day. Although the distinction was even then at times opaque, they can be distinguished into 'psychopannychists' and 'thnetopsychists'. As Norman Burns puts it:

> The psychopannychists believed that the immortal substance called soul literally slept until the resurrection of the body; the thnetopsychists, denying that the soul was an immortal substance, believed that the soul slept after death only in a figurative sense. Both groups of soul sleepers believed in the personal immortality of the individual after the resurrection of the body.[10]

Both groups should be distinguished from those annihilationists who denied both the immortality of the individual soul and the resurrection of the body.

Although mortalism thrived among radical Protestants in Europe, it appears to have had less of an uptake in sixteenth-century England. In its

Lutheran form, however, it was brought to the attention of English believers in Sir Thomas More's *Dialogue* in 1529. This was the year in which the pious Catholic humanist More (1478–1535) became Henry VIII's Lord Chancellor (before, five years later, falling foul of a king who was ambiguously to embrace Protestantism so that he might bigamously embrace Anne Boleyn). For More, heretical views on death and the afterlife were literally matters of life and death. His key criticism of Luther's soul-sleeping focused on the loss of the incentive to lead a moral life: 'What shall he care,' asked More, 'how long he live in sin, that believeth Luther, that he shall after this life neither feel well nor ill in body nor soul till the day of doom?' And not least because 'if they shall be damned, yet they say it shall be long or [before] they feel it. For Luther saith that all souls shall sleep and feel neither good nor bad after this life till doomsday.'[11]

More's *Dialogue* was directed not only against Luther but against the latter's English disciple William Tyndale (1494?–1536), whose English translation of the New Testament had been smuggled into England from 1526. Such vernacular translations were emblematic of Protestantism's determination to replace medieval Catholicism with biblical Christianity. The Catholic debate about mortalism had been conducted within the philosophical space created between Aristotelianism and Platonism. But for Protestant mortalists, it was not a debate within philosophy but against it. For them, revelation was against reason, and Jerusalem opposed to Athens. For them, true Christianity had, in short, been tainted by pagan philosophy. As Tyndale put it in his response to More's *Dialogue*:

> The heathen philosophers [...] did put that the souls did ever live. And the pope joineth the spiritual doctrine of Christ and the fleshly doctrine of philosophers together; things so contrary that they cannot agree [...] And because the fleshly-minded pope consenteth unto heathen doctrine, therefore he corrupteth the scripture to establish it.[12]

Moreover, Tyndale argued (pretty reasonably), the Bible knew nothing of the immortality of the soul. It was focused on the resurrection of the body and the Day of Judgement. Christ and his Apostles, he declared, 'taught no other; but warned to look for Christ's coming again every hour.'[13] Moreover, if souls were in heaven immediately after death, there was no need of any resurrection of the dead: 'And ye, in putting them [souls] in heaven, hell, and purgatory, destroy the arguments wherewith

Christ and Paul prove the resurrection [...] The true faith putteth the resurrection, which we be warned to look for every hour.'[14] The resurrection of the body was, for Tyndale, the beginning of salvation and not just an unnecessary addition to souls already enjoying the Beatific Vision. 'I am not persuaded,' he wrote,

> that they be already in the full glory that Christ is in, or the elect angels of God are in. Neither is it any article of my faith: for if it were so I see not but then the preaching of the resurrection of the flesh were a thing in vain.[15]

William Tyndale and his New Testament collaborator John Frith (1503–33) were the only two English writers openly to endorse soul-sleeping in the sixteenth century. Their commitment to the Protestant cause came at a price. Frith was burnt for denying the doctrines of Purgatory and transubstantiation in London in July 1533; and Tyndale was strangled and then burnt in Holland in October 1536.

It is difficult to estimate the influence of soul-sleeping in the England of the sixteenth century. The first Anglican and genuinely Protestant Prayer Book of Edward VI, published in 1549, showed an afterlife of studied ambiguity. The final prayer at the service of the burial of the dead asked that the souls of the dead 'delivered from the burden of the flesh, be in joy and felicity', while the collect for Holy Communion when there is a burial beseeched God 'to raise us from the death of sin into a life of righteousness, that when we shall depart this life, we may sleep in him'. Still, the overall emphasis is without doubt on the Day of Resurrection: 'when that dreadful day of the general resurrection shall come, make him to rise also with the just and righteous and receive this body again to glory, then made pure and incorruptible.'[16]

If the Prayer Book of 1549 was ambiguous, that of 1552 wasn't. Already by this time, Anglicanism was declaring itself a *via media*, on this occasion between a Catholicism that seemed to deny the necessity of the resurrection of the body and a mortalism that denied the conscious life of the soul between death and the Last Judgement. Thus, the thirty-ninth of the Forty-two Articles of Religion included in this edition of the Prayer Book declared unorthodox those who thought the life to come belonged only to the soul and not also to the body. The fortieth article declared both soul-sleepers and soul-deniers outside of the bounds of right belief:

> They which say, that the souls of such as depart hence, do sleep being without all sense, feeling, or perceiving, until the day of judgment; or affirm that the souls die with the bodies, and at the last day shall be raised up with the same; do utterly dissent from the right belief, declared to us in holy scripture.[17]

That mortalism was considered unorthodox in the Church of England was, theologically at least, the consequence of the dominance of Genevan Calvinism in the Anglican theology of the reigns of Edward VI (1547–53), Elizabeth I (1558–1603) and James I (1603–25). John Calvin (1509–64) was a vehement opponent of mortalism. In his tract *Psychopannychia* (1542), he saw it as an evil that 'has lately begun to send forth sparks, being stirred up by some dregs of Anabaptists', by which he meant the proponents of the Radical Reformation.[18] He was the first to make a clear distinction between those mortalists who 'imagine that [the soul] sleeps in a state of insensibility from Death to the Judgement-day when it will awake from its sleep' and those who maintain that it 'perishes along with the body, and becomes evanescent till the period when the whole man shall be raised again'.[19] It was also Calvin who in this work established the scriptural parameters within which the debate would be carried out for the next century. As a believer in the immortality of the soul, he argued for its conscious existence between death and the Last Judgement, although he studiously avoided any suggestion of purgation or spiritual development beyond the grave. Having got rid of Purgatory, he had to reinstate the Bosom of Abraham. Thus, the state of the soul between death and the final day was a static one. The souls of the elect waited in Abraham's Bosom for the perfection of their happiness when reunited with their bodies, while the reprobate awaited in chains their ultimate and eternal punishment:

> The fact that the blessed gathering of saintly spirits is called 'Abraham's Bosom' is enough to assure us of being received after this pilgrimage by the common father of the faithful, that he may share the fruit of his faith with us. Meanwhile, since Scripture everywhere bids us wait in expectation for Christ's coming, and defers until then the crown of glory, let us be content with the limits divinely set for us: namely, that the souls of the pious, having ended the toil of their warfare, enter into blessed rest, where in glad expectation they await the enjoyment of promised glory, and so all things are held in suspense until Christ the Redeemer appear. The

> lot of the reprobate is doubtless the same as that which Jude assigns to the devils: to be held in chains until they are dragged to the punishment appointed for them.[20]

Calvin's concerns about mortalism were shared by the Swiss reformer Heinrich Bullinger (1504–75). The tenth dialogue of his *An Holsome Antidotus or Counter-poysen, agaynst the Pestylent Heresye and Secte of the Anabaptistes*, published in England in 1548, was primarily a scriptural argument against soul-sleeping. But it also provided philosophical reasons for the immortality and incorruptibility of the soul.[21] His major contribution to the debate occurred in *The Second Helvetic Confession* in 1566, a creed for which he was primarily responsible, and one that was endorsed by all the Reformed Churches. 'We say,' declared Bullinger,

> that man doth consist of two, and those diverse substances in one person; of a soul immortal (as that which being separated from his body doth neither sleep nor die), and a mortal body, which, notwithstanding, at the last judgment shall be raised again from the dead, that from henceforth the whole man may continue forever in life or in death. We condemn all those who mock at, or by subtle disputation call into doubt, the immortality of the soul, or say that the soul sleeps, or that it is part of God.[22]

Radical mortalists

For mainstream Protestantism, the fear of mortalism was as much political as eschatological. Mortalists were uninterested in the destiny of the soul between death and the Last Judgement, not least because they expected the return of Christ imminently. And they were not averse to helping God usher in the Last Day by turning the world upside down. They had heard Jesus say, 'I have not come to bring peace but a sword' (Matt. 10.34), and many were more than willing to assist his Second Coming by taking up arms on his behalf. The mortality of the soul and the imminence of the Last Judgement served revolutionary ideas well. Both thrived, for example, in the English Revolution of the mid-seventeenth century. 'It is no new work of Satan to sow heresies, and breede Heretickes,' declared one pamphleteer in 1651, 'but they never came up so thick as in these latter times.'[23] That heresies abounded, or at least were thought to do so, was demonstrated by the Calvinist Thomas Edwards (*c.*1599–1648) in his 1646 'bestseller' *Gangraena* (Gangrene), the title of which gave eloquent expression to what he thought of the vast number of heresies that he controversially catalogued. Of the 267 heresies that he listed, 11 related to mortalism. He did perhaps draw finer distinctions than really existed. But his list shows the sorts of options that he judged were corrupting the Church. We can classify them into those that support the sleep or death of the soul and those that teach the annihilation of the soul. Among the former we find:

> That the soul of man is mortal as the soul of a beast, and dies with the body [...] That the souls of the faithful after death, do sleep till the day of judgement and are not in a capacity of acting any thing for God, 'tis with them as 'tis with a man that is in some pleasing dream [...] That none of the souls of the Saints go to Heaven where Christ is, but Heaven is empty of the Saints till the resurrection of the dead [...] No man is yet in hell, neither shall any be there until the judgement; for God doth not hang first, and judge after [...] That it is injustice in God to punish the souls of the wicked in Hell while their bodies lie at rest in their graves, for seeing both were sinners together, both must be sufferers together.[24]

Among the heresies that teach the soul's annihilation, Edwards found:

> That man had life before God breathed into him, and that which God breathed into him was part of the divine Essence, and shall return into God again [...] That the soul dies with the body, and all things shall have an end, but God only shall remain forever [...] Every creature in the first estate of creation was God, and every creature is God, every creature that hath life and breath being an efflux from God, and shall return into God again, be swallowed up in him as a drop is in the ocean [...] There is no resurrection at all of the bodies of men after this life, nor no heaven nor hell after this life, nor no devils [...] There is no Hell, but in this life, and that's the legal terrours and fears which men have in their consciences.[25]

The heresies identified by Edwards reflected a number of deep-seated concerns in the seventeenth century. For some at least, the extinction of life at the moment of death was a more comforting prospect than eternal punishment in the fires of hell, or even a temporary punishment followed by extinction. The founder of the Muggletonian sect, Lodowick Muggleton (1609–98), spoke passionately of his youthful fear of being cast into hell after his death and there being tormented by the Devil, eternally and without respite. 'These things,' he wrote, 'wrought in my mind exceeding great Fear, and stir'd me up to a more exceeding Righteousness of life, thinking thereby that my Righteous Life would have cast out those tormenting Fears, but it did not.'[26]

In spite of his fears of hell, Muggleton rejected the annihilation of the individual at the time of death and accepted the desirability of some Day of Judgement on which the good would be rewarded and the wicked punished. He and his cousin John Reeve (1608–58) declared themselves to be the Lord's last two witnesses and prophets (Rev. 11.1–14), thus ensuring salvation to those who believed their teachings and damnation to those who did not. This had the additional benefit of ensuring their own salvation as well, thus mitigating Muggleton's own fears of hell, if not the fears of those not persuaded by his and Reeve's prophetic pretensions. For the unpersuaded, little mercy would be shown. Their *Joyful News from Heaven* brought no joy to the damned. Hell and its devils would be in the very bodies of the wicked. These hellish corpses, they wrote,

> shall be fiery bodies, of spiritual darknesse, yea bodies of all unrighteousnesse, having all their wicked deeds of their former bodies conveyed into these bodies, as fewell to kindle the fire of new sorrows [...] so their bodies shall be their Kingdome of Hell, and their proud spirits, that had pleasure in unrighteousnesse, shall be the Devils; that shall be barr'd in close prisoners within their bodies [...] then [...] shall their spirits and bodies burn together like a flame of fire, that is all dark as pitch, they never stirring from their place of resurrection.[27]

For those mortalists who argued for the annihilation of the individual soul at death, there was no difference between animals and humans. Ecclesiastes 3.19–20 was a favourite biblical text:

> For the fate of humans and the fate of animals is the same; as one dies, so dies the other. They all have the same breath, and humans have no advantage over the animals; for all is vanity. All go to one place; all are from the dust, and all turn to ash again.

Such plebeian materialism was however often uneasily combined with a pantheism that found the divine in everything. Thus, the independent preacher

Richard Coppin (*fl. c.*1645–59) found God in all things: 'The same God which dwels in one dwels in another, even in all; and in the same fullness as he in one, he is in everyone.'[28] The Ranter Joseph Salmon (*fl.* 1647–56) believed that 'God is that pure and perfect being in whom we all are, move and live; that secret blood, breath and life, that silently courseth through the hidden veins and close arteries of the whole creation.'[29]

It is difficult to discern the specific sources of the pantheism of the English radicals. But they were tapping into traditions of Christian mysticism. Many works of religion focused on the 'inner life' were published in the 1640s, any of which might have played a role in the development of pantheism. Translations of some of the works of the Dutch founder of the Family of Love, Hendrik Niclaes (*c.*1502–*c.*1580), began to be published from 1646. From 1645, the better-known books of the Lutheran mystic Jacob Boehme (1575–1624) appeared in English translation. A year later, Nicholas of Cusa's (*c.*1400–64) *The Vision of God* was published in English, followed by the late fourteenth-century mystical work *Theologia Germanica* and the Lutheran mystic Valentine Weigel's *The Vision of God*, both in 1648. In contrast to those Christian traditions that emphasised the qualitative distinction between God and the world – the consequence of God's having created the world out of nothing – the Christian mystical tradition, drawing on the Neoplatonism of Plotinus (204–70 CE), emphasised the participation of the world and the soul in the divine – the result of seeing these as having emanated from and thus still being part of the divine. The eschatological consequence of this was that eternal life was a reabsorption of the soul after death into the divine, whence it originally came.

We can also look to such mystical writings as the sources, directly or indirectly, of radical views of heaven and hell. For members of the Family of Love and for Boehme and Weigel, heaven and hell were not in the hereafter but in the here and now. Such views were common among the English radicals. For the Ranter William Bond (*fl.* 1650s), for example:

> There was neither heaven nor hell except in a man's conscience, for if he had a good fortune and did live well, that was heaven: and if he lived poor and miserable, that was hell, for then he would die like a cow or a horse.[30]

That God was everywhere also led to doubts about a localised heaven. The Ranter Jacob Bauthumley (1613–92), in his *The Light and Dark Sides of God* (1650), claimed to be able to make little sense of God as dwelling in a localised heaven, seeing him rather as an omnipresent spirit 'in low and dark appearances, as well as in the most glorious'. And his idea of a God as equally in everything drove his mortalism: 'I am willing,' he declared,

> to let fall any carnall apprehension of a visible or corporeal enjoyment of God, or any expectation of a happy condition out of God after this life and dayes are ended, being willing to resign and give up to God what he is in me in flesh, that so God may be all in all.[31]

That we, as human beings, are all 'of one piece' and not composed of a mortal body and an immortal soul is a relatively modern idea, often aligned with an implicit scientific materialism. It is tempting to see the radical mortalists of the sixteenth and seventeenth centuries as precursors of it, as evidence of the way in which the Reformation was paving the way for modernity. But their materialism was often united to their pantheism. Spirit and matter, God and nature commingled. They often looked back to biblical images of the unity of the person rather than forward to science. Their doctrines, like their religious allegiances, were fluid. This is especially well exemplified in Laurence Clarkson (1615–67) – an Anglican, a Presbyterian, a Dipper, a Seeker, a Ranter and finally a Muggletonian. On the one hand, he appeared to be a committed materialist. The body, he wrote, after it is laid in its grave, 'is buried in its heaven, glory and happiness, where it shall rot and consume in its own nature for ever and ever'.[32] On the other hand, he also used the typical mystical image of the spirit returning into the ocean of the divine whence it first came:

> even as a stream from the Ocean was distinct in itself while it was a stream, but when returned to the Ocean, was therein swallowed and become one with the Ocean; so the spirit of man while in the body, was distinct from God, but when death came it returned to God, and so became one with God, yea God itself.[33]

A sage from Malmesbury, a Leveller and a poet

Mortalism allied with materialism was not merely the prerogative of Reformed radical riff-raff. It also engaged some of the most respected minds of the seventeenth century. The mortalism of the philosopher from Malmesbury, Thomas Hobbes (1588–1679), for example, did arise from his materialism. For Hobbes, the notion of the soul as a substance incorporeal was a nonsense. Because, according to him, 'substance' and 'body' meant the same thing, then '*Substance incorporeall* are words which, when they are joined together, destroy one another, as if a man should say an *Incorporeall Body*.'[34] Moreover, he viewed the notion of the soul's existence independently of the body as the cause of religious errors – of the doctrine of eternal torments, of the ghosts of the dead walking abroad, of exorcisms, of prayers to the saints, of indulgences and of Purgatory – 'of exemption for a time, or for ever, from the fire of Purgatory, wherein these Incorporeall Substances are pretended by burning to be cleansed, and made fit for Heaven.'[35]

Crucial to Hobbes's critique of the soul was his denial of its *natural* immortality. That the souls of men were substances distinct from their bodies that subsisted after death by virtue of their intrinsic nature was, Hobbes argued, a disease caught by the Church from the Greeks. For Hobbes, Scripture was against any notion of natural immortality. According to the Scriptures, he wrote, 'soul' and 'life' meant the same thing. Thus 'eternal life' could only mean the revivifying of the body on the Day of Resurrection. Immortality was not the soul's natural right, but a supernatural divine gift conferred upon the bodies of the elect in a future time.

This eschatology played a central role in the political theory of his *Leviathan* (1651), for which Hobbes is best remembered. For Hobbes, the Kingdom of God can only be a kingdom on this earth. The biblical type of this kingdom was the civil kingdom inaugurated by God in the covenant made between him and the people of Israel. Moreover, it was one in which ecclesiastical power on the one hand and civil power on the other could not be separated. Thus, Hobbes's interpretation of the biblical notion of the Kingdom of God as an earthly kingdom under the rule of one sovereign with no distinction between his spiritual and temporal powers was a direct criticism, not only of the Catholic Church's belief that *it* was the existing Kingdom of God, but also of its belief that the Kingdom of God was a spiritual and not a temporal matter. Thus, as J. G. A. Pocock writes,

> The tactic of combining apocalyptic with mortalism served [...] to destroy the claim that the Church possessed the keys to an individual's salvation at the hour of his death; he could be saved or damned only by an action

> which God was to take in the future, and the Church was merely a community of faithful expectant of that future act.[36]

The denial of an intermediate state together with an emphasis on the coming Kingdom of God served also as a critique of the Calvinist view that the Kingdom of God had begun with the resurrection of Christ, and that, consequently, the Calvinists, as the representatives of the true Kingdom of God on earth, had authority over civil sovereigns. Against the Calvinists, Hobbes argued that the Kingdom of God did not begin with Christ's resurrection, but would do so only on the Day of Judgement. For Hobbes, therefore, both Catholic and Presbyterian doctrines of God's Kingdom were designed to usurp legitimate sovereign power. The sovereignty of the king was a precursor of the sovereignty of Christ when he returned to earth to usher in the Kingdom of God. The resurrected elect would not be carried from earth into heaven. Rather, on this earth, Christ in his risen body would reign forever over the elect into an infinite future. On that day:

> the Faithfull shall rise again, with glorious and spirituall Bodies, and bee his Subjects in that his Kingdome [...] That they shall neither marry, nor be given in marriage, nor eate and drink, as they did in their natural bodies; but live for ever in their individual persons.[37]

Like the faithful, the wicked too would rise on the Day of Judgement to be punished, both physically and spiritually, in the sight of their sovereign. The wicked would be in the same state as they were after the sin of Adam. They would marry, be given in marriage and reproduce as now. But they would also face the certainty of a second and eternal death: 'For though the Scripture bee clear for an universall Resurrection; yet wee do not read, that to any of the Reprobate is promised an Eternall life.'[38]

Hobbes was hard put to avoid those scriptural passages that implied everlasting torments in eternal fire to be the fate of the damned. However, as we will see later, he foreshadowed John Locke's solution to the same quandary by arguing that everlasting fire does not entail the eternal survival of those within it. Although the fire is everlasting, he argued, 'it cannot thence be inferred that hee who shall be cast into that fire, or be tormented with those torments, shall endure, and resist them so, as to be eternally burnt, and tortured, and yet never be destroyed nor die.'[39]

This notion of the ultimate annihilation of the wicked was philosophically made possible by Hobbes's denial of *natural* immortality and his understanding of it as a supernatural gift. Thus the wicked could – logically would – die a second death. Although he intimated that a sovereign could justly condemn the wicked to eternal torments, theologically he saw the final annihilation of the wicked as a result of the mercy of God. It was this concept of God's mercy that was at the heart of all attempts from the time of Hobbes onwards to mitigate the idea of the eternity of hell's torments. It seems hard to say, he wrote,

> that God who is the Father of Mercies, that doth in Heaven and earth all that hee will; that hath the hearts of all men in his disposing; that worketh in men both to doe, and to will; and without whose free gift a man hath neither inclination to good, nor repentance of evill, should punish mens transgressions without any end of time, and with all the extremity of torture, that men can imagine, and more.[40]

Eight years before the publication of Hobbes's *Leviathan*, the mortalist position which Hobbes exemplified had been publicised in a 1643 work by the Leveller Richard Overton (*fl.* 1640–63). 'All is vanity' (Eccles. 3.19) again provided the proof text. Philosophically, Overton attempted to reduce the concept of the immortality of the soul to absurdity. But the overall weight of his argument for the soul's mortality was scriptural and within the framework of the Christian doctrines of Creation, Fall and redemption. Crucial to his argument was Genesis 2.7: 'Then the Lord God [...] breathed into his nostrils the breath of life; and the man became a living soul.' For Overton, as for Hobbes after him, this could not mean 'an Angelical Entitie; a supernatural, spiritual, infinite Existence to be couched in the flesh, or mens corpulency; whose being doth not depend upon it', but rather a living being who, as such, would have lived forever had he not sinned.[41] Thus, for Overton, the Fall of Adam and Eve did not entail only the mortality of the body but of the whole being. Moreover, he maintained, on the assumption of the immortality of the soul, no sense could be made of the resurrection of the body on the Day of Judgement. As he put it in his typically exuberant way:

> If the Soul (as they say) be the very life [...] and the body but its instrument; then the body now hath no more life in it, then when it is reduced

> to the earth; but is as dead as a dore-naile: And so at the Resurrection cannot be raised from death; and the union of it to the Soul at the Resurrection they Fabulate on, is but an addition of corpulency or gross matter to the Soul which in truth is no Resurrection at all from the dead [...] For Resurrection from the death is not the addition of gross matter to life; but the Restoration of life from death.[42]

It was virtually impossible in the seventeenth century for the orthodox, whether Catholic or Protestant, to contemplate the possibility that sound Christian doctrine should not include the belief in the immortality of the soul. There was a firmly held conviction that the denial of the soul's immortality was the thin end of a wedge that would lead to the collapse of, so to say, civilisation as they knew it. The pugnacious Anglican Alexander Ross (1591–1654) declared:

> These Arabian Pygmies will never be able with such engines to overthrow the soules immortalitie, which is the strong fort and Citadell of every good Christian in his afflictions. Let there be but way given to this doctrine of the Saducees, we must bid farewell to lawes and civility, nay to Religion and Christianity.[43]

They were better suited, he decided, to dwell in the bodies of beasts than in their own.

In their denial of the immortality of the soul and their advocacy of the psycho-physical unity of the human individual, Hobbes and Overton saw themselves as endorsing Scripture against philosophy. Their scriptural interpretations should not be read as a disguised and dishonest philosophical naturalism. The same must be said of the mortalism of John Milton (1608–74). Milton's conviction that individuals shall only rise on the Day of Resurrection was totally based on Scripture. It was clearly stated for the first time in his *De doctrina Christiana* (On Christian doctrine, *c.*1658–60). As with Overton, so also with Milton, Genesis 2.7 was central. Man became a living soul, he wrote,

> whence it may be inferred [...] that man is a living being, intrinsically and properly one and individual, not compound or separable, not, according to the common opinion, made up and framed of two different natures, as of soul and body.[44]

'Flying like an eagle in the air'

All my disciples must be airy,
And dance as nimble as a Fairy,
Must never think of sordid Dying,
But practice must the Art of Flying.

Anon. (1701)

As a result of the Protestant commitment to the principle of *sola scriptura* (Scripture alone), Protestant mortalism moved within a biblical space. The Bible provided the unity within Protestantism, but it also provoked its diversity, not least in views of the afterlife. This was because the only limit on Protestant readings of the Bible was the imagination of its interpreters. Nowhere was this better exemplified than in the case of John Asgill (1659–1738), lawyer, Member of Parliament and (very) amateur theologian. On 18 December 1707, Asgill was expelled from the House of Commons for blasphemy contained in a book that he had published anonymously in 1700. It was a work that provoked consternation, outrage and, as the verse above suggests, not a little mirth. As Daniel Defoe remarked of it in 1704: 'When Men Pore upon the Sacred Mysteries of Religion with the Mathematical Engines of Reason, they make such incoherent stuff of it, as would make one pity them.'[45] The book was entitled *An argument proving that according to the covenant of eternal life revealed in the Scriptures, man may be translated from hence into that eternal life without passing through death, although the humane nature of Christ himself could not be thus translated till he had passed through death.*

According to Asgill, as a result of the Fall of Man, death reigned from Adam until the time of Christ with two exceptions – the Old Testament worthies Enoch and Elijah, who were translated to heaven prior to their deaths (see Plate 23 [BW]). Unlike them, Christ had died. But in his resurrection, he had broken the Law of Death. Having risen, Christ 'stood perfectly qualified to make his *Exit* by way of Translation [...] And thereupon God sent him down one of the Chariots of Heaven to convey him thither.'[46]

The remarkable consequence of Christ's death, resurrection and ascension was that death was no longer necessary for mortals. Those who have faith that Christ has overcome the inexorability of death need not die but can be translated directly to heaven. On the face of it then, since Christ's ascension, death ought to have been abolished. Asgill's explanation for its continuation was a psychological one. In part, men died because they expected to; in part, too, men died because of their fear of death. For those who, like Asgill, had faith in translation, the precedent of death was broken, the fear of death removed. Thus, he declared:

> I shall not go hence *by returning unto the Dust* [...] But that I shall *make* my Exit by way of *Translation*, which I claim as a dignity belonging to that Degree in the Science of Eternal Life, of which I profess my self a graduat, according to the true intent and meaning of the Covenant of Eternal Life revealed in the Scriptures. And if after this, I die like other Men, I declare my self to die of no religion.[47]

From his time on, he believed, translation would be the rule rather than the exception.

But what of those who had died or would die without the benefit of Asgill's faith in translation? Like Overton, Milton and Hobbes, Asgill denied the immateriality and immortality of the soul. Thus, there was no conscious life after death. Asgill's eschatology, however, blended materialism and pantheism. Those who died without faith in translation, he maintained, neither died nor slept after death. Rather, their bodies were reabsorbed into matter, their spirits into God. The body was left to the elements out of which it was first composed. The individual spirit surrendered itself 'into the Ocean of Life, from whence it first flowed', as rivers are 'merged in the Ocean of their original Fountain'.[48]

That said, unlike the radical sectarians, Asgill did not envisage this reabsorption of individual spirits into God to last forever. On the contrary; it would last only until the Day of Resurrection. Then, God would reunite every spirit with its own body. After the just had risen, there would still be a period of time for perfecting the belief in translation. When both the resurrected and those that were still alive on the Day of Resurrection had learnt this faith, the general resurrection of the dead would follow, the righteous 'to be caught up together in the Air'.[49]

Asgill was aware that his work would be controversial. Whoever thinks anything within it unfair to God or man, he wrote, 'let him, or her, burn this Book, and cast a Stone at him that wrote it'.[50] There were indeed many willing to take up Asgill's challenge to burn his work (literally) and to bury him beneath an avalanche of stones (metaphorically, at least). He was denounced for his pride and conceit and lampooned mercilessly. Even if on occasion, perhaps not untypically for members of the legal profession, the pleasure he derived from the presentation of an argument exceeded the genuineness of his belief in it, he was without doubt seriously committed to the unique centrepiece of his theology – translation.

England in the early eighteenth century was neither particularly intolerant nor especially religious. But Asgill signalled to many all the dangers of idiosyncratic scripturalism. His jocularity, his inwardly guided interpretation of the Scriptures, his mortalist tendencies and, above all, his arrogant confidence in his truth about the afterlife – translation into heaven: these were all frightening echoes of a world only recently turned right-side up from the terrors of sectarianism and the fears of papal domination. Parliament returned Asgill to the debtors' prison from which it had called him. There he remained for the next 30 years of his life. No doubt to his eternal chagrin, John Asgill died, untranslated, in 1738.

Variations on an Arabian theme

John Asgill was not alone in his eschatological eccentricities. It was perhaps inevitable that the Protestant principle of *sola scriptura* should foster eccentric theologies, particularly among those laypersons, like Asgill, who came to their Bibles without the theological training to keep them within the limits of orthodoxy. But even the scholarly elite were not immune to idiosyncratic readings of the Bible. Henry Dodwell's (1641–1711) variations on a mortalist theme were met with as much astonishment as John Asgill's, not least because he was renowned for his scholarship and learning. His unusual ideas were not restricted to eschatology alone. His defence of the uses of instrumental music in public worship to counter the influence of devils on the spinal marrow of human beings, along with his inclination to believe that the spinal marrow when decomposed became a serpent, were, to say the least, whimsical, even for his own times. His book on the mortality of the soul in 1706, *An Epistolary Discourse Proving [...] That the Soul is a Principle Naturally Mortal*, brought almost universal opprobrium upon him. The Anglican vicar of Greenwich, John Turner, was particularly severe. He likened Dodwell to a glutton with a bad digestion, who must either vomit up what he has eaten or 'keep the undigested Load to breed filthy Humours and bad Distempers, to his own great Uneasiness and Vexation.'[51] A little unkind, perhaps! But the modern reader, like Dodwell's contemporaries, will find Dodwell's arguments difficult to swallow and his literary style difficult to digest.

He deserves his place in this discussion not least because his position on mortalism was a unique one, making it difficult to determine whether he was a soul-sleeper, a soul-denier or something else altogether. Tentatively, his complex eschatology can be reconstructed along the following lines: God created Adam out of the dust and added his *afflatus* – his breath (*pneuma*) of life – so that man became a living being. He had a natural immortality. God also added his divine breath (*pnoe*) to man. At the Fall, the *afflatus* was lost and man lost his natural immortality. But man retained the divine breath. Thus his immortality was conditional on God's continuing his breathing. This conditional immortality was confirmed at the time of baptism.

The consequence of this was that persons, made immortal by the divine breath, continued to exist immediately after death. The breath of God, declared Dodwell in a later work, 'seems to be the Principle that enables Humane Souls to subsist in Hades in their separate State.'[52] Dodwell also had a unique take on human destiny after the Day of Judgement. Those who had heard the gospel and responded to it would be raised on the Last Day and granted eternal happiness. Those who had heard it and rejected it would incur eternal punishment. This was Protestant orthodoxy. However, those who had remained ignorant of the gospel, having been rewarded or punished in the intermediate state for their merits or demerits, would be raised on the Day of Judgement only to be annihilated shortly afterwards (or perhaps not be raised at all). So the heathen, deserving neither heaven nor hell, would have the divine breath withdrawn from them because there cannot be 'any Third Eternal State suitable to the Nature of a Rational Soul.'[53] Just to confuse matters a little further, however, Dodwell did not expect that, on the Day of Judgement, there would actually be any (or many) who were ignorant of the gospel. For in a revised version of the doctrine of the harrowing of hell (which had been expunged from Protestant theologies) he suggested that all would have an opportunity in the time between death and the Last Judgement to accept or reject Christ:

> on supposition that they, who never heard of the Gospel in this Life, may have it Preached to them in Hades, and may there be admitted

> to Baptism [...] This will qualifie the compliers for the Rewards of Heaven, and expose those, who shall prove Refractory, to a just Sentence of partaking in the Fire prepared for the Devil and his Angels.[54]

In his assertion of the natural mortality of the soul, Dodwell was clearly aligned with the soul-deniers. But his commitment to the intermediate state between death and the Last Judgement through his assertion of its survival by the divine breath was quite out of keeping with the mortalist tradition. He was nonetheless accused of being a soul-denier, even though he had specifically rejected the error of the Arabians (as Eusebius had called the mortalists).[55] He had done so, Dodwell later claimed, to distinguish himself from two latter-day 'Arabians', namely Henry Layton (1622–1705) and William Coward (*c*.1657–1725).

The most prolific of the English mortalists, the lawyer Henry Layton published (anonymously) some 14 pamphlets from the early 1690s until his death that, while endorsing the notion of a general resurrection of the dead, had asserted the mortality of the soul primarily on physiological grounds. Man, like plants, insects and animals, may perform 'all his natural functions', he wrote, 'by the like means of a material spirit, inspiring and acting the proper organs which God hath made apt for such purposes'.[56] He found no verse in the Bible supporting the natural immortality of the soul. Thus, on the grounds of Scripture and reason, souls literally died, although metaphorically they slept. 'Men die', he declared, 'thus they rest, and believers sleep in Jesus, till the time of the restitution of all things' when men will be restored to their former beings.[57]

Similarly, the surgeon William Coward wrote a series of works from 1702 to 1706 in which he argued for the mortality of the soul on philosophical and scriptural grounds and declared that the immortality of the soul was a legacy of the heathenish philosophy of Pythagoras, Plato and Socrates: 'the Ground only of many Absurd; and Superstitious Opinions, Abominable to the Reformed Churches and Derogatory in General to True Christianity'.[58] 'Does man die like a brute beast?' he asked. Yes, he replied,

> in respect of their End in this Life [...] But then Man has thus Prerogative, or Praeeminence above a Brute, That he will be rais'd to Life again, and be made Partaker of eternal Happiness or Misery in the World to come.[59]

The resurrection of John Locke

England's greatest philosopher, John Locke (1632–1704), was the last of the major seventeenth-century supporters of mortalism and the link to its eighteenth-century proponents. In contrast to Overton, Milton, Hobbes or Muggleton, Locke nowhere said clearly that the soul slept or died between death and resurrection, and consequently his mortalism has to be read between the lines. Thus, Locke did not deny the immortality of the soul. He did, however, suggest that men could not *know* that the soul was immaterial; nor could they *know* that God might have merely joined to matter the capacity to think.

More importantly, for Locke, personal or self-consciousness was the key to personal identity regardless of whether this was embedded in body or soul. The afterlife did not depend either on the immortality of the soul or on the continuity of the body before death with the resurrection body. Thus, he argued, we can conceive that, on the Day of Resurrection, the same person would be rewarded or punished regardless of the substance with which they would be united on that day:

> The Sentence that shall be justified by the consciousness all Persons shall have, that they *themselves* in what Bodies soever they appear or what Substances soever that consciousness adheres to, are the *same* [persons] that committed those Actions, and deserve that punishment for them.[60]

This left Locke open to criticism by the orthodox from both directions – from those who believed he was denying the immortality of the soul and from those who saw him as denying the necessity of the resurrection of the *same* body as that which had died.

In ways even more complicated than they thought, both groups of critics were right. Thus, in his notebook 'Adversaria theologica' (1694) Locke argued that the Apostle Paul made no distinction between soul and body, 'material & immaterial as if one died & the other continued living[,] the one was raised & the other not[,] but he speaks of the whole man as dyeing & the whole man as raised.'[61] And he suggested that it appears that when Paul spoke of a spiritual body and an animal body, he was suggesting that 'matter is capable of animality & spirituality [of life and thought].'[62] Little doubt, then, that Locke was here denying the immortality of the soul.

This becomes even clearer in Locke's *The Reasonableness of Christianity, as Delivered in the Scriptures* (1695). This began with a discussion of what it was that Adam had lost in the Fall, namely, the immortality with which God had conditionally created him: 'the state of Paradise was a state of Immortality, of Life without end, which he lost that very day he did eat.'[63] Loss of immortality was the consequence of Adam's sin for all those that followed. Jesus Christ rescued all humankind from this state of mortality to immortality 'which they will receive again at the Resurrection.'[64] This immortality, however, as we will see, belonged only to the righteous.

Locke's views on the Day of Resurrection were fleshed out in his 'Resurrectio et quae sequuntur' (*c.*1699). Locke was here well beyond worries about whether the dead would be raised in their *same* bodies. Out of his reading of the Scriptures, he concluded that there would be two sequential resurrections. The first (following 1 Cor. 15) would be of the righteous. These would rise in *spiritual* bodies and would be 'caught up in the clouds to meet the lord in the air'. The second resurrection would be of the wicked in physical (certainly destructible) bodies before Christ handed over the kingdom to his father. They would be cast into hellfire to be tormented. But Locke did not see them as suffering for eternity. Punishment is everlasting, he wrote, only 'as long as the subject it affects endures.'[65]

The unquenchable fire referred literally, he went on, to the fires of Gehenna outside Jerusalem, which burnt unceasingly to destroy the carcases of beasts and other filth. Yet it did not follow

> that the bodys that were burnt in it were never consumed[,] only that the worms that gnawd & the fire that burnt them was constant & never ceased till they were destroyd. Soe though the fire was not put out yet the chaff was burnt up & consumed.[66]

Locke was unsure how long the punishment of the wicked would last. However:

> that it shall be excessively terrible by its duration as well as sharpness the current of the Scripture seems to manifest, onely if one may conjecture it seems to be before our Saviours delivering up the Kingdome to his father.[67]

The triumph of soul-denying

By the end of the first decade of the eighteenth century, the intellectual space within which the mortalist debate was to be conducted from that time on was in place. The mortalism of the sixteenth century was dominated by those who, accepting the immortality of the soul, imagined the period between death and the Day of Judgement in terms of its sleep. By the end of the seventeenth century, soul-sleeping was in decline and soul-denying in the ascendant. Soul-denying mortalism, arising from the rejection of any natural immortality of the soul, was to become dominant in the eighteenth century. This was driven partly as the consequence of emerging philosophically 'materialist' views of the human that saw no necessity to embrace the existence of incorporeal entities like the soul. It was also determined by a reading of the Bible that found scriptural testimony as a whole in favour of the psycho-physical unity of the individual and against his duality. As the scientist and theologian Joseph Priestley (1733–1804) summed it up in 1782:

> [T]here is no instance, either in the Old or New Testament, of this soul being supposed to be in one place and the body in another. They are always conceived to go together, so that the perceptive and thinking power could not, in fact, be considered by the sacred writers as any other than a *property* of a living man, and therefore as what ceased of course when the man was dead, and could not be revived but with the revival of the body.[68]

Priestley and his mortalist colleagues were pretty right on this. Modern biblical interpretation would generally agree that there is no doctrine of the immortality of the soul within the New Testament.[69]

In the nineteenth century, with the resurgence of apocalypticism, mortalism found a place in those Christian groups whose intellectual roots were not in modern scientific materialism but in the Radical Reformation. As we might expect, mortalism particularly found a place among those groups that expected the imminent return of Christ, notably the Seventh-day Adventists, the Christadelphians and the Jehovah's Witnesses.[70] However, mainstream Protestant theology of the twentieth century did not endorse mortalist views. Nor was it driven by expectations of the immediacy of the Last Judgement. Nevertheless, its tendency to exalt the opposition between faith and philosophy, Scripture and reason, drove it away from the philosophical notion of the immortality of the soul. Added to that, an emphasis on life immediately after death inclined it towards a focus on the biblical ideal of the unity of the individual and the resurrection of the *whole person* on the Day of Judgement. This is exemplified in arguably the greatest twentieth-century theologian, Karl Barth (1886–1968):

> And now the Christian man looks forward. What is the meaning of the Christian hope in this life? A life after death? An event apart from death? A tiny soul which, like a butterfly, flutters away above the grave and is still preserved somewhere, in order to live on immortally? That was how the heathen looked on the life after death. But that is not the Christian hope. 'I believe in the resurrection of the body.' Body in the Bible is quite simply man, man, moreover under the sign of sin, man laid low. And to this man it is said, Thou shalt rise again. Resurrection means not the continuation of this life, but life's completion.[71]

Ironically, the modern popular afterlife did not follow Barth or any of his Protestant colleagues in this understanding of the afterlife. As we will see in the next chapters, the modern afterlife eschewed the resurrection of the body and endorsed an ongoing life of the spirit, which, as Barth put it, did flutter away upwards like a butterfly to live on immortally.

Chapter Six

The Saved and the Damned

> There is a great Gulfe set that is by a divine decree stablished and fixed, a mans state is set for eternity, and there is no longer any hope of a change, a passage there is from death to life, but there is none hereafter; for there is a great Gulfe that God has set between, that there can be no passage, no change of a mans condition, there can be no translation.
>
> William Strong, *The Worm That Dyeth Not* (1672)

The finality of death

One of the chief attractions of mortalism was its rejection of Purgatory. The German Socinian mortalist Joachim Stegmann (1595–1633) argued that any notion of an intermediate state between death and the Day of Judgement opened the door for Catholic abuses: '[Catholics] believe in effect that the dead live [...] Now this is the foundation not only of Purgatory, but also of that horrible Idolatry practised among the Papists, whilest they invocate the Saints that are dead.'[1] The Cambridge Platonist Henry More (1614–87) was no mortalist. But he was in no doubt that the rise of mortalism was due to the 'affrightful Figment of Purgatory'. The great mischief of Purgatory, he declared, is that it created a strong temptation to reject all of religion, 'or any state at all of the Soul after death, but that she is mortal and perishes.'[2]

The orthodox Protestant view on the destiny of souls between death and the Last Judgement was to tread a middle way between Purgatory on the one hand and mortalism on the other. It was a binary view of the afterlife, with heaven or hell the only two options. The delights of heaven or the horrors of hell were to be had immediately after death and before the Last Day. It endorsed both the immortality of the soul and the final resurrection of the body. The Protestant perspective was exemplified in the so-called Westminster Confession of Faith, ratified by the English

Parliament in 1648. Chapter 32, 'Of the state of men after death, and of the resurrection of the dead', reads:

> The bodies of men after death, return to the dust, and see corruption: but their souls (which neither die nor sleep) having immortal subsistence, immediately return to God who gave them: the souls of the righteous being then made perfect in holiness, are received into the highest heavens, where they behold the face of God in light and glory, waiting for the full redemption of their bodies: and the souls of the wicked are cast into hell, where they remain in torments and utter darkness, reserved for the judgement of the great day. Besides these two places, for souls separated from their bodies, the Scripture acknowledgeth none.[3]

In effect, the Last Judgement had become something of a formality. With the rejection of Purgatory, there was no longer any hope of any post-mortem mitigation of sin. As William Strong (d.1654) indicated in the passage with which this chapter began, the ultimate destiny of souls was fixed at death. No 'inward' change was possible for those suffering in hell. Indeed, not only could the damned not improve their state, the wicked actually became worse. The pains of hell, declared E[dward] W[arren] in 1667,

> would provoke the wicked to rage and swell, with anger and impatience; to fret and fume against the providence of *God*, and to curse and blaspheme the Majesty of Heaven for afflicting them; and so will sink them lower, and Chain them faster into the sulphureous Lake and flaming dungeon, rather than any way capacitate them for deliverance.[4]

The wicked, in short, were 'Unalterably confirmed and established in the Habits of sin', declared the Anglican clergyman William Lupton (1676–1726) in a sermon preached before the University of Oxford on 24 November 1706. They deserved punishment for as long as they continued so. And that, he proclaimed, 'is for ever and ever'.[5]

The Westminster Confession of Faith reflected the eschatology of John Calvin. As we noted in the last chapter, he vehemently rejected both soul-sleeping and soul-denying for a commitment to the conscious existence of the soul after death, awaiting its reunion with its body on the Last Day. As a consequence, there was a tension in Calvin's theology. On the one hand, in emphasising the conscious existence of the immortal soul after death, he granted it the full vision of God in Christ. The dead, in Abraham's Bosom, 'enjoy God fully without weariness.'[6] There seems little to be added on the Last Day. Yet Calvin wanted also to argue that, although elect souls did enjoy the vision of God immediately after death, they did not yet do so *perfectly*. Thus, he declared,

> We are more miserable than all men if there is no Resurrection, because, although we are happy before the Resurrection, we are not happy without the Resurrection. For we say that the spirits of saints are happy in this, that they rest in the hope of a blessed Resurrection, which they could not do, were all this blessedness to perish.[7]

It is a case, perhaps, of both fulfilment and expectation. However that may be, Calvin does not underplay the significance of the Last Judgement. On that Last Day, Christ will *finally* separate the elect from the reprobate:

> And he will appear to all with the ineffable majesty of his Kingdom, with the glow of immortality, with the boundless power of divinity, with a guard of angels. From thence we are commanded to await him as our Redeemer on that day when he will separate the lambs from the goats, the elect from the reprobate. No one – living or dead – shall escape his judgement. The sound of the trumpet will be heard from the ends of the earth, and by it all will be summoned before his judgment seat, both those still alive at that day and those whom death had previously taken from the company of the living.[8]

Justified and predestined

There is yet another critical tension within the eschatology of the Magisterial Protestant Reformation of Luther and Calvin that has far more significant ramifications.[9] This tension is present within Protestant thought in particular, although it has resonated within the history of Christian thought at least since the time of Augustine. As we have seen, the Christian doctrine of the afterlife served, among other things, to redress the injustice on this side of the grave by justice on the other. Put simply, because there was no apparent connection between virtue and reward, vice and punishment, in this life, God rewarded the virtuous for their good works and punished the vicious for theirs in the next. The *iustitia Dei* (here the 'justice of God') thus consisted in God's rewarding people for what they were entitled to as a consequence of their actions in this life. In short, men were saved or justified by their merits or works. As we noted in Chapter 4, late medieval Catholicism gave the not unwarranted impression that salvation was for sale and could be purchased for a price.

On the other hand, there had been an alternative understanding of the *iustitia Dei* within the Christian West at least since the time of Augustine. This was to the effect that salvation was not the consequence of any accumulation of merit on the part of men, but a result of God's grace. The *iustitia Dei* is the 'righteousness of God', by which he justifies sinners and imparts righteousness to them. The good works that follow, which earn salvation, are nevertheless God's, not man's. As Augustine put it:

> It follows then, dearly beloved, beyond all doubt, that as your good life is nothing else than God's grace, so also the eternal life which is the recompense of a good life is the grace of God; moreover, it is gratuitously [freely] given.[10]

Luther's concerns about salvation by works were driven in part by the abuses within the Catholic penitential system. But they were embedded in his familiarity with the Augustinian theological tradition. Luther believed that, if merit were a precondition of salvation, and if God judged on the basis of merit, all humanity was doomed, and himself before all others. 'Although I lived blamelessly as a monk,' he wrote, 'I felt that I was a sinner with an uneasy conscience before God; nor was I able to trust that I had pleased him by my satisfaction [works].'[11] And then he realised, he tells us, that the *iustitia Dei* (here the 'righteousness of God') consisted in 'that by which the righteous lives by the gift of God.'[12] Thus, the God of Christianity was not a harsh God of justice who punished the sinner *according to* his demerits, but a merciful and gracious God who bestowed righteousness upon the sinner as a free gift *in spite of* his demerits. As Alister McGrath puts it: 'the "righteousness of God" is not a righteousness which judges whether or not we have met the precondition for justification, but the righteousness which is given to us so that we may meet the precondition.'[13] Men remain sinners, but in the eyes of God, they are righteous (*simul iustus et peccator*). For Augustine, man became righteous in justification. But for Luther, man becomes, if anything, more aware of his own sinfulness. Christians, wrote Luther,

> are always aware of their sin and seek righteousness from God in accordance with his mercy. And for this very reason, they are regarded as righteous by God. Thus in their own eyes (and in reality!) they are sinners; but in the eyes of God they are righteous [...] by the imputation of a merciful God.[14]

As for good works, they were no longer a cause of justification, but a consequence of it. In short, regardless of good works or ill, men were saved by God's grace. Little wonder then that the Church reacted so vehemently, for Luther had made redundant the whole paraphernalia of the penitential system of late medieval Catholicism – penances, suffrages, indulgences – and the profits generated by them.

Thus, with his doctrine of justification by grace, Luther had created a large gulf between Protestantism and Catholicism. Augustine, and the Western Catholic tradition after him, had understood 'justification' as meaning the sinner's being both declared righteous and *made* righteous (both justified and sanctified). Luther had in effect separated salvation and sanctification. In so doing, he had created a chasm between eschatology and ethics. The good works done by the justified sinner had no relevance to his salvation. Men were saved or not regardless of their deserving to be or not.

This was a chasm made even deeper by the doctrine of predestination. It was one thing to have one's eternal destiny determined during life or at death as a result of God's grace regardless of deserts, but quite another to have it predestined before birth. The consequence of Augustine's account of justification was that, since God had made some righteous and not others, God had preselected those who were to be saved, leaving others to be condemned through their own choices and actions. In short, God had predestined some for salvation, but omitted to save others. Calvin went one step further. God's grace now became above all a function of the divine sovereign will. The consequence of this was that God actively, and apparently quite arbitrarily, predestined some to salvation and *others to damnation*. 'As Scripture, then, clearly shows,' wrote Calvin,

> we say that God once established by his eternal and unchangeable plan those whom he long before determined once for all to receive into salvation, and those whom, on the other hand, he would devote to destruction. We assert that, with respect to the elect, this plan was founded upon his freely given mercy, without regard to human worth; but by his just and

> incomprehensible judgment he has barred the door of life to those whom he has given over to damnation.[15]

In marked contrast to that understanding of the *iustitia Dei* that would see God bound to judge persons according to a principle of lawfulness outside of himself (and thus according to their merits), Calvin's God was not bound by anything external to himself, for then, he believed, the Creator would be bound by his creation. On the contrary, God could do whatever he liked. And, as Calvin recognised, God's devoting to destruction whomever he pleased did appear 'more like the caprice of a tyrant than the lawful sentence of a judge.'[16] However, regardless of how it might appear to us, God's will was for Calvin so much the standard of righteousness that whatever he wills, 'by the very fact that he wills it, must be considered righteous.'[17] So it was the will of God that was the law of all laws, inscrutable as it may be to us. Moreover, since all men inherit the corruption of sin from Adam, 'we can only be odious to God, and that not from any tyrannical cruelty but by the fairest reckoning of justice,' for all are drawn from a corrupt mass.[18] From the perspective of original sin, all men deserve damnation anyway. That at least some are saved, and not all damned, is itself therefore a sign of God's infinite mercy.

Except within an understanding of the human condition as one determined by the original sin of Adam, and of a God who does what he pleases, it is hard to take this seriously. A less pessimistic view of human nature than that of either Luther or Calvin might lead to the conclusion that a God acting according to a law of justice, tempered with mercy, might find reason to grant salvation to most, if not all. Still, granted a pessimistic view, predestination did nonetheless provide a beacon of hope to those who believed that, whatever they did to the good, *they* could never merit salvation. And there is a certain comfort in fatalism, theological or otherwise. The early modern age was a melancholy one. As Robert Burton wrote in his *The Anatomy of Melancholy* in 1621, melancholy was 'a disease so frequent [...] in these our daies, so often happening [...] in our miserable times, as few there are that feele not the smart of it.'[19] Predestination to damnation was perhaps both cause and effect of sad times. Certainly, it provided an additional ground for deep melancholy among those who believed that, whatever *they* did to the good and regardless of their striving, they were inevitably doomed to the eternal torments of hell. The key point is that a belief in predestination could cut either way: it could increase or alleviate anxiety. This was a conundrum through which Calvinist preachers recognised that they needed to find a way.

The Norfolk Calvinist preacher John Yates (d.1657) was one of the first Protestants to explore this problem. He recognised the danger that the doctrine of predestination held for those who were melancholic. Such people, he declared, are never able to live with their sins when the 'narrow point of reprobation and election' is 'propounded unto their melancholic braines and hearts, and most miserable polluted souls'.[20] He told of a melancholic virtuous gentlewoman, Mary Honeywood, who, doubting her salvation, fell 'into the gulfe of Gods secret counsels', seeking intellectual certainty about that which was beyond that which can be known.[21] Her minister, John Foxe (1516–87), the famous English 'historian' of the Protestant persecutions under the Catholic Queen Mary I, counselled her against going beyond the Scriptures and to trust 'assuredly that shee might conclude her salvation out of Gods word'.[22]

She went way beyond his advice and

> the temptation grew upon her, insomuch that having a *venice glasse* in her hands [...] presently breakes forth into lamentable words: You have often told mee that I must seeke no further than Gods word, but I have been long without comfort, and can indure no longer; therefore if I must be saved, let this glasse be kept from breaking; and so she threw it against the walls [...] yet the Lord that is rich in mercie, having stamped her with the seale of his election, was content to satisfie the languishing soule with a miracle: the glasse rebounds againe, and comes safe unto the ground.[23]

Thus can the doctrine of predestination cause harm to the melancholic soul when wrongly construed. In itself, Yates went on to say,

> it is the most strong rock of assurance, in al storms of temptations that can befall unto bodie or soule; because predestination is Gods immutable will, the cause and rule of all justice, and uttermost of all reason in his workes.[24]

On the face of it, the doctrine of double predestination was hardly an incentive to lead a life of virtue. Because salvation or damnation was an individual's lot regardless of his behaviour in this life, it mattered little how he behaved. The crucial link between morality and eschatology appeared to be irreparably severed. Thus, the possibility of moral libertinism necessitated

Calvinism reinventing the link between between ethics and eternal destiny. It did so in response to the question, 'How can I be assured that I am among the elect and not the reprobate?' This was a question at the very core of predestinarian piety.

The Puritan Stephen Denison (d.1649), minister of the church of St Katharine Cree in London, was a committed predestinarian. Election and reprobation were at the top of his theological agenda. Election, he declared, 'is the eternall and unchangeable decree of God, whereby of his free grace and favour he hath made choice of some rather then of others, to bestow upon them eternall life and happiness'. Reprobation, he continued, is also the eternal decree of God 'whereby he hath rejected others, leaving them in the fall of *Adam*, to their eternall destruction, and that to the praise of his power and justice'.[25] As a consequence, Denison supported the doctrine of limited atonement, namely, that Christ died to save only the elect, and not all persons. As for the elect, they could and would continue to sin. They must nonetheless persevere in faith. This in itself would lead them towards an assurance of their salvation. Perseverance in faith was one sign of their election. Another was good works. 'Faith must be tried by the Fruits: for faith without good works, is but a carkeise of faith [...] For howsoever faith alone doth justifie the person, yet works must necessarily justifie the faith.'[26]

That said, if faith without works was dead, so too was its converse. Thus did good works need to be balanced by the cultivation of inward piety and personal godliness. This was not salvation by works, so much as the *personal conviction* of salvation through the cultivation of inward piety, the maximising of virtue, the minimising of vice and the strong conviction of the different destinies of the godly and the ungodly. As Max Weber (1864–1920) eloquently put it in his *The Protestant Ethic and the Spirit of Capitalism* (1905), this personal conviction 'cannot, as in Catholicism, consist in a gradual accumulation of individual good works to one's credit, but rather in a systematic self-control which at every moment stands before the inexorable alternative, chosen or damned'.[27]

Purgatory revisited

Even so, whether it was a case of salvation by grace or by works, the expectation was that the number of the damned would be far greater than the number of the elect. There were strong biblical grounds for the small proportion that were to be saved. 'Enter through the narrow gate,' declared Jesus,

> for the gate is wide and the road is easy that leads to destruction, and there are many who take it. For the gate is narrow and the road is hard that leads to life, and there are few who find it. (Matt. 7.13–14)

'Many are called,' he said elsewhere, 'but few are chosen' (Matt. 22.14). Augustine had given this his passionate support. Thus, in a letter to a Mauretanian bishop called Optatus in 418 CE, he wrote of the reprobates who

> by an incomparable multitude outnumber those whom God has deigned to predestine as children of promise in the glory of his kingdom, in order that it might be shown, by their very multitude, that the number of those who are most justly damned, whatever it may be, is of no concern with the righteous God.[28]

This was to be the default position in both Catholicism and Protestantism.

Thus, for example, the Jesuit Jeremias Drexel (1581–1638) asserted that the 100,000 million destined for hell would be contained within a cubic German mile at the centre of the earth, where they will be closely thronged together 'like grapes in a wine-press, or salt herrings in a barrel, or bricks in a kiln [...] or like sheep butcher'd in the shambles.'[29] Not to be outdone by any papist, the Copernican and Anglican Tobias Swinden (1659–1719) declared Drexel's calculation 'a poor, mean and narrow Conception both of the numbers of the Damned, and of the Dimensions of Hell.'[30] How infinitely short, he continued, 'is that Computation to those Multitudes who, as many, are set in Opposition by Christ to the few Saints, which, yet no Man can number?'[31] And one of his main reasons for transferring the location of hell from beneath the earth to the sun was that the inside of the earth could not contain the vast number of lapsed angels and the infinite number of the damned.[32] The unfortunately named Puritan Christopher Love (1618–51), in his sermon on the terrors of hell, followed geographers in dividing the world into 31 parts: 19 possessed by the doomed Jews and Turks, seven by the heathen worshipping 'stocks and stones' and similarly destined for hell, and the remainder by papists and Protestants, the former likewise damned.[33]

All this was difficult to square away with the notion of a God who had died on the cross to save mankind from sin. The German philosopher Gottfried Wilhelm Leibniz (1646–1716) analysed the problem clearly in his *Theodicy* in 1709. It is a terrible judgement, he wrote,

> that God, giving his only Son for the whole human race [...] yet saves so few of them and abandons all others to the devil his enemy [...] And this outcome inspires all the more horror, as the sole cause why all these men are wretched to eternity is God's having exposed their parents to a temptation that he knew they would not resist; as this sin is inherent and imputed to men before their will has participated in it; as this hereditary vice impels their will to commit actual sins; and as countless men, in childhood or maturity, that have never heard or have not heard enough of Jesus Christ [...] die before receiving the necessary succour for their withdrawal from this abyss of sin [...] though in essence they have not been more wicked than others, and several among them have perchance been less guilty than some of that little number of elect, who were saved by a grace without reason, and who thereby enjoy an eternal felicity which they had not deserved.[34]

The Anglican theologian Matthew Horbery (1706–73) was a firm believer in the eternal torments of hell. But he saw the problem to which Leibniz was pointing. He reinterpreted the relevant New Testament texts to suggest that half would be saved and only half damned. With an awareness of the high infant-mortality rates of the time (and ignoring the doctrine of *limbus infantum*), he estimated that dead babies would constitute at least half of the population of the dead. Since, therefore, 'One half of our Species die, perhaps, before they have actually committed any Sin to deserve the Damnation of Hell [...] it may reasonably be hoped that they will escape it.'[35] This was no doubt of comfort to those infants previously deprived of the Beatific Vision and doomed to an eternal limbo. Adult readers of Horbery may have felt less comforted. For Horbery's statistics suggested that although the population of heaven would be greater than that of hell, it would consist largely of babies, the majority of adults having been consigned to the infernal regions.

As we noted in Chapter 4, the doctrine of *particular* judgement, according to which the eternal destiny of individuals was irrevocably fixed at the time of death, denied the possibility of the capacity of individuals to change their destiny. The afterlife was, as a consequence, morally static. Even Purgatory was a place where vice was purged rather than virtue acquired. But during the seventeenth century, many became dissatisfied with the fixing of the destiny of the soul at death. They opted for a morally dynamic state between death and the Last Judgement. In short, the possibilities of individual repentance, of moral and spiritual growth, and consequently of divine forgiveness and the gift of salvation, were extended beyond the grave.

An early example of the morally dynamic afterlife was provided by the seventeenth-century Platonist Henry Hallywell (1641–1703). This amounted to a Protestant rethinking of Purgatory. According to Hallywell, there were rewards for the good immediately after death, and shame and misery for the impious – no sleep of the soul here! But he was not persuaded that the Scriptures held that the good went to heaven and the wicked to hell. Rather, he suggested, on rational grounds, it would be more appropriate were all to go to an intermediate state after death until the Day of Resurrection. He carefully distinguished this state from Purgatory, primarily because, whereas Purgatory was penitential, his intermediate state was purificatory and morally dynamic. 'By this middle State,' he wrote,

> I mean no such condition of Being, as that wherein a man from his impious transactions in this life, shall undergo very sharp and acute torments, the protraction or abbreviation of which yet, depend upon the will and pleasure of his Holiness [the pope] and mercenary priests; and after such a time of penance and purgation, be delivered, and translated into Heaven: but, such a state, wherein, by a due purification of their minds, and subjugation of those stubborn lusts and desires which exalt themselves against the life of God, and which were not thoroughly tamed in this life, the Soul of man becomes wholly dead to every inordinate affection, and daily kindles that fire of Divine Love, till at last it arise to a perfect flame.[36]

In particular Hallywell found it unsatisfactory that 'the infinitely far greater part of men are damned'.[37] And, as a Platonist, he found it inconsistent with the goodness of God to allow the majority to be born into circumstances where there would be little hope of recovering the lost image of God in their souls, with everlasting damnation the inevitable outcome. Consequently, free will was extended beyond the grave and time allotted for moral improvement: '[S]urely it would be a great eye-sore and blemish in Heavens righteous Oeconomy and dispensation in the World, if there were really no time or means allowed for the recovery of these lapsed Souls.'[38]

Hallywell's doctrine of a morally dynamic afterlife opened up the possibility of salvation not only for those who had heard the gospel and responded appropriately or otherwise, but also for those who had lived in ignorance of it. This then was a revised Protestant version of the doctrine of the harrowing of hell (or Hades) for those who had lived *after* Christ rather than *before*. To be sure, this did not imply that all would ultimately be saved. And Hallywell did not deny the possibility of eternal torments after the Day of Resurrection. But he did make it possible that all *could* be saved, and through *their own commitment to moral improvement*.

The belief that in getting rid of the doctrine of Purgatory, the Protestant Reformation might have lost more than it gained, was also held by Archibald Campbell, Anglican bishop of Aberdeen from 1721–44. That the majority were damned was a doctrine he abominated and abhorred as 'Cruel, as Barbarous, as Unbecoming the Infinite Goodness, Love, and Mercy of God'.[39] His account of the state of souls after death was especially reminiscent of Augustine's. At death, he believed, souls proceeded to Hades, where they remained until the Last Day. Hades was divided into two sides with a series of mansions within each – one on the right for righteous souls that would ultimately attain to the Beatific Vision, the other on the left for the wicked who would proceed to hell. For those on the right, progress from mansion to mansion was possible, through a process of purgation, purification and moral improvement.

This idea of a morally dynamic afterlife was an innovation in the history of Christian thought that was to reach its fulfilment in the German philosopher Immanuel Kant (1724–1804). Kant argued that, although we are imperfect human beings, we rationally aspire for perfection. It was obvious to Kant, as to everyone, that moral perfection was unattainable in this life. Thus, he argued in his *Critique of Practical Reason* (1788) that it was reasonable to postulate an infinitely enduring existence immediately after death and before the Last Judgement in which the individual 'may hope for a further uninterrupted continuance of this progress, however long his existence may last, even beyond this life'.[40] Thus may the soul progress endlessly towards God, who is the highest good. That the soul may progress after death entails that it could do so. Thus, the soul had to be free, both on this side of the grave and on the other, to progress in virtue. In the afterlife, God imparted happiness as the result of virtue. In a version of Luther turned upside down, perhaps inspired by Kant's own grounding in Lutheran Pietism, Kant's salvation was by works. Grace (the gift of happiness) did not precede works as in Luther but, rather, grace followed the acquisition of afterlife virtue.

That said, moral progress in the afterlife was not for eternity. It was dependent on time. After the Day of Judgement, declared Kant, there would be no more time. Our eternal destiny – salvation or damnation – would be fixed on that day according to our merits or otherwise. The Last Day, declared Kant in *The End of All Things* (1794),

> is a *Judgement Day*: the decision of the World-Judge in favour of salvation or damnation is, therefore, the proper end of all things in time and the beginning of (blissful or miserable) eternity in which the fate that has fallen to each man endures as it was allotted to him in the moment of its pronouncement [by God].[41]

Hell's torments

It would seem, then, that Kant (perhaps to the surprise of his modern devotees), like Hallywell and Campbell, was convinced that there were those who, whatever the opportunities that there may have been for progress between death and the Last Day, would be inevitably damned to an eternal hell after it. In believing in the possibility of moral progress after death, they were in the minority, but in accepting that, after the Last Judgement, the damned had no further chance for salvation, they were still among the majority in the seventeenth and eighteenth centuries.

At the beginning of the eighteenth century, the Presbyterian John Shower (1657–1715) was not alone in endorsing both the eternal and the extreme nature of hell's torments, even when compared to the familiar horrors of everyday life in the here and now (see Plate 24 [c]). 'We have heard,' he wrote,

> of some who have endured breaking on the Wheel, ripping up of their Bowels, fleaing alive, racking of Joynts, burning of Flesh, pounding in a Mortar, tearing in pieces with Flesh-hooks, boyling in Oyl, roasting on hot fiery Gridirons, etc. And yet all these, tho' you should superad thereto all Diseases, such as the Plague, Stone, Gout, Strangury, or whatever you can name most torturing to the Body [...] they would all come short [...] of

> that Wrath, that Horror, that unconceivable Anguish which the Damned must inevitably suffer every Moment, without any Intermission of their Pains, in Hellish Flames.[42]

While the major part of Richard Baxter's (1615–91) *The Saints' Everlasting Rest* was an exposition of the rewards of the godly, the sufferings of the wicked were not neglected. Baxter's hell was a world of social reversal, a Puritan's revenge for what he saw as the sins of the social elite. The rich man in hell would not be a gorgeous, well-dressed gallant. There would be no powdering or curling of the hair, nor expectations of admiring glances. The good times were no more – no cards, dice, hunting, dancing, theatre or drinking. There would be neither lascivious discourse, amorous songs, nor wanton dalliance. God would laugh at the sufferings of the damned:

> Is it not a terrible thing to a wretched soul, when it shall lie roaring perpetually [...] in the flames of Hell, and the God of mercy himself shall laugh at them? [...] When none in Heaven or earth can help them but God, & he shall rejoyce over them in their calamity?[43]

Baxter's God was an executioner, insensible to mercy, the avenger of sweet-smelling voluptuousness, of hedonistic delights. So was Christopher Love's:

> When thou art scorching in thy flames, when thou art howling in thy torments, then shall God laugh at thy destruction, and then the Saints of God shall sing and rejoice, that thou art a vessel of justice, and so his power and wrath are made known in thee.[44]

On the one hand, the sufferings of hell were magnifications of the pains of illness and disease with which readers of Christopher Love were all too personally familiar. There is no disease, declared Christopher Love, that puts the 'whole body in pain at once: but in hell it is not so, in hell all the parts of your bodies, and powers of your souls shall be tormented.'[45] To Richard Stafford (1663–1703), all the evils, pains, fears, diseases and afflictions throughout the whole earth 'do not make up the ten thousandth part so bad as the Damnation of Hell.'[46]

On the other hand, hell's torments were also exaggerations of the sufferings of criminals. The penal system of the damned in the next world was a projection into the hereafter of criminal punishments in this one. Sadism and piety combined; and the heavenly judge was an omnipotent replica of an earthly judge. So for Richard Baxter, as for his contemporaries, the purpose of punishments for those convicted of crime was retributive, and the deliberate infliction of pain in a public place was crucial; so too were the punishments in hell. Moreover, the terrors of hell were multiplied for Baxter by the shrieks and cries of one's companions, by children crying out against their parents, husbands against wives and wives against husbands, masters and servants, ministers and people, magistrates and subjects, all cursing each other into the infinite future.

The message for progressing pilgrims from John Bunyan (1628–88) was just as clear: progress or else. The worst tortures imaginable on this earth, maintained Bunyan, were as fleabites compared to the sufferings of those in hellfire: 'I will give you the scope of them in a similitude,' he wrote:

> Set case you should take a man, and tie him to a stake, and with red hot Pincers pinch off his flesh by little pieces for two or three years together, and at last, when the poor man cryes out for ease and help, the tormentors answer, Nay but besides all this you must be handled worse. We will serve you thus these 20 years together, and after that we will fill your mangled body full of scalding lead, and run you through with a red hot spit, would this not be lamentable? [...] But he that goes to hell shall suffer ten thousand times worse torments then these, and yet shall never be quite dead under them.[47]

The horrors of this eternal cacophony of misery and blame were augmented by the screams of demons. In this present world, suggested Bunyan, the very thought of demons appearing was sufficient to make the flesh tremble and the hair stand up on end. Even worse there! The spirits of the wicked would be daunted by hobgoblin and foul fiend. What will you do, he asked,

> when not onely the supposition of the devils appearing, but the reall society of all the devils in hell to be with thee howling and roaring, screeching and yelling in such a hideous manner, that thou wilt be even at thy wits end, and be ready to run starke madde again for anguish and torment?[48]

The demons in hell were both tormenting and tormented. According to the Platonist Henry More, wicked souls would be exposed to these grim and remorseless officers of justice, as devoid of any sense of good as those that they would punish. These demons, he wrote, 'satiate their lascivient cruelty with all manner of abuses and torments they can imagine'.[49] However, these demons would themselves be tortured in ways far above 'what the cruellest Tyranny has inflicted here, either upon the guilty or innocent'.[50] The punishments that were inflicted by the demons of hell upon the damned were at God's behest. They were God's torturers manifesting his glory and justice. In both Catholic and Protestant demonology, evil spirits had only as much power as God allowed them to exercise. God could not be excused the malevolence of demons, and he was ultimately responsible for the activities of evil spirits on each side of the grave. Let no man imagine, declared the Calvinist Thomas Goodwin (1600–80),

> that Devils are the greatest Tormenters of Men, or of their Consciences in Hell: or if any would affirm it, I would demand, Who it is that torments the Consciences of Devils themselves? Certainly none but God [...] And it is as sure, that the same God, with whom those Spirits and their Consciences have for ever to do, the Consciences of Men shall also.[51]

From the end of the seventeenth century, at least among a literate elite, hell's population became significantly depleted. References to demons and devils, their presence in hell and their tormenting of the damned disappeared from the literature. The role that the Devil and his minions played in the everyday world went into a similar decline. The baroque fantasy of satanic compacts, of witches' sabbaths and Devil worship, began to lose its purchase in the mental furniture of the cultivated European mind. The philosophical naturalism of the new science banished demons from the natural world. The progressive assumption of an orderly regular universe made untenable the capricious interventions of demons. Without demons, God alone became responsible for the torments of the damned – both judge and torturer.[52] This was to put even more pressure on the doctrine of eternal torments.

Gnawing worms, unquenchable fires and abominable fantasies

A variety of biblical images served to emphasise hell's horrors. It was a bottomless pit of darkness, utter darkness, a furnace of fire, a lake that burnt with fire and brimstone, a dark and tormenting prison, the blackness of darkness, chains of darkness. All were agreed that the wicked would be punished by fire. But there was some debate about the nature of hellfire. While the case could be made that a 'corporeal' fire would not work on spirits, most held to the view that the flames of hell were real, although even then bets were hedged. The Anglican John Brandon (b.1644/5) supposed 'the Fire that shall torment the Bodies of the wicked to be real and corporal fire, as ours is, I mean as real, though perhaps not of the same kind.'[53] In 1670, the Nonconformist Thomas Vincent (1634–78) clearly had the 1666 Great Fire of London in his mind when he suggested that, although corporeal, the dark, irresistible, unquenchable, everlasting fires of hell would far exceed any earthly fires, which would be like the biting of a flea or a pinprick by comparison. The wicked would see 'themselves on fire, Head, Back, Breast, Belly, Hands, Arms, Legs, Feet, every part on fire, and that such a fire though it doth torment them, yet that shall not be able to consume them.'[54]

Paradoxically, in spite of its fires, the major characteristic of hell was its gloominess. The darkness of hell served to emphasise its penal quality – its dungeon-like nature and demonic ambience. The torments of hell were increased by the absence of any consolatory light. The greatest part of the dead, claimed Bishop William Beveridge (1637–1708) in a sermon before Queen Mary in 1690, 'live with the Fiends of Hell in the infernal pit, where they have no light, nothing but darkness and horrour to the utmost extremity roundabout them.'[55]

Even the fires of hell gave out no light. The natural order was overturned. While the righteous enjoyed light without heat, the damned suffered heat without light. John Milton's description of hell in *Paradise Lost* as

> A Dungeon horrible, on all sides round
> As one great Furnace flam'd, yet from those flames
> No light, but rather darkness visible
> Serv'd onely to discover sights of woe

stood in a tradition developed by the early Church Fathers, utilised by medieval Catholic philosophers and articulated by Geoffrey Chaucer.[56] Still, although the flames of hell would give no light, visions of horror would remain: 'The fire it self will give no light,' wrote Thomas Vincent (1634–78),

> all will be dark and black, black Devils, black bodies, black Souls, and they may without light have perceivance one of another, as Devils have now unto whom light is no use; or if there be a duskish light there, to represent one anothers ruful countenances, and other fright-ful spectacles, be sure there will be no refreshing light, there the damned will be in a place and state of darkness forever.[57]

However, in the midst of all this doom and gloom, there was one bright spot, namely that the torments of the damned would be proportionate to their sins. The proportionality of punishment and sin was inherited by Protestantism from the medieval consensus. As we noted in Chapter 4, the doctrine of Purgatory assumed such a proportionality, although one which took into account both the quality and the period of suffering. That the torments of hell were graded was endorsed by the councils of Lyons in 1274 and Florence in 1439. Dante had intricately depicted the grading of both rewards and punishments in the heavenly and infernal realms. Neither Luther nor Calvin, in spite of their belief that works played no role in the hereafter, rejected the gradation of both heavenly joys and hellish pains.[58] No doubt it was more difficult to assert gradations of happiness in heaven than misery in hell. After all, the Beatific Vision *is* the Beatific Vision and the same for all. Still, there was a strong inclination among the majority of Protestant commentators to maintain a symmetry of contrasts between heaven and hell, and thus to endorse the gradation of rewards as well as punishments. Divine justice was thus served in the allocation of both joy and suffering.

The question of degrees of suffering in hell was also intimately connected to the distinction that we made in Chapter 3 between the pain of loss (*poena damni*) and the pain of sense (*poena sensus*). The former was the punishment that consisted in deprivation of the Beatific Vision and the sense of grief, loss and anguish that was its consequence; the latter was the physical punishments primarily inflicted by fire. It was a distinction familiar to John Milton: '[T]he second death, or the punishment of the damned,' he declared, 'seems to consist partly in the loss of the chief good, namely, the favor and protection of God, and the beatific vision of his presence [...] and partly in eternal torment, which is called the punishment of sense.'[59] The scriptural grounds for this distinction were found in Mark 9.48 and Isaiah 66.24: 'And they shall go out and look at the dead bodies of those who have rebelled against me; for their worm shall not die, their fire shall not be quenched, and they shall be an abhorrence to all flesh.'

The debate around the meaning of the 'worm' and the 'fire' had been around since well before the time of Augustine. He had outlined all the possible options for both physical and spiritual readings of these in *De civitate dei*.[60] The same possibilities were still in play in the period of the Reformation over a thousand years later. The popular early modern belief that worms spontaneously generated from putrefying flesh revived the direct impetus for the literal role of worms in hell. The same belief could also be read figuratively as the putrefaction of the wicked soul. Thus, for example, in his posthumously published *The Worm That Dyeth Not* (1672), the independent divine William Strong (d.1672) declared the conscience to be the worm that ever gnaws. It is no wonder, he wrote, if the conscience 'breed a worm as all other putrefactions do; and thus being the worst, it is not strange if it breed the worst and the most devouring Worm.'[61] The fire of hell, on the other hand, was seldom interpreted figuratively. Among the early Church Fathers, only a few, among whom was Origen, interpreted the fires of hell as equivalent to remorse, regret and so on.

The sufferings of the damned in hell were also increased by their ability to see the happiness of the blessed in heaven. The biblical justification for this was again the story of the rich man and Lazarus the beggar. The rich man in hell (Hades) 'looked up and saw Abraham far away with Lazarus by his side' (Luke 16.23). On the basis of this text, John Bunyan saw the torments of hell increased by the sight of friends, neighbours, acquaintances, even one's father, mother, wife, husband, children, brothers and sisters, all enjoying bliss. He rejoiced that

> There shall come from the East and from the West, that is, those that thou didst never see in thy life before, and they shall sit down with thy friends, and thy neighbours, thy wife and thy children in the kingdom of heaven, and thou for thy sins and disobedience shalt be shut out, nay, thrust out. O wonderful torment.[62]

In the contrasting symmetries of heaven and hell, just as the sufferings of the damned were increased by the vision of the joys of the saved, so also the joys of the righteous were heightened by the sight across the great divide of the punishments of the wicked. This 'abominable fancy', as F. W. Farrar called it, was a reversal of the story of the rich man and Lazarus.[63]

It had a long history in the Christian tradition. It was supported by both Tertullian and Augustine. Thomas Aquinas too endorsed it: 'Wherefore in order that the happiness of the saints may be more delightful to them and that they may render more copious thanks to God for it, they are allowed to see perfectly the sufferings of the damned.'[64] America's most famous eighteenth-century Calvinist theologian, Jonathan Edwards (1703–58), passionately championed it in his 1741 sermon:

> The sight of hell torments will exalt the happiness of the saints for ever. It will not only make them more sensible of the greatness and freeness of the grace of God in their happiness; but it will really make their happiness the greater, as it will make them more sensible of their own happiness; it will give them a more lively relish of it; it will make them prize it more. When they see others, who were of the same nature, and born under the same circumstances, plunged in such misery, and they so distinguished, O it will make them sensible how happy they are. A sense of the opposite misery, in all cases, greatly increases the relish of any joy or pleasure.[65]

Still, by the time of Edwards in the first half of the eighteenth century, references to the 'abominable fancy' were few and far between. By the middle of the nineteenth century, it had virtually disappeared from the Protestant tradition. The reasons for its doing so are less clear. Most likely, its decline reflected the beginnings of a change in attitude to the sufferings of others more generally. From the end of the seventeenth until the middle of the nineteenth century, an originally positive attitude to the suffering of others in the here and now was slowly being replaced by a rising sensitivity. As Pieter Spierenburg argues: 'The death and suffering of fellow human beings were increasingly experienced as painful, just because other people were increasingly perceived as fellow human beings.'[66] This change of sensitivity was crucial to the demise of the public spectacle of suffering. Just as this changing sensibility led to the removal of the punishments of the judicially guilty from the earthly public gaze, so, it can be argued, it removed the sufferings of the damned from the sight of the heavenly citizenry. The liberal Protestant theologian Friedrich Schleiermacher (1768–1834) reflected this shift in attitudes to the suffering of others in his rejection of the abominable fancy. Schleiermacher's was a new sensitivity. In marked contrast to the traditional view, he believed that the blessedness of the saved would not be enhanced but severely disturbed by their knowledge of the sufferings of the damned, even when their punishments were just. Eternal bliss, he suggested, cannot include such a diminution. For eternal bliss genuinely to exist, he suggested, eternal damnation cannot.[67]

Similarly, during the same period, there is a diminution in the theological acceptability of the physical punishments of the damned. By the middle of the nineteenth century, the notion of *poena sensus* was under serious attack. Much more acceptable was the belief that the damned would suffer *only* from the loss of heaven and be *only* excluded from fellowship with God. To the liberal Anglican F. D. Maurice (1805–72), for example, the mere thought of the loss of God was sufficiently daunting: '[T]he thought of His ceasing to punish them, of His letting them alone, of His leaving them to themselves, is the real unutterable horror.'[68] Hell had now become the absence of God. The prisoners of hell were there incarcerated no longer *for* punishment but *as* punishment. But whether suffering the punishment of loss or the punishment of sense, there was a further issue upon which attention came to be focused. Would these punishments last forever?

Annihilationists and torments temporary

As much as the torments of hell themselves, it was the emphasis on the eternity of them that was intended to provoke horror, effect repentance and act as an incentive to a good and holy life in the here and now. However, unlike the punishment of criminals in this life at the end of which death often mercifully occurred, the awesome ceremonies of hell went on forever. It was 'the eternity of the Punishment', declared the Anglican divine Matthew Horbery, 'which gives its chief weight and Edge, and makes it pierce deepest into the Hearts of Sinners.'[69] Within the Christian tradition, that the punishments of the damned in hell would be eternal had always been the majority opinion. But from the latter part of the seventeenth and into the eighteenth century, there was a small number by whom it was privately disbelieved, publicly although discreetly questioned, or anonymously challenged. This was done in the name of the conviction that all the damned would be eventually either annihilated or saved after an appropriate period of punishment.

Scripture was the predominant focus of discussions both for and against the eternity of hell. In particular, the debate turned on whether the term 'eternal' (αἰώνιος) in the New Testament meant what it suggested or merely 'of a long duration'. The symmetry of 'eternal happiness' and 'eternal misery' was central. Horbery asked the obvious question of the terms for 'eternal':

> When apply'd to God, they confessedly denote a proper Eternity: when apply'd to the Happiness of the Saints in Heaven, they have hitherto universally been thought to denote the same [...] What Reason then is there why they should not denote the same, when apply'd to the Punishments of the Wicked?[70]

Be that as it may, both annihilationists and universalists nonetheless mined Scripture for support for their respective positions.

Such was the diversity of opinion on the eternity of hell's torments that could be generated by appeal to Scripture that, on occasion, reason was invoked against it. Thus, the English theologian Thomas Burnet (*c.*1635–1715) argued that, granting the ambiguities within the debate,

> every Man is at Liberty to embrace that Opinion which his Conscience shall pronounce to be most agreeable to sound reason; and let him adhere to that Interpretation of the Sacred Scripture upon this Point which the weighty Reasons of the Cause before us will be best able to bear.[71]

It would be simplistic to suggest that the debate over eternal torments in the seventeenth and eighteenth centuries simply reflected a dispute between reason and the Bible. 'Reason over Scripture' was certainly a manifesto for those who perceived themselves progressive and enlightened in contrast to the hidebound traditionalists who supported the eternal punishment of the wicked. For these, 'reason' implied not so much the power of the human mind to arrive independently at truth as a commitment to avoid intolerance, bigotry and extremism. But opponents and advocates of eternal torments alike provided rational arguments that orbited within a biblical space. At the same time, the meaning of the Bible was itself determined within the context of debates about the nature of God. These went particularly to the relationship between the divine attributes of mercy, wrath and justice, and the implications of these for the destiny of the damned.

The wrath of God was for some sufficient reason to punish the wicked eternally. The Calvinist Thomas Goodwin wrote his discourse on the punishment of sin in hell in 1680, as the subtitle indicates, to demonstrate 'the

Wrath of God to be the immediate Cause Thereof'. Eternal punishment, he exclaimed, is 'an act of avenging Wrath'.[72] Jonathan Edwards's sinners were 'in the hands of an angry God'.[73] For Goodwin and Edwards, as for many others, vengeance and retributive justice were closely combined. The doctrine of eternal torments retained a medieval element of the law of vengeance together with an early modern sense of retributive justice. The wicked, proclaimed Jonathan Edwards,

> *deserve* to be cast into hell, so that divine justice never stands in the way, it makes no objection against God's using his power at any moment to destroy them. Yea, on the contrary, justice calls aloud for an infinite punishment of their sins.[74]

It was difficult to integrate the concept of eternal retribution with God's goodness and mercy. The deist Matthew Tindal (1657–1733) in his *Christianity as Old as the Creation* (1731), for example, lamented those who impute such actions to God 'as [to] make him, resemble the worst of beings, & so run into downright Demonism'.[75] As a consequence of this kind of critique, those who argued for eternal torments were forced to reinterpret the goodness and mercy of God accordingly. With the Catholic Francis Blyth (*c.*1705–72), it is difficult to distinguish his rhetorical assertion of the mercy of God from what is in effect a denial of it. For Blyth, the mercy of God can only be understood from the primacy of his retributive justice:

> It is unmerciful, you say, for God to give sinners their desert; is it mercy then for worms, for wretches, to rob God of his due? And must God be more merciful than becomes him as God to be, merely to prove him less just than he really is, and must be?[76]

The implication that, in the light of the eternal torments imposed by God, divine mercy was not up to much, could be mitigated by arguing that the penalties for sins were something that followed naturally and inevitably upon the sinner – self-inflicted wounds rather than externally imposed tortures. They were, after all, the consequence of the misuse of free will. But arguments of this sort did little to solve the issue of God's lack of mercy. As D. P. Walker has pointed out, although a God who allows punishments to happen is less cruel than one who actively imposes them, 'there is little if any moral difference between allowing the occurrence of a disaster together with the resultant suffering, which you could prevent, and actively causing the disaster and the suffering.'[77]

William Whiston (1667–1752) would have agreed. He was Isaac Newton's successor as Lucasian Professor of Mathematics at the University of Cambridge. To Whiston, the doctrine of the love of God was absolutely inconsistent with those 'common but barbarous and savage opinions' of eternal torments,

> as if much the greatest part of mankind are under a state of reprobation, unalterable reprobation, and must inevitably be damned: and that such their damnation is to be *coeternal* with the duration of their Creator himself; and that the torments, the exquisite torments of these most numerous and most miserable creatures, are determined without the least pity, or relenting, or bowels of compassion in their Creator, to be in the flames of Hell; without abatement, or remission, for endless ages of ages. And all this for the sins of this short life; fallen into generally by the secret snares of the Devil, and other violent temptations; which they commonly could not wholly either prevent, or avoid; and this without any other advantage to themselves or to others, or to God himself, than as instances [...] of the absolute and supreme power and dominion of the cruel and inexorable author of their being; for all the infinite ages of eternity.[78]

For his part, Whiston was, at the end of the Last Day, an annihilationist. When he was a student at Cambridge from 1686 to 1691, Whiston was a supporter of eternal torments. But by 1709, perhaps under the influence of the philosopher John Locke, he had changed his mind. A temporary period of punishment followed by annihilation, he suggested, reflected both the divine (retributive) justice and goodness. The punishments were eternal, he maintained, only in the sense that they would 'continue the whole Duration of the Wicked, who are the subjects of it'.[79]

According to Whiston, before the Last Judgement, the wicked would be confined beneath the earth. The Astronomer Royal Edmund Halley's and his own researches demonstrated, he claimed, a large cavity between the internal and external parts of the earth, thus vindicating the biblical and traditional descriptions of Hades being beneath the earth. During this period the wicked would be confined there with the opportunity for repentance. The majority would grab that last chance. Taking a leaf out of Origen's book, Whiston even hoped that Satan and his evil angels might eventually choose to repent and be saved. The incorrigibly wicked, however, would be resurrected on the Last Day with physical bodies that would be punished in flames (fire), and with the same diseases they had at death (worms). Moreover, he surmised, they would then be located on a comet (like Halley's):

> I cannot but think the Surface or Atmosphere of such a Comet to be that Place of Torment so terribly described in Scripture, into which the Devil and his Angels, with wicked Men their Companions, when delivered out of their Prison in the Heart of the Earth, shall be cast for their utter Perdition or second Death; which will be indeed a terrible but a most useful spectacle to God's rational creatures.[80]

The period of time that the wicked would spend in this hellish comet would be proportionate to their sins, to be followed by their second death – annihilation.

Whiston's belief that the wicked would have a 'second death' after an appropriate time of punishment in hell, although without his geology and cometology, remained the standard pattern for theologically driven annihilationist views from this time on. The most significant variations on this theme occurred only in the second half of the nineteenth century among those who were influenced by the Darwinian challenge to the Christian idea of man as unique in the animal world by virtue of his immortal soul. Darwinism served to reinforce the assumption implicit within annihilationism that the soul was not naturally immortal, that immortality was a consequence of divine grace and that man was naturally mortal.[81] The Darwinist notion of the survival of the fittest also served to align the annihilationists' account of the afterlife with the belief that those not fit for salvation would, like many species, just disappear. Thus, for example, the Anglican evangelical Henry Constable (1816–91), in his highly successful *The Duration and Nature of Future Punishment* (1868), declared,

> We find in nature that death and destruction are God's usual agents in removing from their place things animate and inanimate as soon as they cease to discharge the part for which they were intended [...] Whole races of living things have long ceased to exist [...] Lower creatures know not God, and fade away out of life. Higher intelligences knew Him, turned

from Him, made themselves like beasts, and like beasts are treated. Hell will add its fossil remains to those of the quarries of the earth.[82]

Universalists and torments reformative

Advocates of both annihilationism and universalism no doubt comforted themselves with the thought that, even if God's justice was manifested in the punishments the wicked endured in hell, his mercy was demonstrated in the torments of hell being only temporary and not eternal. For universalists, however, in contrast to annihilationists, the end of punishments brought salvation rather than destruction, if only after a period of punishments intended to reform the sinner. Within the history of Christian thought, universalism was a minor tradition, generally viewed with suspicion. Since it was often believed that universal salvation would act as a disincentive to the virtuous life among the hoi polloi, some held it to be a secret doctrine for the few, an esoteric truth not to be revealed to the masses to whom the eternity of hell's torments still needed to be preached. Predominantly embedded in the Platonic tradition of the early Church, particularly with Origen, it re-emerged among some of the Platonists in the seventeenth century (Peter Sterry, George Rust and Jeremiah White), and among supporters of the Radical Reformation (John Denck, Gerrard Winstanley and Richard Coppin).[83] It was during the nineteenth century, however, that it became a matter of mainstream controversy.

The nineteenth-century German liberal Protestant theologian Friedrich Schleiermacher was the first modern major theologian to accept universalism. In his case, it was intriguingly combined with a commitment to predestination and, as we noted above, a rejection of eternal damnation. God did not predestine some to salvation and others (the vast majority) to eternal misery. Rather, he foreordained the salvation of all humanity. In contrast to the view that some obtained the highest bliss while others were lost in irrevocable misery, Schleiermacher proclaimed, we ought to admit 'the equal rights of the milder view [...] that through the power of redemption there will one day be a universal restoration of all souls.'[84]

Schleiermacher's liberal view on salvation was to have little impact on nineteenth-century German theology. In England, by contrast, controversy about universalism was a constant feature of the theological landscape of the second half of that century. We can take the Broad Church Anglican cleric

3. Hades and his wife Persephone, rulers of the underworld.

5. Heaven depicted as a garden.

6. The heavenly city of St Augustine.

9. Souls purified through the fires of Purgatory.

10. Souls passing through Purgatory on their way to Heaven.

11. Dante shown with a depiction of hell on the left, the seven terraces of Purgatory in the background, and the city of Florence on the right.

13. Christ descends into Limbo between his death and resurrection.

15. Souls become 'physicalised' as bodies become 'spiritualised'.

16. The resurrected Christ telling Mary Magdalene 'Touch me not'.

18. 'The trumpets shall sound and the dead shall be raised.'

20. The heavenly choir.

21. The selling of indulgences depicted as *'Regnum Diaboli'* ('Reign of the Devil').

24. The damned tortured in hell.

25. The good being led to heaven by an angel.

26. The Virgin Mary in glory surrounded by the heavenly society of apostles and angels.

27. Doubting the resurrection of the flesh.

32. The Damozel awaits the arrival of her lover in heaven.

F. W. Farrar's collection of sermons entitled *Eternal Hope* (1878) and the arguments it generated as emblematic of the debate around universalism in the mid-Victorian period.[85] It was the third of these sermons, 'Hell – what it is not', that was to provoke the most controversy, not least because Farrar had the virtue of being able not only to preach *to* but to write *for* a large crowd.

Farrar was vehemently opposed to the doctrine of eternal punishment. 'I know nothing,' he declared,

> more calculated to make the soul revolt with loathing from every doctrine of religion than the evil complacency with which some cheerfully accept the belief that they are living and moving in the midst of millions doomed irreversibly to everlasting perdition.[86]

He deemed it a doctrine of 'judicial terrorism', 'a blasphemy against God's exceeding and eternal love.'[87] And of the biblical texts that appeared to endorse it:

> I protest at once and finally against this ignorant tyranny of isolated texts which has ever been the curse of Christian truth, the glory of narrow intellects, and the cause of the worst errors of the worst days of the corrupted Church [...] The devil, as we know, can quote texts for his own purpose.[88]

The words 'hell', 'everlasting' and 'damnation' should be expunged, he declared, from all English Bibles as mistranslations.

It is also clear that, along with eternal torments, Farrar rejected annihilationism. This, on the face of it, would leave universalism as the only remaining option. Yet, he wrote, 'I cannot preach the certainty of Universalism.' There were, no doubt, practical and theoretical grounds for this uncertainty. Practically, Farrar wished to avoid accusations of teaching an unorthodox doctrine. Theoretically, he was agnostic not only about universalism but also about all the options for those who did not merit eternal life at the time of death. God has given us 'no *clear and decisive* revelation on the final condition of those who have died in sin.'[89]

Nevertheless, he did go on to sail very close to the winds of heresy. He had no doubt that the will of God was that all would eventually be saved. He believed that there would be a period of time after death when man would continue in that spiritual death that is alienation from God, although how long that might be – 'that is one of the secret things which God hath not revealed.'[90] Without asserting that *all* would be saved, he did express the hope that the vast majority of the lost would be eventually redeemed. And he strongly hinted that there would be a period of time when those who were not yet ready for salvation 'may have to be purified in that Gehenna of aeonian fire beyond the grave.'[91] This was Purgatory in all but name.

However much he may have tried to avoid endorsing universalism, there were many who believed that he had done precisely that. The debate among the theological elite focused on

> the appeal to a fixed, revealed doctrine on the one hand, and the protest against its morally intolerable nature on the other; a fear of giving licence to sin on the one hand, and a fear of making it impossible for men to believe in a good God on the other; the pitting of text against text, and authority against authority.[92]

Still, however troubled the theological intelligentsia may have been, Farrar received a more sympathetic response among the general public. Thus, for example, a lady from Cornwall wrote to Farrar to tell him that his book had been

> the means of saving from Atheism a young and thoughtful man – a carpenter in our village. Brought up strictly in the narrow views of the United Free Methodists his danger was, from feeling the terrible inconsistency of the hell preached by them with the doctrine that God *is* love. I lent him *Eternal Hope*, which he has since told me saved him when on the verge of Atheism.[93]

For some Victorians, at least, the doctrine of the eternal punishments of the damned in hell was a sufficient cause for disbelief. Atheism was now a serious option for the ethically virtuous. The doctrine of an eternal hell was leading not only to a theological refining of belief but also to a wholesale rejection of it. Farrar, like a number of others, was driven by a Victorian moral seriousness that was rebelling against some parts of Christian orthodoxy. God was decidedly looking ethically a little bit out of touch. As early as 1825, the poet Samuel Taylor Coleridge (1772–1834) had analysed the theological disquiet among his acquaintances:

> I have found the far larger number of serious and inquiring persons little, if at all, disquieted by doubts respecting Articles of Faith, that are simply above their comprehension. It is only where the belief required of them jars with their *moral* feelings; where a doctrine in the sense, in which they have been taught to receive it, appears to contradict their clear notions of right and wrong, or to be at variance with the divine attributes of goodness and justice; that these men are surprised, perplexed, and alas! not seldom offended and alienated. Such are the Doctrines of Arbitrary Election and Reprobation; the Sentence to everlasting Torment by an eternal and necessitating decree; vicarious Atonement, and the necessity of the Abasement, Agony and ignominious Death of a most holy and meritorious Person, to appease the wrath of God.[94]

Thus, the doctrine of eternal punishment in hell had become morally repugnant to many both inside and outside the Church, As Don Cupitt puts it:

> The Victorians thought it a moral duty to believe that no one was quite beyond redemption; they did not like the doctrine of Reprobation [predestination to damnation], and if a Broad Church clergyman questioned the doctrine of eternal punishment he might [...] be reviled by the theologians, but he was sure of the sympathy of a large public of liberal-minded laymen.[95]

Almost at the end of the nineteenth century, the British statesman William Gladstone (1809–98) commented that the doctrine of hell had been 'relegated [...] to the far-off corners of the Christian mind [...] there to sleep in deep shadow as a thing needless in our enlightened and progressive age.'[96] This was an exaggeration. The doctrine of hell remained the orthodoxy within Christianity and that of the eternal torments of the damned in hell continued within both conservative evangelical Protestantism and conservative Roman Catholicism, then as now. Thus, for example, in Thomas Hardy's (1840–1928) novel *Tess of the d'Urbervilles* (1891), the heroine Tess worries about the destiny of her unbaptised and illegitimate baby Sorrow, whom she realises is close to death:

> The clock struck the solemn hour of one, that hour when fancy stalks outside reason, and malignant possibilities stand rock-firm as facts. She thought of the child consigned to the nethermost corner of hell, as its

> double doom for lack of baptism and lack of legitimacy; saw the arch-fiend tossing it with his three-pronged fork, like the one they used for heating the oven on baking days; to which picture she added many other quaint and curious details of torment sometimes taught the young in this Christian country.[97]

James Joyce similarly recalled the kind of 'hellfire and damnation' sermon to which he had been subjected as a young man. 'All were as one before the judgement seat of God,' declared the priest of the moment after death.

> He would reward the good and punish the wicked. One single instant was enough for the trial of a man's soul. One single instant after the body's death, the soul had been weighed in the balance. The particular judgement was over and the soul had passed to the abode of bliss or to the prison of purgatory or had been hurled howling into hell.

The priest was later to remind his young listeners that, at the end of the world, God would cast the unjust from him, crying in his offended majesty: 'DEPART FROM ME, YE CURSED, INTO EVERLASTING FIRE WHICH WAS PREPARED FOR THE DEVIL AND HIS ANGELS.'[98]

Nevertheless, the old certainties were becoming much more problematic. That the soul was naturally immortal was a view that had continued to hold sway throughout the eighteenth century, particularly among the proponents of natural theology. It had received support in the nineteenth century in a philosophical idealism, notably in the thought of G. W. F. Hegel (1770–1831), which viewed Spirit (*Geist*) as the essence of both individuals and the universe. Having said that, the view of man as a mortal body united to an immortal soul had become more questionable in both the eighteenth and nineteenth centuries, not least as the result of a developing naturalistic materialism that denied, on principle, the existence of all things supernatural, including God, spirits angelic and demonic, and souls.

Thus, for example, for the German philosopher Ludwig Feuerbach (1804–72), whose materialism was in essence Hegel's idealism turned upside down, eternal life was nothing but this life imagined as it ought to be, a merely fictional projection of how we wish life really were in the here and now. The future life, declared Feuerbach in his *The Essence of Christianity* (1841), is nothing but 'the present embellished, contemplated through the imagination, purified from all gross matter; or, positively expressed, it is the beauteous present intensified.'[99] For Karl Marx (1818–83), Feuerbach had failed to go far enough. Feuerbach's critique of heaven needed to become a critique of earth, of its material practices and social relations: 'after the earthly family is discovered to be the secret of the holy family, the former must then itself be criticised in theory and revolutionised in practice.'[100] As for Feuerbach and Marx, so also for Sigmund Freud (1856–1939), Heaven was an illusion invented to offer hope against the sufferings of this life and compensation for its injustices: 'it brushes away men's fear of the dangers and vicissitudes of life, in so far as it assures them of a happy ending, and comforts them in their misfortunes.'[101] Unlike Feuerbach and Marx, however, Freud has moved the critique of religion from the social to the psychological. The history of religion was for Freud the history of a spiritual illusion that fulfilled the oldest, strongest and most urgent wishes of mankind. It was the unhealthy persistence of the wishes and needs of childhood into maturity. In short, religion, whether in the evolution of mankind or in the development of each individual, was a neurosis 'which the civilised individual must pass through on his way from childhood to maturity'.[102]

Still, for some nineteenth-century Christians, the adoption of materialism did not necessitate the denial of all eschatology. Materialism found sympathisers among those Christians who advocated the death of the soul (soul-deniers), and focused eschatology on the resurrection of the body. It had appeal also for those annihilationists who, denying the soul's natural immortality, saw its immortality as conditional solely on God's continuing goodwill, and envisaged its ultimate destruction at some time after the Last Judgement. At the very least, that man was by nature immortal now had to be argued for by its supporters and not just assumed as a truth demonstrable by reason.

Nineteenth-century debates about the biblical account of hell had also reached a stalemate. The Bible had become as much a cause of diverse accounts of the afterlife as the source of an authoritative unified view. Along with this, the rise of historical criticism, with its attendant diminution of the authority of the Bible, had rendered disputes about the meaning of biblical terms much less determinative and decisive. Moreover, among the theologically liberal, in the light of modern cosmology, heaven and hell were no longer conceived as *places* that could be geographically located. They had become at best *states* of post-mortem life rather than places. 'Heaven above' and 'hell below' had become merely metaphorical and not literal. For some, 'hell' had become a metaphor more relevant to conditions on this side of the divide than a literal place on the other. Thus, for example, to the eyes of William Booth (1829–1912), the founder of the Salvation Army, industrial England was itself infernal:

> Talk about Dante's Hell, and all the horrors and cruelty of the torture-chamber of the lost! The man who walks with open eyes and with bleeding heart through the shambles of our civilisation needs no such fantastic images of the poet to teach him horror.[103]

In addition to this, nineteenth-century penal reform was coming to view criminal punishments as restorative rather than retributive. The consequence of this was that it was becoming more difficult to conceive of hell as a site of physical punishment (*poena sensus*). Rather, it was transforming into a site only of psychological punishment (*poena damni*), a state that consisted primarily in the soul's despair at its separation from God.

The nineteenth century's belief in the possibility of progress for individuals and humanity as a whole also saw a decline in the acceptance that the destiny of individuals was fixed at death (or at birth). Salvation by grace and predestination to salvation or damnation (or both) were countered by an emphasis on the individual freely creating his ethical self. Thus, on the other side of life, the individual became free to turn towards God after death, morally to advance, and finally to attain salvation. Kant had established philosophical reasons for this. But it was also reinforced by the theological dominance of an eschatology focused on life immediately after death and not after the Last Judgement. At least among liberals, both Catholic and Protestant, there was no expectation of the imminent return of Christ. The eschatology of the Last Day with its assertion of the end of history and its harsh judgement of eternal happiness or eternal misery, while still theoretically endorsed, was practically ignored.

Doubts about the intellectual coherence of the resurrection of the flesh continued. Henry Bowler's (1824–1903) painting *The Doubt: Can These Dry Bones Live?* (1855; Plate 27 [c]) gave eloquent expression to the tensions between doubts about the resurrection of the dead and the biblical certainty of it, between the exhumed remains of 'John Faithful' lying on the ground and the biblical text on the gravestone *from John 11.25* – 'I am the resurrection and the life.' The melancholic expression on the face of the young woman leaning on the gravestone leaves the viewer in no doubt that this *is* a painting about doubt. By the end of the nineteenth century, the balance had shifted irrevocably away from the post-resurrection body and towards the post-mortem spirit.

The division that was progressively hardening during the nineteenth century between conservative and liberal views of life after death was paralleled by another contrast – that between elite views of the afterlife and an emerging popular view. The focus of attention now became the life of the spirit immediately after death in a newly emerging nineteenth-century heaven to which all could reasonably aspire. In this afterlife, hell no longer had a role, and even God and his saints and martyrs faded into the background.

Chapter Seven

Heavens, Sacred and Secular

> There is a land of pure delight
> Where saints immortal reign;
> Infinite day excludes the night,
> And pleasures banish pain.
>
> There everlasting spring abides,
> And never-withering flowers;
> Death like a narrow sea divides
> This heavenly land from ours.
>
> Isaac Watts (1674–1748)

The early modern heaven

Between the torments of the damned and the joys of the saved, there was a contrast of symmetries, of light and dark, joy and misery, pleasures and pains. The nature of the delights of heaven, however, was less commented upon than the horrors of hell. This can be explained by the conviction that concentrating on the torments of the lost was more an incentive to the leading of a godly life than dwelling on its rewards. As the French Catholic François-René Chateaubriand (1768–1848) was to put it:

> Heaven, where boundless felicity reigns, is too far above the human condition for the soul to be strongly affected by the bliss of the elect: one can interest oneself but little in beings who are perfectly happy. This is why poets have succeeded better in the description of hells: at least humanity is there, and the torments of the guilty remind us of the miseries of this life.[1]

That said, in the sixteenth and seventeenth centuries, there was little doubt that, as the torments of the damned would include the eternal absence of

God, so the happiness of the blessed would consist in living eternally in the presence of God. Thus, for example the philosopher Thomas Browne (1605–82) saw heaven as nothing but the presence of God. After God had destroyed the world, he wrote, all that would remain would be an empty space filled with the divine presence. He alone was the place in which the blessed would reside:

> when this sensible world shall bee destroyed, all shall then bee as it is now there, an Empyreall Heaven [...] To aske where Heaven is, is to demand where the presence of God is, or where wee have the glory of that happy vision.[2]

This image of the God-centred heavenly life reached its classic Puritan statement in Richard Baxter's *The Saints' Everlasting Rest* (1650). For Baxter, the focus of heaven was God alone:

> As all Good whatsoever is comprised in God, and all in the creature are but drops of this Ocean: So all the Glory of the blessed is comprised in their enjoyment of God; and if there be any mediate Joys, they are but drops from this. If men and Angels should study to speak the blessedness of that estate in one word, what can they say beyond this, That it is the nearest enjoyment of God?[3]

There were, as Baxter suggested, 'drops of joy' other than the presence of God. He, like a number of his contemporaries, did distinguish between the primary glory of the vision of God and a secondary glory that consisted of fellowship with the saints and angels. He looked forward to the day when he would sit down with Enoch, Noah, Abraham, Isaac, Jacob, Moses and David. He anticipated with joy eternally dwelling with Peter and Paul, Augustine and Jerome, and with the Reformation worthies: Luther, Calvin, Zwingli, Beza and Bullinger – indeed with 'all the Saints of all ages, whose faces in the flesh we never saw, whom we shall there both know and comfortable enjoy'.[4]

Baxter's heaven is a God-centred one. But it is also a heavenly society. He was deeply committed to the belief that our present knowledge would be increased, and therefore that we would once again know our friends in heaven. We would not know each other according to our physical appearance – by stature, voice, colour, complexion or outward shape – nor by titles of honour and worldly dignity, by age or sex. But, he confidently declared, 'by the Image of Christ, and spiritual relation, and former faithfulness in improving our Talents, beyond doubt, we shall know and be known.'[5]

Many of these themes in Baxter recurred throughout the writings of the period. Andrew Marvell (1621–78), Milton's assistant and Oliver Cromwell's court poet, somewhat toadyingly placed the Lord Protector alongside Moses, Joshua and David.[6] To the Anglican William Gearing (*fl.* 1660–90), the blessed would behold the glory of God and would see the face of Christ as do friends now behold each other's faces, albeit with glorified vision. They would also see not only the faces of all the saved but also those of the patriarchs, saints, prophets, Apostles and martyrs. They would also reacquaint themselves with old friends. If the soul can carry with it a sociable inclination, Gearing surmised,

> then may it for the use and exercise of this desire be admitted to the knowledge of other Souls, and of those especially with whom it had sojourned on Earth, that like fellow-travellers [...] they may thenceforth interchangeably communicate their joys, springing from their present rest and peace.[7]

This issue of friends in heaven was extensively dealt with in 1698 by John Dunton (1659–1733), the founder of the Athenian Society. Written on the death of his wife Elizabeth, *An Essay Proving We Shall Know Our Friends in Heaven* claimed (and rightly so) to be the first book totally devoted to this subject. It was the hope of being reunited with his deceased wife that motivated Dunton's essay. To this end, he assembled a number of sources in which the expectation of meeting husbands, wives and children in the afterlife was mooted.

For Dunton, life in heaven would be a continuation of the social relations present in this world. Society, he argued, was not comfortable without familiar acquaintance, and heaven would be no different. 'Be assured,' he wrote, that familiar acquaintance

> shall not be wanting in the Height and Perfection of all Glory, Bliss, and Joy. Nay, our Minds being abundantly and beatifically illuminated with all Wisdom and Knowledge, we shall be acquainted to know, not only those of former Holy Acquaintance, but also Strangers, and such as we never knew before.[8]

Dunton was familiar with Baxter's *Everlasting Rest*. In contrast to Baxter, however, he maintained that we would know each other by face, stature, voice and difference of sex. Indeed, on the issue of whether sexual identity would be retained in heaven, he specifically argued against Baxter. Thus, while he maintained that there would be no sexual relations between husbands and wives, the heavenly body would conform to the disposition of the soul, which was eternally male or female:

> [T]he soul [...] of the one is Resolute and Constant, that of the other Light, Wavering and Changeable [...] The Soul of one takes a pride in being Grave, and speaking little; the other talks much, and cannot forbear *twatling upon every thing*.[9]

A similar stereotype of women had appeared in 1691 in the *Athenian Gazette*, which Dunton edited, although the discussion of sexual identity in heaven was different. In answer to a reader's question, 'Are there sexes in heaven?' the columnist argued that in a state of perfection and bliss, anything imperfect and accidental would be removed, and consequently sexuality should be. He couldn't resist the following:

> We won't add for another Reason what, as we remember, one of the Fathers has said – That *were there any women in Heaven, the Angels cou'd not stand long*, but would certainly be seduced from their Innocency, and Fall as *Adam* did.[10]

Still, in spite of any standard 'sexist' leanings, that Dunton was distraught by the death of his wife and deeply comforted by the thought of their eventual union is clear. 'Her Death,' he poignantly wrote, 'has made me so very melancholy, that I had pin'd away in a few days, had not the hopes of finding her again in Heaven, given me *some Relief*.'[11]

Similar sentiments were expressed in the poet Elizabeth Singer Rowe's (1674–1737) *Friendship in Death*, first published in 1728, with more than 30 editions in the eighteenth century and a readership into the nineteenth.[12] In these 20 letters from the dead to the living, the reader was assured that human love was an essential part of life in the beautiful celestial realm. Rowe's heaven had tinges of embodied eroticism and flavours of Eden. For her, death could not sever the bonds of love, whether between parents and children, husbands and wives, or brothers and sisters. According to Peter

Walmsley, Rowe's heaven is 'a new Christian society whose bounds are affective and natural rather than disciplinary and conventional, a society of loving souls which extends from this world to the next'.[13] It is a sign of things to come. For it is a heaven from which God is conspicuously absent, a secular Paradise. The spirit of this work is amply conveyed by the letter of Altamont, who had died grieving for his wife Almeria:

> The first gentle Spirit that welcom'd me to these new Regions, was the lovely *Almeria*; but how Dazling! How divinely Fair! Extasy was in her Eyes, and inexpressible Pleasure in every smile! Her Mien and Aspect more soft and propitious than ever was feign'd by Poets of their Goddess of Beauty and Love: What was airy Fiction *there*, was *here* all transporting Reality. With an inimitable Grace she received me into her aetherial Chariot, which was sparkling Saphire studded with Gold [...] But how shall I describe this fair, this fragrant, this enchanting Land of Love! The Myrtle Shades and rosy Bowers, the bright Cascades and chrystal Rivulets rolling over Orient Pearls and Sands of Gold: Here they spread their silent Waves into broad transparent Lakes, smooth as the Face of Heaven; and there they break with rapid Force through arching Rocks of Diamond and Purple Amethist.[14]

These visions of the reunion in heaven of families and friends were no doubt the consequence of changing patterns of human relationships. In particular, the desire to be reunited with spouses reflected the growth during the early modern period in the companionate marriage, one in which each partner contributed to the spiritual, emotional and intellectual well-being of the other. And the sacralisation of the companionate marriage in the afterlife in such works as Rowe's no doubt helped to normalise the companionate marriage in this life.

What is also clear is that the boundaries between life and death were breaking down. Heaven was more a continuation of this life than discontinuous with it, albeit one where pain and sorrow are no more. As Isaac Watts put it in the hymn with which this chapter began, death is now merely 'a narrow sea' dividing this 'heavenly land from ours'. Watts had himself created a version of the social heaven combined with a traditional God-centred one. There is little doubt that Watts's two main works on the afterlife were highly influential. His *The World to Come* went through five editions in the eighteenth century, while his *Death and Heaven* saw 16 by 1818. In Watts's heaven, for the saved, there will be clear and unerring knowledge, unspotted holiness and everlasting joy. We will progress in all of these. We will know things in

> a manner something akin to the Way whereby God knows us [...] such a sort of Knowledge as we have of a Man when we see his Face [...] a certain and unwavering Knowledge, without remaining Doubts, without Error, or Mistake.[15]

Holiness and happiness will combine in the love and service of God and our fellow creatures. There will be no envy, ambition and malice, for a universal benevolence runs through the whole kingdom. We do not know what senses the resurrected body will have. The organs of light and sound, however, will be such as transcend those we have in our present state. Certainly, there will be no pain: '[N]o Gout nor Stone, no Infirmity nor Distemper, no Head-ach nor Heart-ach shall ever attend them.'[16]

In heaven, the blessed will be eternally awake, not least because heaven is a place where there is neither night nor darkness (in contrast to hell, where all is gloom). The light of heaven, Watts wrote, 'is constant without Interruption, and Everlasting or without end.'[17] So, no rest there for the virtuous! Who could get to sleep, he asked, 'under the full Blaze of divine Glory, under the incessant Communications of divine Love?'[18] All the regions of Paradise are constantly illuminated by the glory of God. Not so much a place of eternal rest, Watts's heaven is a place of never-ending activity. The saved would not have it otherwise. Those who have actively served God on earth 'can hardly bear the Thoughts of paying no active Duties, doing no work at all for him in heaven, where Business is all over Delight, and Labour is all Enjoyment.'[19] It will be a delight because our faculties will then be so suited to our work that we will never feel fatigued by it. Everlasting active service will combine with eternal delight and satisfaction. 'Business and Pleasure,' Watts declared, 'are for ever the same among all the inhabitants.'[20] The ideal of the dignity of labour predominates in this very Protestant heaven.

Work in heaven will reflect its variety in the human world. Our various skills will there be put to use. Scientists will continue their research.[21] Theologians will continue to ply their trade.[22] Thus, souls will work in heaven in ways suited to their former earthly capacities, although some of them will be trained to undertake higher duties. Indeed, there will be a form of governance there, for some spirits 'may be appointed Visitors and Superintendents over whole Provinces of intelligent Beings in lower Regions, who are yet labouring in their State of Probation.'[23] Similarly, there will be degrees of reward in heaven relative to the level of virtue attained in this life. In the theatre of heaven, the more virtuous will have the better seats:

> Can we think that Abraham and Moses, who were train'd up in converse with God face to face, as a Man converses with his Friend [...] were not prepar'd for a greater intimacy with God, and nearer views of his Glory in heaven, than Sampson and Jephthah those rude Heroes, who spent their Days in bloody Work, in hewing down the Philistines and the Ammonites?[24]

Much time will be spent in worship, songs and prayer. But there will also be lectures and sermons given to the younger spirits by those more exalted. Watts's heaven resembles an eternal academic conference held at a fashionable resort. Conversations with angels will inform the saved of their transactions with men. Adam will acquaint us with the nature of innocence, of the trees of Knowledge and of Life, and of how he fell. Enoch and Elijah will tell us how they were translated to heaven, while Noah will speak of the Ark, and Abraham of his converse with God and angels. Paul and Moses will speak of the Jewish Law, and the Reformation worthies – Thomas Cranmer and Nicholas Ridley, Calvin and Luther – will tell of how they threw off 'the Chains, the Darkness and the Defilements of [papal] Antichrist.'[25] And if it should seem unreasonable that they should have to do this for every new arrival in heaven,

> 'tis very unreasonable to suppose, that Spirits made perfect and glorify'd have not a Power of communicating their Thoughts to many more Thousands by immediate Converse: and 'tis past our Reach to conceive what unknown Methods may be in use amongst them, to transmit their Ideas and Narratives.[26]

In any case, memories will be good, and older spirits can give accounts of such matters to the newly arrived. There will also be opportunities for travel. The blessed, 'active and swift as Sun-Beams', will be able to make journeys to distant 'Planetary Worlds' (perhaps other 'soular systems'), to boldly go where no man has gone before. Thence they can bring back 'new

Lectures of Divine Wisdom or Tidings of the affairs of those Provinces, to entertain our Fellow-Spirits.'[27] These will not be especially lengthy journeys, for heavenly bodies, as John Shower suggested and most would have agreed, could move at a speed of many 'thousands of Miles in an hour'.[28]

The doctrine of the communion of saints (*communio sanctorum*) had always implied a union between Christians on earth with one another and with those in heaven or Purgatory. By implication, it included communion between those in heaven. As early as the third century, Roman beliefs about the reunion of friends and family in heaven had found their way into Christianity. Thus, Augustine quoted Cyprian (d.258) to the effect that 'A great number of those who are dear to us are expecting us there – a dense and abundant crowd of parents, brethren, sons, are longing for us; already secure of their own safety, but still anxious about our salvation.'[29] That said, it remained very much a minor tradition within Christianity until the early modern period.

However, that the nature of the afterlife had become, by the second half of the eighteenth century, a part of general conversation and speculation about reunion with friends crucial to it, is demonstrated by Boswell's *Life of Johnson* (1791). In March 1772, Samuel Johnson's (1709–84) biographer James Boswell (1740–95), anxious to know Johnson's opinion about the future state, led him into a discussion of the afterlife. It will consist, declared Johnson, in a consciousness of the favour of God, in the contemplation of truth and in the possession of felicitating ideas. 'Is there any harm,' asked Boswell, 'in our forming to ourselves conjectures as to the particulars of our happiness, though the Scripture has said but very little on the subject?' To which Johnson replied, 'Sir, there is no harm.' And he went on to recommend the last word in philosophy on the matter, namely, the Platonist Henry More, the two-volume folio of whose works was for sale at the cost of about eight shillings. One of the most pleasing thoughts, Boswell continued, is 'that we shall see our friends again'. On this, Johnson was less confident. 'Yes, Sir,' he pronounced,

> but you must consider, that when we are become purely rational, many of our friendships will be cut off. Many friendships are formed by a community of sensual pleasures: all these will be cut off. We form many friendships with bad men, because they have agreeable qualities, and they can be useful to us; but, after death, they can no longer be of use to us. We form many friendships by mistake, imagining people to be

> different from what they really are. After death, we shall see everyone in a true light. Then Sir, they talk of our meeting with relations: but then all relationship is dissolved; and we shall have no regard for one person more than another, but for their real value. However, we shall either have the satisfaction of meeting our friends, or be satisfied without meeting them.[30]

There were others similarly worried about a heaven that was becoming too earthly. In 1739, for example, the *Gentleman's Magazine* published a reader's letter complaining about authors who, following John Milton's *Paradise Lost*, were

> corrupting our Notions of Spiritual Things and sensualizing our Ideas of Heaven to a Degree that may have ill Effects on Religion in general: It is letting Fancy obtrude its wild Luxuriance into the Place of Truth and Reason, and making room for the grossest and most absurd kind of Enthusiasm, and if one is to interpret his [Milton's] other Descriptions of Heaven by this Hint, it is every whit as sensual as the Mahometan's.[31]

In the early modern period, as in earlier centuries, heavenly bodies, like heavenly places, were ambiguous mixtures of the corporeal and the spiritual. That the bodies of those in the afterlife were fashioned after the virtues and vices of the souls who inhabited them was a common theme: lucid, refulgent, glorious, spiritual, heavenly, transparent and angelic for the good; gross, dark, foetid, diseased and demonic for the wicked. The much-admired (by Samuel Johnson) Henry More saw heavenly bodies as manifesting visibly the nature of the soul:

> For if Vertue and Vice can be ever seen with outward eyes, it must be in these aerial Vehicles [...] that the Soule in a manner becomes perfectly transparent through them, discovering her lovely beauty in all the efflorescencies thereof, to the ineffable enravishment of the beholder.[32]

The *Athenian Gazette* described our resurrection bodies as 'shining and bright'.[33] The contrast between light and dark, heaven and hell, was interestingly expressed in the same journal in answer to the question of whether 'negroes' would rise so on the Last Day: 'Black is of the colour of the night,' we are informed,

> frightful, dark and horrid; but White of the Day and Light, refreshing and lovely. Taking then this blackness of the Negro to be an accidental Imperfection [...] we conclude thence, that he shall not arise with that Complexion, but leave it behind him in the darkness of the Grave, exchanging it for a brighter and a better at his return agen into the World.[34]

The form of the heavenly body was also much discussed. For More, heavenly bodies would appear in the ordinary form of angels, 'such a countenance, and so cloathed, as they'.[35] And the angelic form was very much like the human. Although for More there would be no lust, nor difference of sex between heavenly beings, there would be some discrimination of beauty into male and female. The scientist Thomas Burnet agreed that heavenly bodies would be like those of the angels, lucid and ethereal, and consisting of celestial matter 'as pure and thin, as the finest Air or Aether'.[36] But unlike More, who believed that souls would have hearing, sight, touch, smell and taste, Burnet's heavenly bodies would have neither palate, throat, bowels nor sexual parts; in fact, bodies that, while recognisably angelic, were not obviously human. The bodies of the blessed would also be of a perfect age – that of Christ during his ministry on earth, that is, about 30 to 33. Those who had died in infancy or were severely deformed would be made perfect. In Elizabeth Rowe's *Friendship in Death*, the deceased two-year-old child found itself immediately after death 'an active and reasonable Being'.[37] William Gearing was unwilling to specify an 'age' for the heavenly body, but he was nonetheless convinced of its physical perfection: '[T]he Infant and the Dwarf shall be made a proper man! [...] when the Child that left its own soul before it left the Womb, shall in an instant, without growth, be as big as the Mother.'[38]

In their work *Heaven: A History*, Colleen McDannell and Bernhard Lang make much of the transition from a God-centred heaven focused on the eternal worship and praise of God to a modern heaven characterised by four features. First, only a thin veil separates heaven from earth, and heavenly life begins immediately after death. Second, rather than heaven being structurally opposite to life on earth, it is a continuation and fulfilment of material existence. Third, although heaven remains a place of rest, the saints are increasingly active in heaven, making progress in a joy-filled environment. Finally, a focus on human love replaces the primacy of the divine love experienced in the form of the Beatific Vision. Social relationships are fundamental to the afterlife, not a distraction from it, and God is loved primarily through the love shown to other heavenly spirits.[39]

As we have seen, all of these features were coming into play in the period between 1500 and 1750. Be that as it may, the dominant feature of the early modern heaven remained the gulf fixed not only between earth and heaven but also between heaven and hell. The sufferings of this world were swallowed up in eternal felicity, or intensified in the horrors of hell. This world was, in the main, a mixed realm halfway between the two kingdoms of good and evil, of light and dark.

Between 1750 and 1900, this was to change. The God-centred heaven was taken over by one centred on human relationships; the sacred heaven became secularised, especially in the popular imagination. This was not least because of the influence of a Swedish Lutheran visionary: Emanuel Swedenborg (1688–1772; Plate 28 [BW]) – 'that divinely chosen seer of our age', as Goethe described him, 'who was impregnated with the joys of heaven, to whom the spirits spoke through all senses and the entire body, in whose bosom the angels lived'.[40] For Swedenborg claimed, in his visions, to have crossed the narrow sea, to have experienced life on the other side, and to have conversed with the spirits there, all of whom once lived a normal life on earth. In Swedenborg, we have a new source of knowledge of the afterlife beyond both reason and revelation, namely, personal visionary experience.

The visions of Emanuel Swedenborg

For Immanuel Kant, as we have seen, practical reason demanded the postulation of the immortality of the soul. About the details of the afterlife, however, Kant had nothing to say. For him, they were beyond what could be known. So it is a matter for little surprise that Kant described Swedenborg's major work, the *Arcana coelestia* (Heavenly mysteries; 1749–56) as 'full of nonsense' and 'void of the last drop of reason'.[41] Kant's attack ended the intellectual respectability of a man who, until he had a vision from God in London in 1745 in which he saw heaven and hell, was an esteemed scientist. For the rest of his life, Swedenborg set out to map the worlds of spirits. Thus, it is as the seer and not as the scientist that he is remembered, albeit as one who attempted to come to terms with a secular world – one that had been scientifically disenchanted – by his visions of a spiritual world 'alongside' the material one and corresponding to it. Strongly influenced by the body–mind dualism of the French philosopher René Descartes (1596–1650), this was Cartesianism gone cosmic. Ironically, body and soul, matter and spirit, science and religion were reconciled by emphasising their fundamental differences.

According to Swedenborg, the material world that we now inhabit is one of innumerable such populated planets.[42] It is located between heaven and hell, in the former of which the inhabitants love the Lord and their neighbour, in the latter of which the inhabitants love the world and themselves. Both of these kingdoms try to influence those in this world by means of spirits from hell and angels from heaven. These forces balance each other out, with the result that individuals are free to choose the one or the other. As a consequence, our eternal destiny is in our hands alone. We are saved or damned not by faith or by predestination, but through our own free choice for good or evil and through the active expression of these in our lives. Life in the here and now, as in heaven, is a matter of active thoughtfulness for our neighbour:

> [T]he life that leads to heaven is not one of withdrawal from the world but a life in the world [...] a life of thoughtfulness, a life of behaving honestly and fairly in every duty, every affair, every task, from our deeper nature and therefore from a heavenly source. The source of this life is within us when we act honestly and fairly because doing so is in accord with divine laws.[43]

Thus, the good life is active and not contemplative. In virtuous and active living, we mimic the angels: 'the life of angels is cheerful and blessed. It consists of worthwhile activities that are deeds of thoughtfulness.'[44]

At the time of death, we enter the world of spirits (*mundus spiritum*). Here, there is a vast number of spirits gathered. As the place of preparation to enter heaven or hell, there is no fixed limit to our stay in this world of spirits. Some have only barely entered and are taken up into heaven or cast down into hell. Some stay for weeks, others for years, although no more than 30. The more that our deeper nature is in correspondence with our outward nature, the less time is spent in the world of spirits. Upon arrival there is a careful sorting by the Lord. Evil people are connected with the hellish community that their ruling love (self-love) had affiliated them with while still in the world, and good people with those of love, thoughtfulness and faith with whom they had connected while still in the world. Even so, for a while at least, people seem to be more or less the same as they were in the material world. We are free to talk to anyone that we wish to:

> friends and acquaintances from our physical life, especially husbands and wives, and also brothers and sisters. I have seen a father talking with his six sons and recognising them. I have seen many other people with their relatives and friends.[45]

In the next state after death, people are transformed into their true selves. This is the result of being taken up by angels who instruct them about the Lord, heaven and the angelic life. Arrivals with an overall disposition to evil soon wish to get away from their angelic instructors. When the angels notice this, they leave them. These people will drift towards others of a similarly evil nature, thus turning away from God and towards the hell they were united with in this world. Those whose good nature dominates will eventually slough off any remaining evil and be purified. At this point, their appearances change. The face becomes very different from the face of the body and 'comes to look like the ruling affection in which the deeper reaches of our mind were engaged in the world, the kind of affection characteristic of the spirit within the body'.[46] People who were 'engaged in good affections have lovely faces, while people who were engaged in evil affections have ugly ones'.[47] Hypocrites, skilled as they are in counterfeiting good affections, take longer to become even uglier. It is now that the final separation of the good from the wicked occurs. The wicked choose to go into hell, while the good prepare to enter heaven.

Swedenborg's most radical innovation now occurs. The good now enter the world of the angels. More importantly, they become angels: '[F]or we have been created to enter heaven and become angels.' Not surprising, then, that angels have a truly human form! 'I can say with full confidence,' declared Swedenborg on the grounds of several years of experience,

> that in their form, angels are completely human. They have faces, eyes, ears, chests, arms, hands, and feet. They see each other, hear each other, and talk to each other. In short, they lack nothing that belongs to humans except that they are not clothed with a material body.[48]

Angels talk to each other about various 'everyday' things – domestic matters, community concerns, issues of moral and spiritual life. They cannot, however, speak any human languages. The angelic language that they speak is differentiated into words, is articulated in sound, and is innate. But most importantly, it is unlike any human language because it is the language of Adam before the Fall, or of mankind before Babel (resembling Hebrew).[49] In the language of the angels, there is a perfect 'natural' correlation between words and ideas, not a merely artificial one, as in human languages. That we will be able to speak it (and Swedenborg could understand it) is the result of its remaining deep within us after the Fall. Thus, the angels can speak the universal language, the quest for which had occupied many theologians, linguists, mystics and magicians during the seventeenth and eighteenth centuries.[50] This was no doubt an idea that Swedenborg drew from his reading of the Lutheran John Engelbrecht's (1599–1642) *True Account and Vision of Heaven and Hell*. Engelbrecht too purported to translate into his own language that of the angels.[51]

Be that as it may, according to Swedenborg, like-minded angels may come together to live in communities, the larger ones consisting of tens of thousands of individuals, the smaller of thousands, the smallest of hundreds. There are nonetheless people who live alone. Within these communities, the blessed – that is, the angels – live in houses. These are much the same as earthly homes, only more beautiful: 'They have chambers, suites, and bedrooms in abundance, and courtyards with gardens, flower beds, and lawns around them.'[52] The houses are arranged in the form of a city, with streets, lanes and public squares, 'just like the ones we see in cities on our earth.'[53] There are also palaces, beautiful beyond description, and parklands 'where everything sparkled in the same way, here and there the leaves like silver and the fruits like gold, with the flowers in their beds making virtual rainbows with their colours.'[54]

Granting that the form of the angels is like that of their earlier human selves, the angels are divided into male and female. This leads Swedenborg again to break with the long Christian tradition of there being no marriage in heaven (or at least of no weddings in heaven).[55] Marriage in heaven is, however, different to that on earth. It is a meeting not of bodies but of minds. 'Marriage love,' he wrote,

> finds its source in the union of two people in one mind. In heaven, this is called 'living together', and they are not called 'two' but 'one.' Consequently two spouses in heaven are not called two angels but one angel.[56]

Because the heavenly communities consist of like-minded people, it is a matter of instant attraction: 'So at first sight they love each other most deeply, see each other as married partners, and enter into their marriage.'[57] Heavenly weddings are followed by feasts that are attended by many. The key difference between earthly and heavenly marriages is procreation. Although there are sexual relations between couples in heaven, in place of the procreation of children, there is only 'the procreation of what is good and true'. There is no place in heaven for the Beatific Vision. Rather, the emphasis is on the erotic union of two people, in which the love of the man is the truth flowing towards the good, and the love of the woman is the good flowing towards the true. Here erotic love has replaced divine love as the ultimate source of goodness. Conjugal sex is the exemplar of the sacred.

Swedenborg was far more interested in the heavenly than the infernal life. It will come as no surprise that evil spirits were former human beings, destined to spend eternity in hell. However, unlike in Christian orthodoxy, this could not be the consequence of any direct action by a God who was goodness itself. Rather, it was the result of the cultivation by the spirits in hell of a disposition to evil in their earthly life that continued to assert itself when they entered the world of spirits after death. 'So after death, it is we,' Swedenborg declared, 'not the Lord, who cast ourselves into hell.'[58] The tortures of hell were physical, but not divinely inflicted. Rather, 'The Hellish mob craves and loves nothing more than inflicting harm, especially punishing and torturing.'[59] And there was no escape because our nature is already fixed for eternity, as good or evil, at death. The evil lived there in various hells, according to the degree of their wickedness, in what amounted to a post-apocalyptic world beneath the earth of caves of fire and darkness, of the ruins of cities and houses, of brothels full of filth and excrement, of deserts and dark forests 'where hellish spirits roam like wild beasts', of the wicked raging against each other.[60] The most evil of them were able to attack those on earth, 'making themselves unnoticeable and floating around others like ghosts, doing their harm covertly, spraying it around like the venom of snakes'.[61]

All of this was the consequence of what Swedenborg claimed was an intensely personal vision. He was forbidden, he somewhat disingenuously claimed, 'to read authors on dogmatic and systematic theology, before heaven was opened to me; because unfounded opinions and fictions might have easily insinuated themselves thereby, which afterwards could only have been removed with difficulty.'[62] Readers of Swedenborg look in vain for any references to those who might intellectually have influenced him. Church people, declared Swedenborg in 1758, know practically nothing about heaven and hell or their life after death. For the sake of those of simple heart and simple faith, wrote Swedenborg,

> it has been granted to me to be with angels and to talk with them person to person. I have also been enabled to see what is in heaven and hell, a process that has been going on for thirteen years.[63]

That he was innovative is beyond doubt. During the eighteenth century, as a consequence of the scientific revolution, nature had come more and more to be seen as 'disenchanted', indeed as merely 'dead' matter. This had rendered intellectually redundant the tradition of Renaissance esotericism, embedded in Neoplatonism and the Hermetic tradition, which had seen nature in its essence as 'enchanted', as imbued with life and spirit. Although undoubtedly influenced by the esoteric tradition, the significance of Swedenborg lay in his rejecting nature as 'alive', accepting its 'death' and discovering a spiritual realm 'over against' it rather than 'deep' within it or part of it. Simply put, from the time of Swedenborg, the realm of spirit becomes 'the other side' rather than the reality underpinning 'this side'.[64]

Swedenborg's angels were more than merely sexually active. Like earthly life should be, heavenly life was highly active in a number of ways. As on earth, so also in heaven, there was a variety of heavenly occupations – ecclesiastical, civic and domestic. Churchgoing occurred, but the essential worship of God in heaven was the life of active love, thoughtfulness and right faith. Some spirits took care of people on earth as guardian angels, while others worked in hell, ensuring that those there were not tortured beyond set limits. Some cared for new arrivals as they awakened from death in the world of the spirits, while others prepared new arrivals, both Christian and non-Christian, to enter heaven.[65] No longer doomed to limbo, nor destined to spend eternity as an infant or child, every child that died (whether a member of the Church or not, baptised or not) was admitted into heaven to become an angel. Thus, some communities took care of babies while others taught young boys and girls while they were growing up.

Swedenborg's was a vision of heaven that was to find expression in the work of William Blake (1757–1827), particularly in his illustrations for *The Grave*, an 1808 poem by Robert Blair. Blake had been, at least for a time, a devotee of Swedenborg, and had studied his *Heaven and Hell*. Thus, his drawing of *The Meeting of a Family in Heaven* (Plate 29 [BW]) shows a couple reunited after death with two other 'couples' in close embrace. To the modern viewer, it all looks innocent enough. But contemporary viewers were shocked. One declared in the 7 August 1808 edition of the newspaper the *Examiner* that 'the salutation of a man and his wife meeting in the pure mansions of Heaven' presented 'the most indecent attitudes' because 'libidinousness intrudes itself upon our thoughts'.[66]

Blake was not alone in his vision of an eroticised, or at least romanticised, afterlife. The art and poetry of Dante Gabriel Rossetti (1828–82), founder of the Pre-Raphaelite Brotherhood, was characterised by its evocations of sensuality. Thus, in the final version of his poem 'The blessed Damozel' (1881), while the damozel looked longingly over the bar of heaven upon the earth beneath hoping for the soul of her lover to come to her,

> Around her, lovers, newly met
> 'Mid deathless love's acclaims
> Spoke evermore among themselves
> Their heart-remember'd names;
> And the souls mounting up to God
> Went by her like thin flames.[67]

This vision of the afterlife as the reunion of lovers in heaven is also found in the background to Rossetti's painting *The Blessed Damozel* (Plate 32 [c]). Here are depicted the embraces of reunited lovers in heaven above the damozel, who looks down, past the angels, to her earthly lover resting beside a river in a wooded landscape.

All this is not to say that the God-centred heaven disappeared from the nineteenth-century imagination. Bishop Reginald Heber (1783–1826), most remembered for his 'politically incorrect' hymn 'The heathen in his blindness bows down to wood and stone', reminded churchgoers on Trinity Sunday in his hymn 'Holy, holy, holy' that

> all the saints adore thee,
> Casting down their golden crowns upon the glassy sea;
> Cherubim and Seraphim falling down before thee
> Which wert, and art, and evermore shalt be.[68]

In a more secular vein, the God-centred heaven was reinforced by Christina Rossetti (1830–94), Gabriel Rossetti's sister, for whom her brother's heaven of 'The blessed Damozel' fell short of the highest view. For her, in the poem 'From house to home', the love between couples was swallowed up in the divine love. Although hands locked never to be separated again, there was much plucking of harps and casting of crowns as

> Each face looked one way like a moon new-lit,
> Each face looked one way towards its Sun of Love;
> Drank love and bathed in love and mirrored it
> And knew no end thereof.[69]

The Gates Ajar

Arguably, Swedenborg was ultimately responsible for the idea in modern Western popular culture that heaven is the continuation of a life only minimally different to the best of life on this side – a place of spiritual growth, of social relations, of enjoyable labours and pleasant pastimes. But for the history of eschatology, he was more than this. He signalled the end of a spirituality dominated by philosophers, pastors and priests. Others wished to go where he had gone, to see the delights of heaven for themselves and to commune with the world of spirits. As early as 1810, of a rural community in Leicestershire, the English poet George Crabbe (1754–1832) wrote that

> Some Swedenborgians in our street are found,
> Those wandering walkers on enchanted ground,
> Who in our world can other Worlds survey,
> And speak with Spirits though confined in clay.[70]

In short, Swedenborg was in the vanguard of those who, in the nineteenth century, oversaw the democratisation of spirituality and, in some cases, its political radicalisation. Thus, for example, Andrew Jackson Davis (1826–1910), the so-called 'Poughkeepsie seer', was especially influenced by Swedenborg as the latter's writings began to influence North America. He dictated his 800-page *The Principles of Nature, Her Divine Revelation, and a Voice to Mankind by and through Andrew Jackson Davis* (1847) while in a trance. Going through 34 editions in less than 30 years, the work involved (very) lengthy explanations of the nature of the universe and visionary schemes for social reform. As a consequence, the 'Harmonial Philosophy' struck a chord as much among this-worldly dreamers of social reform (abolitionists, prohibitionists, educationalists, animal protectionists and feminists) as among other-worldly visionaries. It was as much about preparing for a heavenly utopia on this side of the grave as preparing us for a utopian heaven on the other.[71]

More focused on informing her readers of the next world than reforming this one, Elizabeth Stuart Phelps (1844–1911) was among the most influential popularisers of the social heaven. Her book *The Gates Ajar* (1868) was the second-best-selling novel of the nineteenth century.[72] It told the story of Mary Cabot, a New England woman finding it difficult to come to terms with the death of her brother Roy in the American Civil War. Mary was the better able to do so after the arrival of her Aunt Winifred, who was able to console her with a different understanding of heaven, one not of the vision of God but of social relations and useful activities.

Phelps was familiar with the writings of Swedenborg. She has Aunt Winifred rather cutely declare that she was a Swedenborgian '[u]ntil I read his books.'[73] But around Phelps's heaven there is nonetheless a distinctly Swedenborgian air. Her brother Roy is only out of sight, but he is 'here, close beside you all this time.'[74] Along with Roy, we all become angels in the next life. Death is simply 'the slipping off of the outer body, as a husk slips off from its kernel.'[75] God is represented primarily by a very human Jesus with whom we will talk 'as a man talketh with a friend.'[76] She endorses Swedenborg's view that babies will outnumber adults and will be 'given into the care of those women especially fond of them.'[77] She even quotes Swedenborg's *Heaven and Hell* on the nature of heavenly housing.[78]

On the other hand, hell was conspicuously absent. And Phelps would have firmly rejected Swedenborg's eroticised heaven.[79] Her heaven was about romantic love, family life and 'Victorian' values. So it was a much more domesticated, genteel and well-mannered affair. It just as firmly rejected the Protestant orthodoxy of a God-centred heaven:

> There was something about adoration, and the harpers harping with their harps, and the sea of glass, and crying, Worthy the Lamb! and a great deal more that bewildered and disheartened me so that I could scarcely listen to it. I do not doubt that we shall glorify God primarily and happily, but can we not do it in some other way than by harping and praying?[80]

Thus, Phelps's heaven was a projection into the afterlife of the bourgeois sensibilities of provincial life in nineteenth-century New England. As Mark Twain rather unkindly put it, hers was 'a mean little ten-cent heaven about the size of Rhode Island'.[81]

Although in heaven we will be in spiritual bodies, we will be very much ourselves, easily recognisable to others. Thus, it will be a place of companionship, of amiable conversation, of 'talk and laugh and joke and play'.[82] We will see both sacred and secular heroes – King David and Paul, the poets William Cowper and Elizabeth Barrett Browning, and Abraham Lincoln. Domestic life is made divine and divine life domesticated. 'A happy home is the happiest thing in the world,' declared Aunt Winifred. 'I do not see why it should not be in any world [...] I expect to have my beautiful home, and my husband, and [my daughter] Faith, as I had them here.'[83] Children will play the piano, have toys and eat strawberries and gingersnaps. Adults will have books and music, art galleries and orchestral halls, and perhaps there will be travel to other planets. Pleasant labour will be available to all. The humble Abinadab Quirk takes heart from the assurance of Aunt Winifred that there will be work for him in heaven: 'Perhaps I could help 'em build a church, or hist some of their pearl gates, or something like!'[84]

This popular social heaven was not the preserve of Protestants alone. The Jesuit François-René Blot's (1825–98) *In Heaven We Know Our Own* was Catholicism's version of *The Gates Ajar*. This consisted of a series of letters intended to provide solace for a bereaved mother who had lost a child by assuring her of reunion in the next life with family and friends, and of friendship with the angels. While Blot did not ignore the vision of God as the essence of beatitude, he mined the lives of the saints and the writings of the Church Fathers for testimony to the certainty of reunion in heaven. 'This certainty of a special reunion with our relations in a blessed eternity is a consolation so pure and so sweet, that the saints themselves have made it the subject of their delight.'[85] Blot did not follow Swedenborg or Phelps down the path of us all becoming angels, although we will occupy thrones in the angelic choirs left behind by fallen angels. But he did strongly hint that baptised infants would become 'little angels'.[86] The idea of infant angels remains theologically unorthodox both in Protestantism and Catholicism. But it still continues to find popular support as a consolation among those bereaved by the loss of a child on this side of the grave.

Elizabeth Stuart Phelps's *The Gates Ajar* also reflected new relationships between people and animals. Phelps was open to the notion that people would be reunited with their companion animals in heaven. To the question of whether animals have souls, 'I never should have had the heart to say no to that,' she declared.[87] This was not such an original idea as it may seem. Certainly, the weight of the Western philosophical tradition was on the side of those who, emphasising the radical qualitative distinction between the human and animal realms and viewing the former as having divinely decreed authority over the latter, denied the immortality of animals. Aristotle, Augustine and Aquinas had ruled against animals having rational souls. This perspective was only increased in the seventeenth century by Descartes's view of nature as dead. This relegated animals to the status of nothing more than machines. Yet, during this same century, the developing practice of keeping pets led to new understandings of the connections between people and animals.[88] It became progressively more difficult to conceive how happiness in heaven could be complete in the absence of animals who had loved and been loved so much.

Faith in a just and loving God was also much tried by the sufferings of animals in this present life having no compensation in a future one. Ironically perhaps, the decline of belief in the natural immortality of the human soul in the nineteenth century served to open up immortality to those never before conceived to have had the chance of it. Thus, in removing any absolute distinction between men and animals, Darwin's account of evolution served to exacerbate the problem of animal immortality. For granted that men had evolved from animals, either all had immortal souls or none had. Science and sentimentality now combined in favour of the animals. The parson-naturalist and popular science writer the Reverend J. G. Wood (1827–89) set out to minimise the differences between humans and animals. For him, both revelation and reason pointed to a life after death for animals. Thus, he concluded his study *Man and Beast: Here and Hereafter* by claiming for animals 'a future life in which they can be compensated for the sufferings which so many of them have to undergo in this world'. He did so by decisively breaking with the mechanistic view of nature. 'I do so chiefly,' he continued, 'because I am quite sure that most of the cruelties which are perpetrated on the animals are due to the habit of considering them as mere machines, without susceptibilities, without reason, and without the capacity of a future.'[89]

Technologies of the afterlife

In the middle of the nineteenth century, the spirits themselves decided that, rather than us seeking them out in their homes, they would seek us out in ours by 'manifesting' themselves to us (see Plate 30 [BW]). They did so in a bewildering variety of ways, as William Lloyd Garrison discovered when he attended a seance (sitting) conducted by a 12-year-old girl in 1867:

> Bells ringing over the heads of the circle, floating in the air, and dropping upon the table; a spirit hand seen to extinguish the light; spirit hands touching the hands or garments of all present; pocket books taken out of pockets, the money abstracted, and then returned; watches removed in the same manner; the contents of one table conveyed by an invisible power from one end of the parlor to another; the bosoms of ladies partially unbuttoned, and articles thrust therein and taken therefrom; powerful rappings on the table and floor [...] a basket, containing artificial oranges and lemons, emptied, and its contents distributed around the circle, and the basket put successfully upon the head of everyone present in a grotesque manner; striking and tickling of persons by spirit hands – etc., etc.[90]

The beginnings of spiritualism are often dated to 31 March 1848, when the Fox family of Hydesville, New York, claimed to have communicated with spirits that were the cause of the mysterious rappings that had been heard in the house into which they had moved in December of the previous year.[91] Within the next several years, the three Fox sisters, Margaret, Kate and Leah, were hailed as the leading figures in a new mass movement that promoted communication with the world of the spirits. By 1851, it was estimated that there were 100 mediums in New York City and 50 to 60 'private circles' in Philadelphia.[92]

Seances undoubtedly provided consolation to those who received a message from a deceased loved one. But they served a variety of other functions. They provided entertainment for the curious; they provoked frissons of horror for the believer, moments of amusement for the sceptic and phenomena to be explained for the scientist. They continually crossed the boundary between the religious and the secular. For the conservative Christian, to attend a seance was to dabble with the Devil. For the more credulous and adventurous, this was perhaps part of their attraction. But they also appealed to those of a liberal faith and of no faith at all.

While the activities of the Fox sisters undoubtedly led to the popularisation of such manifestations, communication with the spirits was part of a long tradition that went back to the biblical story of the Witch of Endor conjuring the spirit of Samuel for King Saul (1 Sam. 28.7–20). The manifestations within spiritualism form part of the history of ghosts. That said, spiritualism was also heir to more recent events. Thus, for example, communications with the recently departed, along with accompanying 'physical' phenomena, were reported among Swedenborgian circles as early as the 1780s. In 1776, at seances in Copenhagen, it was reported that a light used to appear 'with a phosphorous appearance, which [gave] precise answers to questions posed to it, by two signs, one of which meant yes and the other no'.[93] The German Friederike Hauffe (1801–29), the so-called 'Seeress of Prevorst', entered trances in which she communicated with the dead, who manifested with knocks, raps and flying furniture. And, as we noted above, Andrew Jackson Davis, the Poughkeepsie seer, was receiving his information from the 'other side' well before the Fox sisters. Both he and the Swedenborgians disapproved of popular spiritualism, not least because, by democratising communication with the spirits, it diminished the uniqueness of their respective philosophies. After all, if mediumship was open to everyone, its value was correspondingly lessened. Be that as it may, women jumped at the opportunity to become active specialists in the sacred even if they were still only the passive vessels of the world of the spirits.[94]

Still, spiritualism did adopt most of the features of the modern social afterlife and promulgated them. Hell was non-existent and heaven was available to everyone. The spiritualist afterlife was very much a continuation of this one. We would all be recognisably the same people, our spiritual bodies very much like our physical bodies, with all imperfections removed. The heavenly landscape would be a more perfect version of that left behind on earth. Spiritual and moral progress towards perfection in heaven would continue from where it had been left on earth. The spiritualist magazine, the *Banner of Light*, insisted in 1857 that spiritualism

> conjures up no awful visions of the future, of burning lakes and pitfalls [...] It tells of an eternal progression in all that is bright and pure, and beautiful, until the soul becomes a part of the glorious harmony of God.[95]

Within spiritualism as within the social heaven more generally, God played a minimal role. Life was lived in the here and now, not under the eye of God, but under the close scrutiny of the dead. As R. Laurence Moore neatly puts it: 'God as a fearsome judge abdicated completely his role as an enforcer of morality in favour of an assorted set of relatives hovering about sixty miles out beyond the earth's atmosphere.'[96]

Beyond this, spiritualism was an amorphous movement and developed no fixed creed. Its core beliefs were really only twofold: first, that the individual soul survived death; second, that the dead were able to communicate with the living. As the declaration from a spiritualists' convention in 1859 put it:

> We recognise as Spiritualists [...] all who hold to the one fact that human spirits have a conscious personal existence after the death of their physical bodies, and can and do manifest themselves, and do communicate to those in the body, under suitable conditions. Beyond this, on questions of philosophy, morals, theology, reform, etc., we profess no full agreement and take no responsibility for each other's opinions.[97]

Not only did spiritualism not have any opinions on such matters, it had little interest in them. The poet Elizabeth Barrett Browning (1806–61) was an early supporter of spiritualism when it reached England in 1852. She was convinced of the reality of the spirit world. But like many others, she was far more interested in the fact that there were spirits than in the often trite and insignificant messages that they brought. She would probably have thought the same about that heir of the nineteenth-century medium, the twentieth-century 'channeller'. 'As to the spirits,' she wrote in a letter in March 1853,

> I care less about what they are capable of communicating, than of the fact of there being communications. I certainly wouldn't set about building a system of theology out of their oracles – God forbid. They seem abundantly foolish, one must admit.[98]

In July 1855, she and her husband, the poet Robert Browning (1812–89), had a seance with the renowned Scottish medium D. D. Home (1833–86). Robert Browning was convinced that Home was a complete fraud. Elizabeth, on the other hand, was further confirmed in her beliefs: 'The medium [in trance],' she wrote in a letter shortly afterwards, 'talked a great deal of much such twaddle as may be heard in any fifth rate [Nonconformist] conventicle. But according to my theory [...] it does not militate at all against the general facts.'[99] It was, after all, the medium and not the message that mattered.

By virtue of the emphasis on manifestations of the spirits that could not only be heard but also be seen and touched, spiritualists saw the world of the spirits as, in principle, open to 'scientific' enquiry. This was a religion that could be scientifically proven. In part, this was because the belief that there was a necessary conflict between religion and science was yet to become part of the intellectual discourse of the time. The result of this was that spiritualism could be both a 'religion' and an object of 'scientific' enquiry. In part, it was because the boundaries between what might be construed as 'mainstream' and 'orthodox' science on the one hand and 'pseudo-' or 'heterodox' sciences on the other were yet to be constructed. In part too it reflected the recognition that 'science' was increasingly being perceived as the final arbiter of truth, and that anything that was to be taken seriously had to be subsumable under that category in one way or another.[100]

For the spiritualist scientist, this was a quest to bring the phenomena of the spirit into the realm of the natural, or rather, to extend the realm of the natural into the realm of the spirit. It was the quest for immortality adapted to an age of science. For such spiritualist science, the boundary between the natural and the spiritual became more fluid, and the distinction between matter and the soul more blurred. Spiritualists, declared the *British Spiritual Telegraph* in 1859, have realised that natural law is

> of far wider scope than had hitherto been imagined – as extending to, and pervading the spiritual universe, as linking together many planes, many graduated systems of life and intellect, into a whole, grander and higher, teaching than had yet been dreamt of by philosophy.[101]

As for those scientists who vehemently opposed it and set about to debunk it, crass materialists that they were thought to be, they were not gifted with the requisite spiritual sight. 'Slowly, but certainly,' colourfully declared James H. Powell, the editor of the *Spiritual Times*, in 1864, 'the mist of materialism is clearing before the dawn of a new sun – the sun of Spiritualism [...] The old ideas of ghostly appearances wear new forms and come to us up out of the dust of ages.'[102]

Some scientists at least were sufficiently sympathetic and interested in 1882 to form the Society for Psychical Research, 'to examine examine [mesmeric, psychical and spiritualistic phenomena] without prejudice or prepossession of any kind, and in the same spirit of exact and unimpassioned inquiry which has enabled Science to solve so many problems, once not less obscure nor less hotly debated.'[103] Without putting too fine a point on it and to the great disappointment of many spiritualists, evidence for the existence of the spirit world was not forthcoming, although plentiful evidence of mediumistic trickery and chicanery was. Eventually, 'spirit' was to disappear from its purview and it would focus its attention only on the 'paranormal'.

Others of a scientific inclination would have nothing whatever to do with what they considered mystical mumbo-jumbo. The naturalist and Darwinian Thomas Henry Huxley (1825–95; Plate 31 [BW]), for example, refused an invitation from the Dialectical Society to join them in an investigation of spiritualism because the instance of it with which he was familiar 'was as gross an imposture as ever came under my notice.'[104] About the existence of immortality, he was as agnostic as he was about the existence of God. The required evidence for belief was absent in both cases. Even if spiritualist phenomena were genuine, he had no interest: 'The only good that I can see in the demonstration of "Spiritualism",' he derisively remarked, 'is to furnish an additional argument against suicide. Better live a crossing-sweeper than die and be made to talk twaddle by a "medium" hired at a guinea a séance.'[105]

Others besides scientists took a more active interest in exposing what they took to be the activities of frauds and charlatans. Magicians were more adept at spotting the tricks than scientists. The magician Harry Houdini (1874–1926) certainly was. He had always been interested in spiritualism, although he became progressively more sceptical about its claims. With a significant increase of interest in contacting those who had perished on the battlefields of World War I, spiritualism surged in popularity in the 1920s. Houdini crusaded vigorously during this period against fraudulent mediums: 'I believe the work I am doing,' he told a reporter, 'is the greatest humanitarian achievement of my life [...] I am helping to alleviate the years of worry that is driving many to the brink of insanity by their inordinate desire to communicate with the dead.'[106]

Twentieth-century variations, new themes and old

The emergence of the modern social heaven and the spiritualist technologies that confirmed it were the last major innovations in the history of the afterlife in the West. This is not to argue that eschatology no longer played a significant role in modern religious life. But it is to suggest that the twentieth century witnessed an ever-increasing array of conflicting visions of the afterlife, in keeping with the increasing cultural pluralism of the West.

In part, this was the consequence of the ongoing rift between the certainties of Swedenborg and the uncertainties of Kant and the consequent differences between elite and popular views of eternity that these generated. Immortality may have survived (just) the Kantian test of reason, but nothing could be known about the afterlife. As the German liberal Protestant David Friedrich Strauss (1808–74) remarked in 1842, the Kantian view had become that of the educated believer. The modern mind, he declared, 'leaves, without showing particular emotion, the complete inventory of ecclesiastical eschatology to be burnt at the stake of criticism, content with rescuing for itself the mere survival of death.'[107] By contrast, Swedenborg, at least in principle, opened to all the possibility of gaining a new knowledge of things eternal, not through recourse to reason or Scripture but through personally validated experience of the other side beyond the gates of death.

Thomas Huxley's indifference and agnosticism about the afterlife was one outcome of the Kantian turn. Charles Darwin's was another. In his autobiography, Darwin wrote of how once, while standing in the midst of the grandeur of a Brazilian forest, he was 'convinced that there is more in man than the mere breath of his body'. But, he continued, 'now the grandest scenes would not cause any such convictions and feelings to rise in my mind.'[108] On immortality as on the existence of God, he, like his friend Huxley, was to declare himself agnostic.

At the turn of the twentieth century, Darwinian agnosticism was to segue, in the face of scientific materialism, into philosophical certainty. The German Darwinist Ernst Haeckel (1834–1919), for example, had no doubts that science had rendered invalid any claims for personal immortality, or 'athanatism', as he called it. Thus, in his bestselling 1899 work *Die Welträthsel* [*sic*] (The riddle of the universe), he concluded his chapter on the immortality of the soul by concluding: 'The belief in the immortality of the human soul is a dogma which is in hopeless contradiction with the most solid empirical truths of modern science.'[109] He believed that the most plausible ground for belief in immortality was the hope that we would be reunited with friends and family, but he was not unaware of some of the more practical impediments to its realisation: 'It is more than questionable,' he wrote, 'whether Henry VIII would like the prospect of living eternally with his six wives; or Augustus the Strong of Poland, who had a hundred mistresses and wives and three hundred and fifty-two children.'[110]

In contrast to materialist certainties, Kantian uncertainty was to play a key role in twentieth-century liberal theology's reluctance to say much at all about the afterlife. The nineteenth century's reticence about hell had now become a virtual silence about heaven as well. Eschatological questions, as the Protestant theologian Jürgen Moltmann (1926–) put it, 'have dried up like fish in a drained pond.'[111] Within liberal theology, the meaning of life was not to be found after it, but during it, through radically transformed individuals (in existentialist theologies) or radically transformed society (in liberation theologies). As the leading feminist theologian Rosemary Ruether (1936–) summed it up:

> We can do nothing about the 'immortal' dimension of our lives. It is not our calling to be concerned about the eternal meaning of our lives [...] Our responsibility is to use our temporal life span to create a just and good community for our generation and for our children.[112]

In short, the search for the meaning of life was replaced by the quest for meaning in life.

The God-centred heaven too was transferred from the afterlife to the present. To the question 'What happens after death?' Karl Rahner (1904–84), arguably the twentieth century's most influential Catholic theologian, answered: 'Absolutely nothing.' Rahner invoked that distinction between two forms of eternity that we distinguished in Chapter 3: between an eternity defined as a succession of moments extending into an infinite future and an eternity outside of time. According to Rahner, the dead have only this latter form of eternity. When we speak of the dead who live, he declared, 'We do not mean that "things go on" after death, as though we only changed horses, as Feuerbach puts it, and rode on.'[113] Rather, as a state outside of time, it can be achieved 'in time.' Eternity, he wrote, 'is not an immeasurably long-lasting mode of pure time, but a mode of the spirit and freedom which are fulfilled in time.'[114] We meet the living dead, concluded Rahner, not in the seances of the spiritualists but

> when we open our hearts to the silent calm of God himself, in which they [the dead] live; not by calling them back [like the spiritualists] to where we are, but by descending into the silent eternity of our own hearts, and

> through faith in the risen Lord, creating in time the eternity which they have brought forth for ever.[115]

In twentieth-century Protestant and Catholic theology, at least on the liberal side, the afterlife had become an afterthought. The reluctance of elite theologies to say anything about the afterlife (or little of substance compared to earlier times), together with the democratisation of spirituality, led to the emergence in that century of an array of popular theories and practices, from the this-worldly to the other-worldly, filling the gap left by an agnostic or at least reticent elite.

From here to eternity

Like the nineteenth, the twentieth century continued to narrow the gap between this life and the next. Emblematic of this narrowing is the modern American cemetery. Here the architecture of the modern heaven is replicated on earth. The body lives in a space that mimics the place of the soul. Soul and body, heaven and earth are aligned. An earthly Eden reflects its heavenly counterpart. The cemetery now becomes a place not of sorrow but of joy, a site to celebrate life lived and life continuing. Its most famous instance? Forest Lawn Memorial Park in Glendale, California. The 1917 dream of its founder Hubert Eaton (1881–1966) is inscribed in stone adjacent to the entrance to the Great Mausoleum: 'I believe in a happy eternal life,' he there declares. 'I believe those of us who are left behind,' he continued,

> should be glad in the certain belief that those gone before [...] have entered into that happier life [...] I therefore know the cemeteries of today are wrong, because they depict an end, not a beginning [...] I shall endeavour to build Forest Lawn as different, as unlike other cemeteries as sunshine is unlike darkness, as Eternal Life is unlike Death [...] a great park. Devoid of misshapen monuments and other customary signs of earthly Death, but filled with towering trees, sweeping lawns, splashing fountains, singing birds, beautiful statuary, cheerful flowers; noble memorial architecture, with interiors of light and colour, and redolent of the world's best history and romances [...] a place where lovers new and old shall love to stroll and watch the sunset's glow [...] where school teachers bring happy children.[116]

It was a combination of 'paganism, spiritualism, Swedenborgianism, and infantile optimism' that all turned out pretty much as Eaton had hoped.[117] This was the Disneyland of death that Evelyn Waugh (1903–66) was to satirise in his novel *The Loved One* (1948). There too, the memorial park, Whispering Glades, has the dream of its founder Wilbur Kenilworth sculptured in marble. In his dream, the 'narrow sea' that Isaac Watts saw dividing this 'heavenly land from ours' has now become merely a 'narrow stream': 'I saw the Waiting Ones,' declared Kenilworth,

> who still stood at the brink of that narrow stream that now separated them from those who had gone before. Young and old, they were happy too. Happy in Beauty, Happy in the certain knowledge that their loved ones were very near, in Beauty and Happiness such as the earth cannot give.[118]

The modern social heaven is essentially a vigorous assertion of the importance of individuals and of their personal relationships. The modern afterlife is, however, not always a matter of individual immortality, but on occasion one of final absorption into the divine (or the recognition that the self and the divine are one). This is a view that can be traced back through the traditions of Christian mysticism to the Neoplatonism of the third century. Be that as it may, it has had its impact in modern Western consciousness as a result of that creative synthesis between Eastern and Western mystical traditions known as 'the perennial philosophy'. Popularised by the English writer Aldous Huxley (1894–1963) in his 1945 book of the same name, the perennial philosophy was based on the notion that truth is manifested in many forms, but it flows from a single fountain. For Huxley, this amounted to the view that the essence of each individual (soul) was equivalent to the essence of the universe (God): 'the Atman, or immanent eternal Self is one with Brahman, the Absolute Principle of all existence; and the last end of every human being is to discover this fact for himself, to find out Who he really is.'[119]

The perennial philosophy advocated by Huxley was not the Western *philosophia perennis* grounded in Neoplatonism[120] but the late nineteenth-century neo-Advaita Hindu tradition of Swami Vivekananda (1863–1902), itself an attempt to impose on the multiplicity of religious traditions in India an underlying philosophical unity. In this tradition, the mystical experience of personal identity with God in this life foreshadows the liberation of the individual at death from individual consciousness. For Huxley, then, the afterlife did not have to do with 'a happy posthumous condition of indefinite personal survival'. Those who have accepted the perennial philosophy

> aspire to be delivered out of separate selfhood in time and into eternity as realized in the unitive knowledge of the divine Ground. Since the Ground can and ought to be known in the present life [...] 'heaven' is not an exclusively posthumous condition. He only is completely 'saved' who is delivered here and now.[121]

Within the Indian traditions, liberation from this world of Samsara only occurs after an infinite series of reincarnations within this world. Thus, there is, as it were, an infinite number of afterlives in the future (as in the past) before liberation finally and mercifully brings them to an end. Thus, in the Indian traditions, reincarnation is the great horror from which freedom is sought. But within the modern West, reincarnation operates in a different register. The sequence of lives is not so much to be escaped from as to be embraced as a series of ongoing opportunities for progress, learning and growth. In this sense, it is a 'this-worldly' variation on those opportunities for progress provided by the 'other-worldly' social heaven. Thus, Western reincarnation synthesises Eastern understandings of the infinite cycle of birth and rebirth with Western ideals of spiritual progress. Not so much the wheel of Samsara as an ever-upwards spiral. This synthesis reaches back to the late nineteenth century Theosophical Society of Helena Blavatsky (1831–91). Thus, in her *Isis Unveiled* (1877), she wrote: 'If the Pythagorean metempsychosis [reincarnation] should be thoroughly explained and compared with the modern [Darwinian] theory of evolution, it would be found to supply every "missing link" in the chain of the latter.'[122]

It is also to Madame Blavatsky that the modern Western awareness of karma is owed. For her, this was the natural law that underlay all spiritual progress. Crucially, it both provided an explanation of why in this life bad things happen to good people (or the reverse) and obviated the necessity for a divine recompense (or punishment) in the next. In this balancing out of the good and the evil, God has become redundant. As one of the 'Ramala Masters' puts it:

> Karma is the eastern name for the Law which you in the West call Cause and Effect and which I call Equalisation. What you have sown, what you have done in thought, word and deed has an effect and that effect will in

> turn be felt by you. It is as simple as that. What you have done not only in this life but also in your many previous lives has had an effect on the pool of life, and when you step into that pool you will be affected by the ripples that you have created both now and in the past [...] The purpose of karma is not punishment. It is rather a process of balance and education.[123]

On 21 September 1920, Sir Arthur Conan Doyle (1859–1930), the celebrated author of the Sherlock Holmes stories, arrived in Adelaide, South Australia. As a proud South Australian myself, I note that he described Adelaide as one of few cities 'so pretty, so orderly and so self-sufficing'.[124] Adelaide was the first official stop on a four-month tour of Australia and New Zealand to promote spiritualism. As early as 1887, Doyle had put himself on the public record as a student of psychic matters, and he had become a member of the Society for Psychical Research in the early 1890s. It was during this period that he was to become more and more impressed by the spiritualist position. Although he was later to lose faith in Madame Blavatsky, he was also around this time deeply interested in theosophy, which 'presented a very well thought-out and reasonable scheme, parts of which, notably reincarnation and karma, seemed to offer an explanation for some of the anomalies of life'.[125] By the time he had arrived in Australia, he had become a passionate evangelist for spiritualism. Like many others who had lost loved ones in the Great War of 1914–18 and the subsequent Spanish flu (his own son having survived the war but succumbed to influenza), he was drawn to the proofs spiritualism offered of life after death and he was eager to embrace the opportunity it gave to communicate with those nearest and dearest – and departed.

So it was to an audience of 2,000 people in the grandly Victorian Adelaide Town Hall that Doyle delivered his lecture on Saturday 25 September 1920 'on a subject which concerns the destiny of every man and woman in this room'.[126] Elsewhere, he was vividly to depict the afterlife as it had been gleaned from communications from the other side:

> The information we have depicts a heaven of congenial work and of congenial play, with every mental and physical activity of life carried on to a higher plane – a heaven of art, of science, of intellect, of organization, of combat with evil, of home circles, of flowers, of wide travel, of sports, of the mating of souls, of complete harmony. This is what our 'dead' friends describe.[127]

When the truth of spiritualism was recognised, he believed, the result would be, quite simply, peace on earth and goodwill between all men – an earthly utopia, but one continually in touch with its heavenly counterpart.

For Doyle, the spirits of the dead were part of a larger world of spiritual beings that included fairies. His interest was particularly piqued when he heard, in May 1920, while in the midst of planning his Australian trip, that five photographs of fairies had been taken by two cousins, Elsie Wright and Frances Griffiths, who lived in the village of Cottingley in West Yorkshire. The first two photographs had come to public attention in mid-1919 when they were displayed at the Theosophical Society's annual conference in Harrogate, Yorkshire. The leading Theosophist Edward Gardner saw the girls' capacity to see fairies as a sign of the evolving new consciousness that the theosophists were prophesying:

> [T]he fact that two young girls [...] had not only been able to see fairies, which others had done, but had actually for the first time ever been able to materialise them at a density sufficient for their images to be recorded on a photographic plate, meant that it was possible that the next cycle of evolution was underway.[128]

Doyle was writing an article on fairies for the *Strand Magazine* when, fortuitously, he heard of the photographs. He and Gardner were soon collaborating on the story. Having gained permission from Elsie and her father, Doyle included the two photographs in his article (see Plate 33 [BW]). In spite of his doubts, he had a determination to believe in the validity of the photos, not least because they bore witness to the 'new world' of spirits that he believed was on the verge of discovery. 'When Columbus knelt in prayer upon the edge of America,' he concluded,

> what prophetic eye saw all that a new continent might do to affect the destinies of the world? We also seem to be on the edge of a new continent, separated not by oceans but by subtle and surmountable psychic conditions.[129]

For the sceptics, and there were many, Doyle was only metaphorically and definitely not literally 'off with the fairies.' They would have agreed with the sentiments of Max Weber in his 1918 lecture that the rise of science had led to 'the disenchantment of the world' ('*die Entzauberung der Welt*').[130] As Michael Saler puts it, 'disenchantment' entailed the loss of the 'overarching meanings, animistic connections, magical expectations, and spiritual explanations' that had characterised the pre-modern world.[131] A disenchanted world may have resonated among the elites. But Doyle was in the vanguard of a twentieth-century re-enchantment of the world or, rather, the recollection of a spiritual world that had never really disappeared among the hoi polloi but had only been marginalised by the elites since the middle of the eighteenth century, in spite of the protests of the Romantics of the nineteenth century.

This re-enchantment of the world was the consequence of the closing of the gap within modern popular culture between this life and the next, between this world and the other world. The connection between the two is the key theme in the film *Photographing Fairies* (1997), directed by Nick Willing. It tells the story of a sceptical and world-weary photographer, Charles Castle (see Plate 34 [BW]), who has lost his new bride in a mountaineering accident shortly after his wedding day. As sceptical about the afterlife as he is about the other world, he attends a lecture at the Theosophical Society at which he debunks a picture of the Cottingley fairies, in spite of Arthur Conan Doyle's declaration to the audience that the fairies are exiles from heaven and dwell on 'the borderland between this world and a better one'. Subsequently, he himself is converted from unbelief after experiencing and photographing fairies at 'the great tree' in the Birkenwell Woods. This 'isn't the only world', he concludes: 'There is another world, as close to this one as I am to you.' The film ends with his reunion with his wife in the other world. Here 'science' (in the form of photography) has turned from its role as the master of disenchantment to that of the servant of re-enchantment.

Enchanted worlds now abound alongside a disenchanted one. Boundary riders and border crossers have proliferated, both good and evil: fairies, but also vampires, witches and wizards, werewolves and wraiths, shape-shifters and superheroes, angels and aliens, demons and zombies. Tolkien's (1892–1973) Endor (Middle-earth) is populated with the angelic Ainur, Elves, Dwarves, Hobbits, Ents, Orcs and Trolls. C. S. Lewis's (1898–1963) Narnia is populated by humans, talking animals and assorted creatures – dwarves, centaur, cruels, dragons, giants, fauns, fairies and nymphs, ghouls, incubi, marsh-wiggles, merpeople, werewolves, and so on. Around 100 fantastic and exotic creatures live in the imaginary world of Harry Potter.

In Ursula Le Guin's (1929–) world of Earthsea, the good wizards, like Taoist sages, live in harmony with the world, while bad wizards always threaten to upset the balance. But her land of the dead – the dark, changeless Dry Land – unlike the modern afterlife, references the Greek Hades and the Hebrew Sheol with echoes of the tenth of Rilke's *Duino Elegies*. The Dry Land is not a place where punishment and reward are allocated according to vice and virtue. Regardless, all the dead are gathered together in that vast realm. Like Hades, the Dry Land is a place of gloom where the sun neither rises nor sets and the unmoving stars cast only a dim light. The country of the innumerable dead is empty: 'No tree or thorn or blade of grass grew in the stony earth under the unsetting stars.'[132] There the dead stand still or move slowly with no purpose. They are to be pitied but not feared. The young prince Arren

> saw the mother and child who had died together, and they were in the dark land together; but the child did not run, nor did it cry, and the mother did not hold it, nor even look at it. And those who had died for love passed each other in the streets.[133]

Utopias new and apocalypses old

In an age in which we have the capacity to bring about the end of humanity and the planet, to bring to reality the mythical images of an end to the earth through fire or flood, the Dry Land is as much the image of a post-apocalyptic world as it is of a post-mortem realm – a place without meaning, pattern or hope. Thus, the Dry Land of Le Guin is of a piece with the gloomy (presumably) post-nuclear, ash-covered earth of Cormac McCarthy's (1933–) *The Road*, along which a man and his son push their shopping trolley of meagre possessions, seeking a warmer place. It is a journey across a bare landscape towards nothing hopeful, even if it is carried out in hope. The sun barely shines, the only food is tinned or other humans, and mummified corpses are stuck in the tar of the road that melted beneath them as they tried to escape.

This is a world that proclaims the non-existence of God. When the man and the boy encounter Ely (Elijah?), in an inversion of the Muslim confession of faith he tells them, 'There is no God and we are his prophets.'[134] There is no way back to the world as it once was, one of meaning and pattern – and perhaps of design. Thus, the book's concluding paragraph:

> Once there were brook trout in the streams in the mountains. You could see them standing in the amber current where the white edges of their

> fins wimpled softly in the flow [...] On their backs were vermiculate patterns that were maps of the world in its becoming. Maps and mazes. Of a thing which could not be put back. Not be made right again. In the deep glens where they lived all things were older than man and they hummed of mystery.[135]

Such a post-apocalyptic world signals the end of history, and renders it meaningless. The only things that have meaning are human relationships as exemplified in that between the father and his son. These survive even death. After his father dies, the boy is taken in by another family. Sometimes, we read, the woman in this family would talk to him about God. He 'tried to talk to God but the best thing was to talk to his father and he did talk to him and he didn't forget.'[136] It is an immortality of a sort – to live on in the memories of loved ones left behind, one that many in the modern world embrace – but a pretty poor one for all that.

Such dystopian pessimism finds its contrast in utopian optimism. There remains the belief that humanity as a whole is not so much on the eve of destruction as at the dawn of an ever-ascending evolutionary path of progress. This explains, within the theosophical tradition, how a heavenly utopia on earth can eventually be created. The theosophists saw this as a long-term project over thousands, even millions, of years. But others believed that a new human consciousness that would lead to an earthly Paradise was imminent. The dawning of the Age of Aquarius, the beginning of the New Age, was now! Thus, for example, in 1980, Marilyn Ferguson (1938–2008) presented her manifesto for a radical transformation of human society as the consequence of the cultivation of the radical transformation of individual human consciousness:

> Those who believe in the possibility of impending social transformation are not optimistic about human nature; rather they trust the transformative process itself. Having experienced positive change in their own lives [...] they concede that others may change, too. And they believe that if enough individuals discover new capacities in themselves they will naturally conspire to create a world hospitable to human imagination, growth, and cooperation.[137]

Arguably the most influential source of the idea of the human consciousness evolving towards an eschatological end point was the Jesuit priest, philosopher and palaeontologist Pierre Teilhard de Chardin (1881–1955). In his *Le phénomène humain* (*The Phenomenon of Man*), posthumously published in the year of his death, Teilhard viewed evolution as a process leading from the single cell to the thinking animal, and thence to human consciousness in ever-increasing complexity. The emergence of man was a new stage in evolutionary consciousness. Man, declared Teilhard, 'discovers *he is nothing else than evolution become conscious of itself*.'[138] The increase in knowledge that has accumulated, especially through the growth of science and technology, has led to the further emergence of a 'noosphere', a sphere of mind that is nothing but the collective consciousness of humanity in which we are all embedded. And in the future, the evolution of human consciousness will culminate in the 'Omega Point' (the Christ who is both Alpha and Omega), which 'fuses and consumes' all things 'integrally into itself'.[139] This is not, however, the loss of the individual in the divine, as in the Hindu neo-Advaita. Rather, it is the enrichment of the individual. This is the Christian mystic's union (but not identity) of the soul with God transposed into a grand history of cosmic evolution. This is Christian Hegelianism gone viral. The conclusion is inevitable, Teilhard wrote,

> that the concentration of a conscious universe would be unthinkable if it did not reassemble in itself *all consciousnesses* as well as all *the conscious*; each particular consciousness remaining conscious of itself at the end of the operation, and even [...] each particular consciousness becoming still more itself and thus more clearly distinct from others the closer it gets to them in Omega.[140]

Christ as the end point of the process of history has continued to play a role in the expectations of twentieth-century conservative Protestant Christians. Their hopes are dominated not so much by our becoming Christ as by his coming to us, more specifically, by the expectation of his imminent return and his reign on a utopian earth that will last for a thousand years prior to the Last Judgement. The pre-eminence of this view within the last 40 years can be traced to the popular impact of a bestselling non-fiction book of the 1970s, the American evangelist Hal Lindsey's (1929–) *The Late Great Planet Earth* (1970). God's Kingdom on earth will be a Paradise restored,

> characterized by peace and equity, and by universal spirituality and knowledge of the Lord. Even the animals and reptiles will lose their ferocity

> and no longer be carnivorous [...] The Great Society which human rulers throughout the centuries have promised, but never produced, will at last be realized under Christ's rule. The meek and not the arrogant will inherit the earth.[141]

Eschatological expectations of the imminent end of the world through the hand of God are part of a grand historical narrative, replete with meaning, harmony, symmetry and purpose – the unfolding of a divine plan determined at the creation of the world and laid out in the Bible from Genesis to Revelation. This was what Hal Lindsey's apocalyptic vision tapped into. It is an eschatological scenario that continues to resonate among Conservative evangelical Protestants. Thus, the life of believers, grounded in the events of the past and determined by the events of the future, has meaning in the present. This is both by virtue of the life assured immediately after death through the cross and resurrection of Christ, and also as a result of the special place occupied by each person within the story of history – a history that begins with the creation of the world, proceeds through Fall to redemption and culminates in the Last Judgement. Then the righteous will become part of the heavenly kingdom and the wicked will be doomed to an eternity of punishment in the domain of the lost. Unlike the unbelievers, the believers know this and live by it. Unbelievers don't, and perish without it. For unlike the unbelievers, the believers have read the biblical script. They alone know how the drama will end. Only they have any assurance of salvation. And they are few rather than many, or so they believe.

Thus has Western eschatology turned full circle. With the expectation of the imminent coming of the Kingdom of God and the final return of Christ, the disappointed eschatological hopes of the earliest Christians have become alive in the present, charging the present with the deepest meaning. Predictions of the imminent end of the world are never daunted by its failure to arrive. The hope that Christ will come again ever exceeds the disappointments of his failure thus far to arrive when expected, just as the hope that there is meaning in history and in the lives of individuals always survives any amount of evidence against it. Thus has the expectation that the end of the world is nigh, that Christ is on the verge of returning, reasserted itself in the modern world. It has done so continually at regular intervals throughout the history of Western religious thought since that day when a prophet from Nazareth appeared in Galilee, 'preaching the gospel of the Kingdom of God, and saying, "The time is fulfilled, and the Kingdom of God is at hand; repent ye, and believe the gospel"' (Mark 1.14–15).

In contrast to this grand theological narrative of Creation, Fall, redemption and last things, modern 'secular' histories find neither meaning nor pattern in the facts, neither a divine providence outside of history overseeing all things nor a principle within it guaranteeing a point to it all. History lacks any final explanation, either from that which is outside it or from that within it. As Paul Boyer sums it up: 'With secular historians no longer speaking the language of progress or portraying the majestic unfolding of a divine plan in history, prophecy popularizers took up the slack and found a vast audience in the process.'[142]

Yet the determination to find meaning in history in spite of the apparent absence of it, to find meaning in the present despite the world's apparent disenchantment, has very recently re-emerged. In the physical sciences, it is manifest in the quest to find the unifying law of nature that would underpin all other laws. As the astrophysicist Paul Davies (1946–) puts it, the ideal would be if such a law were to be expressed in a mathematical scheme in a single and simple formula 'compact enough to wear on your T-shirt'.[143] Analogously, in the historical sciences, there has recently emerged the attempt to unite all of the scientific disciplines under a grand evolutionary history of the universe and humanity from the beginning to the present. The aim of its leading exponent, historian David Christian (1946–), is to produce 'a map of time that embraces the past at all scales'.[144] Such 'Big History' intends to construct a unified scientific account of the origin and history of all things. But it is more than this. It means to produce a 'modern creation myth' and thus to provide 'universal coordinates within which people can imagine their own existence and find a role in the larger scheme of things'. Creation myths, he writes, speak to our 'need for a sense of place and a sense of belonging'.[145] Thus Christian's Big History rediscovers the values and meaning lost from modern lives. And thus his unified account of science (in theory) makes possible a new and modern spirituality – an Aboriginal 'Dreaming' for the modern West.[146] A grand narrative of evolutionary progress provides a secularised substitute for divine providence. Secular history becomes sacred once again; or, perhaps better, the gap between secular and sacred history becomes more blurred. Secular history has been spiritualised and sacred history secularised.

So too, in this century, the gap between this life and the next is more opaque. More generally, the distinction between an enchanted and a disenchanted world is harder to sustain intellectually. The enchanted imagination lives alongside disenchanted reason. The spaces between here and eternity, now and then, fact and fiction, the literal and the metaphorical, the religious and the magical, the rational and the imaginary are blurred. The modern world is one of multiple meanings, both enchanted and disenchanted. We can inhabit both an enchanted and a disenchanted world, a secular and a sacred history, this realm and the next, as a matter of leisure, or pleasure, or the utmost seriousness. Belief can be embraced and disbelief happily and willingly suspended.

Epilogue

In the year 627, King Edwin of Northumbria, contemplating acceptance of the Christian faith, conferred about it with his friends and counsellors. One of his chief men eloquently expressed our ignorance of our final destiny:

> The present life of man upon earth, O king, seems to me, in comparison with that time which is unknown to us, like to the swift flight of a sparrow through the house wherein you sit at supper in winter, with your ealdormen and thegns, while the fire blazes in the midst, and the hall is warmed, but the wintry storms of rain or snow are raging abroad. The sparrow, flying in at one door and immediately out at another, whilst he is within, is safe from the wintry tempest; but after a short space of fair weather, he immediately vanishes out of your sight, passing from winter into winter again. So this life of man appears for a little while, but of what is to follow or what went before we know nothing at all.[1]

That we all die, we know. But of what may lie beyond our deaths we remain, like Edwin's adviser, completely ignorant. As for myself, I expect death is one event that unfortunately I shall not live to regret, even though I live in hope that I might be pleasantly, and not unpleasantly, surprised when my life and this world is to me no more.

This book has explored the history of our imaginings about the afterlife, both after death and after the end of history. It is a testimony to the hope that most have for an extension of life beyond the grave. It speaks to the desire that many have expressed for light beyond the darkness of death, for ultimate goodness beyond present evils, and for final justice over earthly inequities. It gives voice to the faith that the drama of history, and the minor role that each of us has played in it, has an ultimate meaning and purpose, one that is discernible from the vistas of eternity if not from our present perspective. And it resonates with the confidence that St Paul had when he comforted those who despaired of this life with words of hope for a better life to come: 'For I reckon that the sufferings of this present time are not worthy to be compared with the glory that shall be revealed to us' (Rom. 8.18).

Notes

Abbreviations

ANF	Alexander Roberts, James Donaldson and A. Cleveland Coxe (eds), *Ante-Nicene Fathers*, 10 vols (Buffalo, NY: Christian Literature, 1885–97).
NPNFI	Philip Schaff (ed.), *Nicene and Post-Nicene Fathers: First Series*, 14 vols (Buffalo, NY: Christian Literature, 1886–90).
NPNFII	Philip Schaff and Henry Wace (eds), *Nicene and Post-Nicene Fathers: Second Series*, 14 vols (Buffalo, NY: Christian Literature, 1890–1900).
PL	J.-P. Migne (ed.), *Patrologia Latina*, 221 vols (Paris, 1844–64).

1. The Destiny of the Dead

1 Wojciech Kosior, 'The underworld or its ruler? Some remarks on the concept of Sheol in the Hebrew Bible', *Polish Journal of Biblical Research* 13 (2014), p. 40. See also Alan E. Bernstein, *The Formation of Hell: Death and Retribution in the Ancient and Early Christian Worlds* (Ithaca, NY, and London: Cornell University Press, 1993). I am indebted to Bernstein for this discussion.
2 Homer, *The Iliad*, trans. A. T. Murray (Cambridge, MA, and London: Harvard University Press and Heinemann, 1924), 15.187–92.
3 Walter Burkert, *Greek Religion: Archaic and Classical*, trans. John Raffan (Oxford: Blackwell, 1985), p. 196. See Homer, *Iliad*, 20.67ff.
4 Homer, *Iliad*, 23.64–75.
5 Homer, *The Odyssey*, trans. A. T. Murray (Cambridge, MA, and London: Harvard University Press and Heinemann, 1919), 24.7–8.
6 Ibid., 11.18.
7 Ibid., 24.203–4.
8 Ibid., 11.37–44.
9 Ibid., 11.217–20.
10 Ibid., 11.486–9.
11 Homer, *Iliad*, 8.14–16.
12 Homer, *Odyssey*, 11.595–8.
13 Ibid., 4.61–3.
14 Hesiod, *Works and Days* 167–73, in Hesiod, *The Homeric Hymns, and Homerica*, trans. Hugh G. Evelyn-White (London: Heinemann, 1914), p. 15.
15 George W. E. Nickelsburg, *1 Enoch 1: A Commentary on the Book of Enoch Chapters 1–36; 81–108* (Minneapolis, MN: Fortress Press, 2001), p. 300.

16 2 Baruch 30.2–5, in James H. Charlesworth (ed.), *The Old Testament Pseudepigrapha*, vol. 1: *Apocalyptic Literature and Testaments* (New York, NY: Doubleday, 1983), p. 631.
17 4 Ezra 5.8, in James H. Charlesworth (ed.), *The Old Testament Pseudepigrapha*, vol. 1: *Apocalyptic Literature and Testaments* (New York, NY: Doubleday, 1983), p. 532. See also p. 523 for notes on Whiston, as well as Christopher Columbus, Bishop Hugh Latimer and John Milton.
18 Ibid., 7.80–1 [p. 539].
19 Ibid., 7.36–7 [p. 538].
20 Hippolytus, *Against Plato, On the Cause of the Universe* 1, trans. J. H. MacMahon, in *ANF*, vol. 5, p. 221. (*Josephus's Discourse to the Greeks Concerning Hades* is now attributed to Hippolytus and not to Josephus, and known by the title *Against Plato*.)
21 Ibid., 1 [p. 222].
22 Ibid.
23 Ibid.
24 Ibid.
25 Tertullian, *A Treatise on the Soul* 55, trans. Peter Holmes, in *ANF*, vol. 3, p. 231.
26 Ibid., 58 [p. 235].
27 Tertullian, *Against Marcion* 34, trans. Peter Holmes, in *ANF*, vol. 3, p. 406. See also Henri Crouzel, 'L'Hades et la Gehenne selon Origene', *Gregorianum* 59 (1978), p. 292.
28 *The Letters of St Augustine*, ed. W. J. Sparrow-Simpson (London and New York, NY: SPCK and Macmillan, 1919), p. 201.
29 See J. A. MacCulloch, *The Harrowing of Hell: A Comparative Study of an Early Christian Doctrine* (Edinburgh: T. & T. Clark, 1930), p. 344.
30 2 Enoch 8.1–3, in James H. Charlesworth (ed.), *The Old Testament Pseudepigrapha*, vol. 1: *Apocalyptic Literature and Testaments* (New York, NY: Doubleday, 1983), p. 114. It should be noted that the date of this text is much disputed, although probably no later than the first century CE.
31 The Apocalypse of Paul 14, in J. K. Elliott (ed.), *The Apocryphal New Testament: A Collection of Apocryphal Christian Literature in an English Translation* (Oxford: Clarendon, 1993), p. 624.
32 Ibid., 15 [p. 624].
33 Ibid., 16 [p. 625].
34 Ibid., 22 [p. 629].
35 Ibid., 31 [p. 633].
36 Ibid., 32 [p. 634].
37 Ibid., 41 [p. 637].
38 Ibid.
39 Ibid., 40 [p. 636].
40 Ibid., 51 [p. 674].
41 Matt. 11.23, 16.18; Luke 10.15, 16.23; Acts 2.27, 2.31; Rev. 1.18, 6.8, 20.13, 20.14.
42 With the one exception of 1 Cor. 15.55, where he used 'death' (*mors*).
43 St Jerome, *Commentary on Ecclesiastes*, ed. and trans. Richard J. Goodrich and David J. D. Miller (New York, NY, and Mahwah, NJ: Newman Press, 2012), p. 63.
44 4 Ezra 7.36, in James H. Charlesworth (ed.), *The Old Testament Pseudepigrapha*, vol. 1: *Apocalyptic Literature and Testaments* (New York, NY: Doubleday, 1983), p. 538.

45 Matt. 5.22, 5.29, 5.30, 10.28, 18.9, 23.15, 23.33; Mark 9.43, 9.45, 9.47; Luke 12.5; Jas. 3.6. See especially Chaim Milikowsky, 'Which Gehenna? Retribution and eschatology in the synoptic Gospels and in early Jewish texts', *New Testament Studies* 34 (1988), pp. 238–49.
46 See ibid., pp. 243–4.

2. *The Geography of the Underworld*

1 Dante, *Purgatorio*, ed. and trans. Robin Kirkpatrick (London: Penguin, 2007), 7.33.
2 Dante, *The Divine Comedy*, trans. A. S. Kline (n.p.: Poetry in Translation, 2014), 4.43. Available at http://www.poetryintranslation.com/PITBR/Italian/Danthome.htm.
3 Albert the Great, *Scriptum super sententiis* 4.1.20, quoted in Amilcare A. Iannucci, 'Dante's limbo: at the margins of orthodoxy', in James Miller (ed.), *Dante and the Unorthodox: The Aesthetics of Transgression* (Waterloo, Ontario: Wilfrid Laurier University Press, 2005), p. 76.
4 Dante, *Inferno*, ed. and trans. Robin Kirkpatrick (London: Penguin, 2006), 3.25–7.
5 Ibid., 4.26–7.
6 Ibid., 4.30.
7 Ibid., 4.37–42.
8 Ibid., 4.63.
9 On Bonaventure, see Jacques Le Goff, *The Birth of Purgatory* (Chicago, IL: University of Chicago Press, 1981), pp. 250–6.
10 Thomas Aquinas, *Scriptum super sententiis* 3.22.2.1–2, quoted in Amilcare A. Iannucci, 'Dante's limbo: at the margins of orthodoxy', in James Miller (ed.), *Dante and the Unorthodox: The Aesthetics of Transgression* (Waterloo, Ontario: Wilfrid Laurier University Press, 2005), p. 77.
11 Gregory of Nyssa, *On Infants' Early Deaths*, trans. William Moore and Henry Austin Wilson, in *NPNFII*, vol. 5, pp. 372–81.
12 Ibid., pp. 374.
13 Ibid.
14 Ibid., p. 376.
15 Ibid., p. 377.
16 *Pelagius's Commentary on St Paul's Epistle to the Romans*, trans. Theodore de Bruyn (Oxford: Clarendon, 1993), p. 94. For Pelagius on original sin, see especially Pier Franco Beatrice, *The Transmission of Sin: Augustine and the Pre-Augustinian Sources*, trans. Adam Kamesar (Oxford: Oxford University Press, 2013). I am indebted to Beatrice for this discussion.
17 Quoted in Augustine, *A Treatise on the Grace of Christ, and on Original Sin* 2.14, trans. Peter Holmes and Robert Ernest Wallis, rev. Benjamin B. Warfield, in *NPNFI*, vol. 5, p. 241.
18 Ibid. At least, according to Augustine, this was a statement that Caelestius was not willing to disavow.
19 Augustine, *De gratia Christi et de peccato originali*, in K. F. Urba and Joseph Zycha (eds), *Corpus scriptorum ecclesiasticorum Latinorum*, vol. 42 (Vienna: Tempsky, 1902), p. 182: '*sine baptism paruuli morientes, quo non eant, scio; quo eant nescio.*'

20 Quoted in Beatrice, *Transmission of Sin*, p. 79.

21 Augustine, *De libero arbitrio* 3, in Augustine, *On Free Choice of the Will*, trans. Thomas Williams (Indianapolis, IN: Hackett, 1993), p. 116.

22 Augustine, *Sermo* 294.16.16, in *PL*, vol. 38, col. 1345: '*Omnis generatus, damnatus: nemo liberatus, nisi regeneratus.*'

23 Augustine, *A Treatise on the Merits and Forgiveness of Sins* 1.28, trans. Peter Holmes and Robert Ernest Wallis, rev. Benjamin B. Warfield, in *NPNFI*, vol. 5, p. 25.

24 Ibid., 1.21 [p. 23].

25 Gregory the Great, *Morals on the Book of Job by St Gregory the Great, Translated with Notes and Indices*, vol. 1, trans. James Bliss (Oxford and London: John Henry Parker and J. G. F. and J. Rivington, 1844), 9.21.32.

26 Anselm, *The Virgin Conception and Original Sin* 23, in *Anselm of Canterbury*, vol. 3, ed. and trans. Jasper Hopkins and Herbert Richardson (Toronto and New York, NY: Edwin Mellen Press, 1976), p. 172.

27 Ibid., 28 [p. 178].

28 Peter Abelard, *Commentary on the Epistle to the Romans*, trans. Steven Cartwright (Washington DC: Catholic University of America Press, 2012), pp. 221–2.

29 Bonaventure, *Scriptum super sententiis* 2.33.3. See Amilcare A. Iannucci, 'Dante's limbo: at the margins of orthodoxy', in James Miller (ed.), *Dante and the Unorthodox: The Aesthetics of Transgression* (Waterloo, Ontario: Wilfrid Laurier University Press, 2005), p. 79.

30 Thomas Aquinas, *Summa theologica*, appendix 1, question 2, in Thomas Aquinas, *Summa theologica*, trans. Fathers of the English Dominican Province (New York, NY: Benziger Brothers, 1947). Available at http://www.ccel.org/ccel/aquinas/summa.html. This passage was inserted into the text of the *Summa* from Aquinas's commentary on the *Sentences* of Peter Lombard.

31 Thomas Aquinas, *Quaestiones disputatae de malo*, question 5, article 3, in Thomas Aquinas, *On Evil*, trans. Richard Regan, ed. Brian Davies (Oxford: Oxford University Press, 2003).

32 See J. A. MacCulloch, *The Harrowing of Hell: A Comparative Study of an Early Christian Doctrine* (Edinburgh: T. & T. Clark, 1930). See also especially Jeffrey A. Trumbower, *Rescue for the Dead: The Posthumous Salvation of Non-Christians in Early Christianity* (Oxford: Oxford University Press, 2001).

33 William Joseph Dalton, *Christ's Proclamation to the Spirits: A Study of I Peter 3:18–4.6* (Rome: Pontificio Istituto Biblico, 1989). Dalton notes that, in spite of the very early tradition of Christ's descent into hell, Clement of Alexandria (*c.*150–*c.*215 CE) was the first to link this tradition to 1 Pet. 3.19. See p. 32.

34 The dating of the Gospel of Nicodemus, from the first century CE onwards, has been much disputed. See G. C. O'Ceallaigh, 'Dating the commentaries of Nicodemus', *Harvard Theological Review* 56 (1963), pp. 21–58.

35 See M. R. James (ed. and trans.), *The Apocryphal New Testament* (Oxford: Clarendon, 1953), p. 95.

36 The Gospel of Nicodemus [Greek] 18.2, in M. R. James (ed. and trans.), *The Apocryphal New Testament* (Oxford: Clarendon, 1953), p. 126.

37 Ibid., 21.3 [p. 134].

38 Ibid., 24.1 [p. 138].

39 Ibid., 27.1 [p. 143]. The Gospel of Nicodemus was the first to name the two thieves crucified with Christ: Dismas, crucified to Jesus's right, and Gestas, to his left.

40 The Gospel of Nicodemus [Latin B] 24, in M. R. James (ed. and trans.), *The Apocryphal New Testament* (Oxford: Clarendon, 1953), pp. 135–6.
41 Ibid., 26 [p. 139].
42 Ibid., 25.2 [p. 139].
43 Irenaeus, *Against Heresies* 1.27.3, trans. Alexander Roberts and William Rambaut, in *ANF*, vol. 1, p. 352.
44 Ibid.
45 Ibid., 4.27.2 [p. 499].
46 Clement, *Stromata* 6.6, trans. William Wilson, in *ANF*, vol. 2, p. 491.
47 Ibid., 6.6 [p. 490].
48 Origen, *Against Celsus* 2.43, trans. Frederick Crombie, in *ANF*, vol. 4, p. 448.
49 Henri Crouzel, 'L'Hades et la Gehenne selon Origene', *Gregorianum* 59 (1978).
50 Augustine, Letter 163, trans. J. G. Cunningham, in *NPNFI*, vol. 1, p. 515. For Augustine on the descent into hell, see Basil Studer, 'Der Abstieg Christi in die Unterwelt bei Augustinus von Hippo', in I. Scicolone (ed.), *Psallendum: miscellanea di studi in onore del Prof. Jordi Pinelli i Pons, OSB* (Rome: Pontificio Ateneo Sant'Anselmo, 1992), pp. 267–74.
51 Augustine, Letter 164 2.3, trans. J. G. Cunningham, in *NPNFI*, vol. 1, p. 515.
52 J. N. D. Kelly, *Early Christian Creeds* (London: Longman, 1972), p. 289.
53 Augustine, Letter 164 3.6 [p. 516].
54 Ibid.
55 Ibid., 3.7 [p. 517].
56 Ibid., 3.8 [p. 517].
57 Augustine, Letter 187 6, in Augustine, *Selected Writings*, ed. and trans. Mary T. Clark (Mahwah, NJ: Paulist Press, 1984), p. 405.
58 Ibid.
59 Augustine, Letter 187 34 [p. 421].
60 Augustine, *De haeresibus* 79, in *PL*, vol. 42, col. 45.
61 Gregory the Great, Book 7, Epistle 15, trans. James Barmby, in *NPNFII*, vol. 12, p. 217.
62 *The Letters of Saint Boniface*, trans. Ephraim Emerton (New York, NY: Norton, 1976), p. 102.
63 Quoted in MacCulloch, *Harrowing of Hell*, p. 260, n. 2.
64 Quoted in Ralph V. Turner, 'Descendit ad inferos: medieval views on Christ's descent into hell and the salvation of the ancient just', *Journal of the History of Ideas* 27 (1966), p. 179. Since Erasmus, this work has been ascribed to 'Ambrosiaster'.
65 See *Abelard's Christian Theology*, ed. and trans. J. Ramsay McCallum (Oxford: Blackwell, 1948), p. 52.
66 Thomas Aquinas, *Compendium theologiae* 253, in Thomas Aquinas, *Compendium of Theology*, trans. Richard J. Regan (Oxford: Oxford University Press, 2009), p. 194.
67 Aquinas, *Summa theologica*, supplement 69.4.
68 Ibid., 69.5.
69 Thomas Aquinas, *Quaestiones disputatae de veritate* 14.11, in Thomas Aquinas, *The Disputed Question on Truth*, vol. 2, trans. James V. McGlynn (Chicago, IL: Henry Regnery, 1953). Available at http://dhspriory.org/thomas/QDdeVer.htm.
70 Ibid.
71 Dante, *Purgatorio*, 7.7–8.

3. Souls and Bodies

1 The authorship and date of this work have been much disputed. See David Rankin, *Athenagoras: Philosopher and Theologian* (Farnham: Ashgate, 2009). Rankin argues for the traditional ascription to Athenagoras.
2 Athenagoras, *On the Resurrection of the Dead* 15, trans. B. P. Pratten, in *ANF*, vol. 2, p. 157.
3 Ibid.
4 Plato, *The Phaedo* 106e, in *The Collected Dialogues of Plato, Including the Letters*, eds Edith Hamilton and Huntington Cairns (Princeton, NJ: Princeton University Press, 1961), p. 88.
5 Ibid., 114c [p. 94].
6 Plato, *The Gorgias* 525c, in *The Collected Dialogues of Plato, Including the Letters*, eds Edith Hamilton and Huntington Cairns (Princeton, NJ: Princeton University Press, 1961), p. 305.
7 Plato, *Republic* 614d, in *The Collected Dialogues of Plato, Including the Letters*, eds Edith Hamilton and Huntington Cairns (Princeton, NJ: Princeton University Press, 1961), p. 839.
8 Ibid., 615e [p. 840].
9 Ibid., 621b [p. 844].
10 Caroline Walker Bynum, *The Resurrection of the Body in Western Christianity, 200–1336* (New York, NY: Columbia University Press, 1995), p. 10.
11 Augustine, Letter 166 2.3, trans. J. G. Cunningham, in *NPNFI*, vol. 1, p. 523.
12 For an excellent overview, see A. W. Argyle, 'The Christian doctrine of the origin of the soul', *Scottish Journal of Theology* 18 (1965), pp. 273–93.
13 See especially Peter Martens, 'Origen's doctrine of pre-existence and the opening chapters of Genesis', *Zeitschrift für Antikes Christentum* 16 (2013), pp. 516–49.
14 Origen, *On First Principles* 2.9.1, in Origen, *On First Principles*, trans. G. W. Butterworth (Gloucester, MA: Peter Smith, 1973), p. 129.
15 Ibid., 1.8.1 [p. 67].
16 Ibid., 3.6.3 [p. 248].
17 Ibid., 2.10.1 [p. 139].
18 See Lodi Nauta, 'The pre-existence of the soul in medieval Europe', *Recherches de théologie ancienne et medievale* 63 (1996), pp. 93–135; Philip C. Almond, *Heaven and Hell in Enlightenment England* (Cambridge: Cambridge University Press, 2008).
19 See Philip C. Almond, *The British Discovery of Buddhism* (Cambridge: Cambridge University Press, 1988); Raymond Schwab, *The Oriental Renaissance: Europe's Rediscovery of India and the East* (New York, NY: Columbia University Press, 1984).
20 We can distinguish a 'material' and a 'spiritual' version of traducianism. In the former, represented by Tertullian, the soul is 'within' the seed. In the latter, represented by Gregory of Nyssa, the soul is transmitted 'along with' the seed. This latter version is sometimes called 'generationism' or 'spiritual traducianism'. Augustine's sympathies lay more with Gregory than with Tertullian. The one exception in all this was Jesus, whose soul, according to Augustine, was created afresh by God.
21 Jerome, Letter 126.1, in *NPNFII*, vol. 6, p. 252.
22 Tertullian, *A Treatise on the Soul* 27, trans. Peter Holmes, in *ANF*, vol. 3, p. 208.
23 Ibid.

24 Thomas Aquinas, *Quaestiones disputatae de potentia dei* 3.9.29, in Thomas Aquinas, *On the Power of God*, trans. English Dominican Fathers (Westminster, MD: Newman Press, 1952). Available at http://dhspriory.org/thomas/QDdePotentia.htm. Aquinas is quoting from a work long attributed to Augustine entitled *De ecclesiasticis dogmatibus* (Of Church doctrine). The author was in fact the fifth-century priest Gennadius of Massilia. That an immortal soul is present from the moment of conception is of course the theological grounds for Catholic opposition to abortion.

25 See Don Cameron Allen, *Doubt's Boundless Sea* (Baltimore, MD: Johns Hopkins Press, 1964), p. 160.

26 Ibid., pp. 184–5.

27 See Thomas Aquinas, *Summa theologica* 1.10.1, in Thomas Aquinas, *Summa theologica*, trans. Fathers of the English Dominican Province (New York, NY: Benziger Brothers, 1947). Available at http://www.ccel.org/ccel/aquinas/summa.html.

28 See ibid., 1.10.3.

29 See ibid., 1.10.5.

30 Ibid., 1.10.3.

31 See D. P. Walker, 'Eternity and the afterlife', *Journal of the Warburg and Courtauld Institutes* 27 (1964), pp. 241–50. I am indebted to Walker for this discussion.

32 Mark 12.18–27, Matt. 22.23–33, Luke 20.27–40.

33 See Peter Carnley, *The Structure of Resurrection Belief* (Oxford: Clarendon, 1987).

34 For a recent analysis of modern exegetical complexities around 1 Cor. 15, see Wolfgang Kraus and Martin Kraus, 'On eschatology in Paul's First Epistle to the Corinthians', in Jan G. van der Watt, *Eschatology of the New Testament and Some Related Documents* (Tübingen: Mohr Siebeck, 2011), pp. 197–224.

35 'Medieval sourcebook: twelfth ecumenical council: Lateran IV 1215', in H. J. Schroeder (ed.), *Disciplinary Decrees of the General Councils: Text, Translation and Commentary* (St Louis, MO: B. Herder, 1937). pp. 236–96 (my italics). Available at http://www.fordham.edu/halsall/basis/lateran4.asp.

36 See for example John Calvin, *Institutes of the Christian Religion*, ed. John T. McNeill (Louisville, KY, and London: Westminster John Knox Press, 2006), 3.25.8.

37 Athenagoras, *On the Resurrection of the Dead* 15 [p. 157].

38 Ibid., 17 [p. 158].

39 Ibid., 3 [p. 150].

40 Ibid., 20–1 [pp. 160–1].

41 Ibid., 25 [p. 162].

42 Tertullian, *On the Resurrection of the Flesh* 1, trans. Peter Holmes, in *ANF*, vol. 3, p. 545.

43 Ibid., 15 [p. 555].

44 Ibid., 17 [p. 557].

45 Ibid.

46 Ibid., 52 [p. 585].

47 Augustine, *On Faith and the Creed* 10.24, trans. S. D. F. Salmond, in *NPNFI*, vol. 3, p. 333.

48 Augustine, *The City of God* 13.19, trans. Marcus Dods, in *NPNFI*, vol. 2, p. 255 (my italics).

49 Ibid., 13.20 [p. 256].

50 Ibid., 22.17 [p. 496].
51 Ibid., 13.22 [p. 257].
52 Augustine, Letter 92, trans. J. G. Cunningham, in *NPNFI*, vol. 1, p. 381. See also Letter 148.
53 Augustine, *City of God* 22.29 [p. 508].
54 On the incorporeality of the soul and its location in the body, the whole and each part of which it completely fills (as does a liquid its container), see Augustine, Letter 166, trans. J. G. Cunningham, in *NPNFI*, vol. 1, p. 524. See also R. J. Teske, 'Saint Augustine on the incorporeality of the soul', *Modern Schoolman* 60 (1983), pp. 220–35.
55 See Andrew Louth, *The Origins of the Christian Mystical Tradition: From Plato to Denys* (Oxford: Oxford University Press, 2007).
56 See Vladimir Lossky, *The Mystical Theology of the Eastern Church* (Crestwood, NY: St Vladimir's Seminary Press, 1976).
57 Quoted in Bynum, *Resurrection of the Body*, p. 267.
58 Although this distinction is often attributed to Abelard, I can find no reference to these terms used contrastingly before Thomas Aquinas.
59 Thomas Aquinas, *Compendium theologiae* 179, in Thomas Aquinas, *Compendium of Theology*, trans. Cyril Vollert (St Louis, MO, and London: Herder, 1947), p. 195.
60 Ibid., 180 [pp. 195–6].
61 Athenagoras, *The Resurrection of the Dead* 4, trans. B. P. Pratten, in *ANF*, vol. 2, p. 151.
62 Tertullian, *On the Resurrection of the Flesh* 61, trans. Peter Holmes, in *ANF*, vol. 3, p. 593.
63 Augustine, *City of God* 22.12–20 [p. 493ff.].
64 Quoted in Bynum, *Resurrection of the Body*, p. 123. See also Caroline Walker Bynum, *Fragmentation and Redemption: Essays on Gender and the Human Body in Medieval Religion* (New York, NY: Zone, 1992), ch. 7.
65 Thomas Aquinas, *Summa contra Gentiles* 4.81.13, trans. Charles J. O'Neil, in Thomas Aquinas, *Summa contra Gentiles*, ed. Joseph Kenny (New York, NY: Hanover House, 1955–7). Available at http://dhspriory.org/thomas/ContraGentiles4.htm.
66 Ibid.
67 Thomas Aquinas, *Compendium theologiae* 153 [p. 162].
68 Ibid., 157 [p. 169] (my italics).
69 Ibid., 168 [p. 179].
70 Ibid., 176 [p. 192].
71 Robert Boyle, *The Works of the Honourable Robert Boyle*, vol. 4, ed. Thomas Birch (2nd edn, London, 1772), p. 196. On Birch and resurrection, see Salvatore Ricciardo, 'Robert Boyle on God's "experiments": resurrection, immortality and mechanical philosophy', *Intellectual History Review* 24 (2014), pp. 1–17.
72 Humphrey Hody, *The Resurrection of the (Same) Body Asserted* (London, 1694), p. 187.
73 Ibid., p. 189.
74 Ibid., pp. 194–5.
75 Ibid., p. 205.
76 See Bernard McGinn, John J. Collins and Stephen J. Stein (eds), *The Encyclopedia of Apocalypticism* (New York, NY, and London: Continuum, 1998).
77 See Norman Cohn, *The Pursuit of the Millennium: Revolutionary Millenarians and Mystical Anarchists of the Middle Ages* (London: Pimlico, 1993).

4. Purgatory and Beyond

1 See Caroline Walker Bynum, *The Resurrection of the Body in Western Christianity, 200–1336* (New York, NY: Columbia University Press, 1995), pp. 283–91; and D. Douie, 'John XXII and the Beatific Vision', *Dominican Studies* 3 (1950), pp. 157–74. I am indebted to the latter for this discussion.
2 D. Douie, 'John XXII and the Beatific Vision', *Dominican Studies* 3 (1950), p. 168.
3 Benedict XII, *Benedictus Deus* (1336). Available at http://www.papalencyclicals.net/Ben12/B12bdeus.html.
4 Ibid.
5 Bynum, *Resurrection of the Body*, p. 283.
6 Thomas Aquinas, *Compendium theologiae* 181, in Thomas Aquinas, *Compendium of Theology*, trans. Cyril Vollert (St Louis, MO, and London: Herder, 1947), p. 197.
7 Ibid., 174 [p. 190].
8 The Second Epistle of Clement 16, ed. M. B. Riddle, in *ANF*, vol. 7, p. 552.
9 Ibid., 8 [p. 519] (my italics).
10 Cyprian, *An Address to Demetrianus* 25, trans. Robert Ernest Wallis, in *ANF*, vol. 5, p. 465 (my italics).
11 Chrysostom, *Homilies of St John Chrysostom, Archbishop of Constantinople, on the Gospel according to St Matthew* 36.3, trans. George Prevost, rev. M. B. Riddle, in *NPNFI*, vol. 10, p. 241.
12 Augustine, *On the Soul and Its Origin* 2.8, trans. Peter Holmes and Robert Ernest Wallis, in *NPNFI*, vol. 5, p. 334.
13 Quoted in Jeffrey A. Trumbower, *Rescue for the Dead: The Posthumous Salvation of Non-Christians in Early Christianity* (Oxford: Oxford University Press, 2001), p. 129.
14 Augustine, *Enchiridion* 110, trans. J. F. Shaw, in *NPNFI*, vol. 3, p. 272.
15 Ibid., 113 [p. 273].
16 Ibid., 68 [p. 260].
17 Ibid., 69 [p. 260].
18 Augustine, *The City of God* 21.13, trans. Marcus Dods, in *NPNFI*, vol. 2, p. 464.
19 Clement, *Stromata* 7.6, trans. William Wilson, in *ANF*, vol. 2, p. 491.
20 See Lawrence Hennessey, 'The place of saints and sinners after death', in Charles Kannengiesser and William L. Petersen (eds), *Origen of Alexandria: His World and his Legacy* (Notre Dame, IN: University of Notre Dame Press, 1988), pp. 295–312.
21 Jacques Le Goff, *The Birth of Purgatory* (Chicago, IL: University of Chicago Press, 1981), pp. 59–60.
22 Ambrose, *Enarrationes in XII psalmos davidicos* 1.54, in *PL*, vol. 14, col. 993. See also Brian E. Daley, *The Hope of the Early Church* (Grand Rapids, MI: Baker Academic, 2010), pp. 98–9.
23 Caesarius of Arles, Sermon 179, in Caesarius of Arles, *Sermons*, vol. 2, trans. Mary Magdeleine Mueller, Fathers of the Church 47 (Washington DC: Catholic University of America Press, 1964), p. 453.
24 *The Dialogues of Saint Gregory, Surnamed the Great: Pope of Rome and the First of That Name*, ed. Edmund G. Gardner (London: Philip Lee Warner, 1911), 4.39. The phrase translated 'Purgatory fire' is better translated 'fire of purgation'. On Gregory, see R. R. Atwell, 'From Augustine to Gregory the Great: an evaluation of the emergence of the doctrine of Purgatory', *Journal of Ecclesiastical History* 38 (1987), pp. 173–86.

25 A list of which particular sins fell into which category was never formalised.
26 William of Auvergne, *De universo* 679aD-bA, quoted in Alan E. Bernstein, 'Esoteric theology: William of Auvergne on the fires of hell and Purgatory', *Speculum* 57 (1982), p. 511.
27 Le Goff, *Birth of Purgatory*, p. 228.
28 Quoted ibid.
29 Quoted in Patrick Toner, 'Prayers for the dead', *The Catholic Encyclopedia*, vol. 4 (New York, NY: Robert Appleton, 1908). Available at http://www.newadvent.org/cathen/04653a.htm.
30 Augustine, *Enchiridion* 110 [p. 272].
31 Ibid.
32 Quoted in Le Goff, *Birth of Purgatory*, pp. 102–3. See also *PL*, vol. 94, col. 30, and Megan McLaughlin, *Consorting with Saints: Prayers for the Dead in Early Medieval France* (Ithaca, NY: Cornell University Press, 1994).
33 See Le Goff, *Birth of Purgatory*, p. 341.
34 Dante, *Purgatorio*, ed. and trans. Robin Kirkpatrick (London: Penguin, 2007), 13.124–9.
35 Ibid., 13.50–1.
36 Ibid., 4.31–3.
37 Ibid., 13.69–72.
38 Ibid., 27.49–51.
39 Ibid., 4.88–93.
40 On the history of the connection between money and the afterlife in early Western Christianity, see Peter Brown, *The Ransom of the Soul: Afterlife and Wealth in Early Western Christianity* (Cambridge, MA: Harvard University Press, 2015).
41 Henry Bettenson and Chris Maunder (eds), *Documents of the Christian Church* (Oxford: Oxford University Press, 1999), p. 203.
42 See Robert W. Shaffern, 'The medieval theology of indulgences', in Robert N. Swanson (ed.), *Promissory Notes on the Treasury of Merits in Late Medieval Europe* (Leiden: Brill, 2006), pp. 11–36. I am especially indebted to Shaffern for this discussion on Purgatory and indulgences.
43 See Robert W. Shaffern, 'Learned discussions of indulgences for the dead in the Middle Ages', *Church History* 61 (1992), p. 369.
44 Quoted in Shaffern, 'Medieval theology of indulgences', p. 35 (my italics).
45 Henry Charles Lea, *A History of Auricular Confession and Indulgences in the Latin Church*, vol. 3 (Philadelphia, PA: Lea Brothers, 1896), p. 346.
46 Le Goff, *Birth of Purgatory*, p. 12.
47 Carter Lindberg (ed.), *The European Reformations Sourcebook* (Oxford: Blackwell, 2000), p. 31.
48 *Works of Martin Luther with Introduction and Notes*, vol. 1, ed. and trans. Adolph Spaeth (Philadelphia, PA: A. J. Holman, 1915), pp. 25–6.
49 Ibid., p. 27.

5. *The Sleep of Death*

1 Quoted in George Hunston Williams, *The Radical Reformation* (Philadelphia, PA: Westminster Press, 1962), p. 23. On Christian mortalism more generally, see

Norman T. Burns, *Christian Mortalism from Tyndale to Milton* (Cambridge, MA: Harvard University Press, 1972) and Brian W. Ball, *The Soul Sleepers: Christian Mortalism from Wycliffe to Priestley* (Cambridge: James Clarke, 2008). I am especially indebted to these two groundbreaking works.

2 Pietro Pomponazzi, 'On the immortality of the soul', trans. William Henry Hay, in Ernst Cassirer, P. O. Kristeller and J. H. Randall (eds), *The Renaissance Philosophy of Man* (Chicago, IL: University of Chicago Press, 1948), p. 313. See also Don Cameron Allen, *Doubt's Boundless Sea* (Baltimore, MD: Johns Hopkins Press, 1964), ch. 2.

3 Pomponazzi, 'On the immortality of the soul', p. 364.

4 Ibid.

5 See ibid., p. 362.

6 *Luther's Works*, vol. 4: *Lectures on Genesis Chapters 21–25*, eds Jaroslav Pelikan and Walter A. Hansen (St Louis, MO: Concordia Publishing House, 1964), p. 312.

7 [Martin Luther], *An Exposition of Salomons Booke, Called Ecclesiastes or the Preacher* (London, 1573), p. 151v.

8 Martin Luther, 'Gospel sermon, twenty-fourth Sunday after Trinity', in *A Compend of Luther's Theology*, ed. Hugh T. Kerr (Philadelphia, PA: Westminster Press, 1943), p. 242.

9 Williams, *Radical Reformation*, p. xxv. Williams (p. xxiv) divides them into 'Anabaptists', 'Spiritualists' and 'Evangelical Rationalists'.

10 Burns, *Christian Mortalism*, p. 18.

11 More, *The Dialogue Concerning Tyndale* 4.9 and 4.10, quoted in Burns, *Christian Mortalism*, p. 99. For an excellent overview of More on heresy (of which Lutheranism was the exemplar), see Richard Rex, 'Thomas More and the heretics: statesman or fanatic?', in George M. Logan (ed.), *The Cambridge Companion to Thomas More* (Cambridge: Cambridge University Press, 2011), pp. 93–115.

12 William Tyndale, *An Answer to Sir Thomas More's Dialogue*, ed. Henry Walter (Cambridge: Cambridge University Press, 1850), pp. 180–1.

13 Ibid., p. 189.

14 Ibid., p. 180.

15 Willyam Tindale [*sic*], *The New Testament Diligently Corrected and Compared with the Greek* (Antwerp, 1534), sig. xxv.v.

16 Joseph Ketley (ed.), *The Two Liturgies, AD 1549, and AD 1552* (Cambridge: Cambridge University Press, 1844), p. 147.

17 Ibid., p. 537.

18 John Calvin, *Psychopannychia*, in John Calvin, *Tracts Relating to the Reformation*, vol. 3, trans. Henry Beveridge (Edinburgh: Calvin Translation Society, 1851), p. 415.

19 Ibid.

20 John Calvin, *Institutes of the Christian Religion*, ed. John T. McNeill (Louisville, KY, and London: Westminster John Knox Press, 2006), 3.25.6.

21 Heinrich Bullinger, *An Holsome Antidotus or Counter-poysen, agaynst the Pestylent Heresye and Secte of the Anabaptistes* (London, 1548), p. 215ff.

22 Philip Schaff (ed.), *The Creeds of Christendom*, vol. 3: *The Creeds of the Evangelical Protestant Churches* (New York, NY: Harper, 1919), p. 842.

23 Quoted in Norman Cohn, *The Pursuit of the Millennium: Revolutionary Millenarians and Mystical Anarchists of the Middle Ages* (London: Pimlico, 1993), p. 290.

24 Quoted in Burns, *Christian Mortalism*, pp. 73–4. See also Ann Hughes, *Gangraena and the Struggle for the English Revolution* (New York, NY: Oxford University Press, 2004).
25 Quoted in Burns, *Christian Mortalism*, pp. 74–5.
26 Lodowick Muggleton, *The Acts of the Witnesses of the Spirit* (London, 1699), pp. 12–13.
27 John Reeve and Lodowick Muggleton, *Joyful News from Heaven* (London, 1658), p. 11v.
28 Richard Coppin, *Divine Teachings* (London, 1653), p. 8.
29 Joseph Salmon, *Heights in Depths* (London, 1651), pp. 37–8.
30 Quoted in Christopher Hill, *The World Turned Upside Down* (Harmondsworth: Penguin, 1975), p. 228.
31 Quoted in Nigel Smith (ed.), *A Collection of Ranter Writings from the Seventeenth Century* (London: Junction, 1993), pp. 236, 239.
32 Quoted ibid., p. 172.
33 Quoted ibid., p. 182.
34 Thomas Hobbes, *Leviathan* (London: Dent, 1973), p. 211.
35 Ibid., p. 338.
36 J. G. A. Pocock, 'Time, history and eschatology in the thought of Thomas Hobbes', in J. H. Elliott and H. G. Koenigsberger (eds), *The Diversity of History* (Ithaca, NY: Cornell University Press, 1949), p. 186.
37 Hobbes, *Leviathan*, p. 342.
38 Ibid., p. 247.
39 Ibid.
40 Ibid., p. 342.
41 R[ichard] O[verton], *Man Wholly Mortal [...]* (London, 1655), pp. 32–3.
42 Ibid., pp. 38–9.
43 Alexander Ross, *The Philosophicall Touch-stone [...]* (London, 1645), pp. 122–3.
44 *The Works of John Milton*, vol. 15, ed. Frank A. Patterson (New York, NY: Columbia University Press, 1931–8), pp. 40–1.
45 Daniel Defoe, *An Enquiry into the Case of Mr. Asgil's General Translation* (London, 1704), p. 8.
46 [John Asgill], *An argument proving that according to the covenant of eternal life revealed in the Scriptures, man may be translated from hence into that eternal life without passing through death, although the humane nature of Christ himself could not be thus translated till he had passed through death* (London, 1700), p. 61.
47 Ibid., p. 95.
48 Ibid., p. 82.
49 Ibid., p. 93.
50 Ibid., p. 106.
51 John Turner, *Justice Done to Human Souls [...]* (London 1706), pp. 7–8.
52 Henry Dodwell, *A Preliminary Defence of the Epistolary Discourse, Concerning the Distinction between Soul and Spirit* (London, 1707), pt 1, p. 97.
53 Henry Dodwell, *An Epistolary Discourse Proving [...] That the Soul is a Principle Naturally Mortal* (London, 1706), p. xliii.
54 Dodwell, *Preliminary Defence*, pt 2, p. 32.
55 Ibid., p. xxvi.
56 Quoted in Ball, *Soul Sleepers*, p. 133.

57 Ibid., p. 135.
58 Subtitle to William Coward, *Second Thoughts Concerning Human Soul [...]* (London, 1702).
59 Ibid., sig. A7v.
60 John Locke, *An Essay Concerning Humane Understanding* (London, 1690), p. 188.
61 John Locke, *Writings on Religion*, ed. Victor Nuovo (Oxford: Clarendon, 2002), p. 29.
62 Ibid.
63 Ibid., p. 92.
64 Ibid., p. 95.
65 Ibid., p. 236.
66 Ibid.
67 Ibid.
68 Joseph Priestley, *An History of the Corruptions of Christianity*, vol. 1 (Birmingham: J. Johnson, 1882), p. 401. On mortalist readings of apparently immortalist biblical texts, see Ball, *Soul Sleepers*, pp. 201–7.
69 Although controversial, see Oscar Cullman, *Immortality of the Soul or Resurrection of the Dead?* (New York, NY: Macmillan, 1958).
70 See Le Roy Edwin Froom, *The Conditionalist Faith of Our Fathers* (Washington DC: Review & Herald, 1965–6).
71 Karl Barth, *Dogmatics in Outline* (New York, NY: Philosophical Library, 1949), p. 154.

6. The Saved and the Damned

1 [Joachim Stegmann], *Brevis disquisitio: Or, a Brief Enquiry Touching a Better Way [...] to Refute Papists, and Reduce Protestants to Certainty and Unity in Religion* (London, 1653), p. 27. Stegmann was a follower of the radical reformer Faustus Socinus (1539–1604). As well as being mortalists, Socinians tended to deny the existence of Christ before his incarnation. The Unitarian tradition in its denial of the doctrine of the Trinity has its intellectual roots in Socinianism.
2 Henry More, *A Modest Inquiry into the Mystery of Iniquity [...]* (London, 1664), p. 86.
3 *The Confession of Faith [...] First Agreed upon by the Assembly of Divines at Westminster* (Glasgow, 1669), p. 66.
4 E[dward] W[arren], *No Praeexistence: Or a Brief Dissertation against the Hypothesis of Humane Souls, Living in a State Antecedaneous to This* (London, 1667), p. 44.
5 William Lupton, *The Eternity of Future Punishment Proved and Vindicated* (Oxford, 1708), p. 6.
6 John Calvin, *Psychopannychia*, in John Calvin, *Tracts Relating to the Reformation*, vol. 3, trans. Henry Beveridge (Edinburgh: Calvin Translation Society, 1851), p. 434.
7 Ibid., p. 472.
8 John Calvin, *Institutes of the Christian Religion*, ed. John T. McNeill (Louisville, KY, and London: Westminster John Knox Press, 2006), 2.16.17.
9 'Magisterial Protestant Reformation' refers here generally to the Reformation of the Lutheran and Reformed Churches, and excludes the Radical Reformation (typified by the Anabaptist traditions). More specifically, it refers to those Protestant Churches

(like the Lutheran and Reformed Churches) who saw themselves as subject to the secular agencies of government.

10 Augustine, *On Grace and Free Will* 8.20, trans. Peter Holmes and Robert Ernest Wallis, in *NPNFI*, vol. 5, p. 452.
11 Quoted in Alister E. McGrath, *Luther's Theology of the Cross* (Chichester: Wiley-Blackwell, 2011), p. 129.
12 Ibid., p. 130.
13 Alister E. McGrath, *Reformation Thought: An Introduction* (Oxford: Blackwell, 1993), p. 100.
14 Quoted ibid., p. 107. I am indebted to McGrath for this discussion of Luther.
15 Calvin, *Institutes*, 3.21.7.
16 Ibid., 3.23.2.
17 Ibid.
18 Ibid., 3.23.3.
19 Robert Burton, *The Anatomy of Melancholy*, vol. 1, ed. Thomas C. Faulkner, Nicholas K. Kiessling, Rhonda L. Blair (Oxford: Clarendon, 1989), p. 110. See Angus Gowland, 'The problem of early modern melancholy', *Past and Present* 191 (2006), pp. 77–120.
20 John Yates, *Gods Arraignment of Hypocrites* (London, 1615), pp. 357–8.
21 Ibid., p. 356.
22 Ibid., p. 357.
23 Ibid.
24 Ibid., p. 358. See also Leif Dixon, *Practical Predestinarians in England, c.1590–1640* (Farnham: Ashgate, 2014).
25 Stephen Denison, *A Compendious Catechisme [...]* (London, 1621), pp. 2–3. On Denison, see Peter Lake, *The Boxmaker's Revenge: 'Orthodoxy', 'Heterodoxy' and the Politics of the Parish in Early Stuart London* (Stanford, CA: Stanford University Press, 2001).
26 Stephen Denison, *The Doctrine of Both the Sacraments: To Witte, Baptisme, and the Supper of the Lord [...]* (London, 1621), pp. 145–6.
27 Max Weber, *The Protestant Ethic and the Spirit of Capitalism*, trans. Talcott Parsons (New York, NY, and London: Charles Scribner's Sons and George Allen & Unwin, 1950), p. 115.
28 Augustine, Letter 190, quoted in Alan D. Fitzgerald (ed.), *Augustine through the Ages: An Encyclopedia* (Grand Rapids, MI: Eerdmans, 1999), p. 44.
29 Hieremy Drexelius, *A Pleasant and Profitable Treatise of Hell* (n.p., 1668), p. 148.
30 Tobias Swinden, *An Enquiry into the Nature and Place of Hell* (London, 1727), p. 92.
31 Ibid.
32 Ibid., p. 87.
33 Christopher Love, *Hells Terror: Or, A Treatise of the Torments of the Damned, as a Preservative against Security* (London, 1653), p. 66. By the time this was published, he had already met his destiny, having been executed for treason in 1651.
34 G. W. Leibniz, *Theodicy: Essays on the Goodness of God, the Freedom of Man and the Origin of Evil*, trans. E. M. Huggard (London: Routledge & Kegan Paul, 1951), p. 126.
35 Matthew Horbery, *An Enquiry into the Scripture-doctrine Concerning the Duration of Future Punishments [...]* (London, 1744), p. 207.

36 [Henry Hallywell], *A Private Letter of Satisfaction to a Friend* (n.p., 1667), p. 35.

37 Ibid., p. 36.

38 Ibid., pp. 38–9.

39 Archibald Campbell, *The Doctrines of a Middle State between Death and the Resurrection [...]* (London, 1721), p. 112.

40 Immanuel Kant, *Critique of Practical Reason*, trans. Lewis White Beck (Indianapolis, IN: Bobbs–Merrill Co., 1956), p. 128.

41 Immanuel Kant, *On History*, trans. Lewis White Beck (Indianapolis, IN: Bobbs–Merrill Co., 1957), p. 70. In reading the later Kant, it is difficult to determine the extent to which Kant accepts that there is 'literally' any life after death, rather than heaven and hell being *only* 'ideas of reason' that we should use to govern our ethical life in the here and now. What is true is that Kant separates our lives as truly ethical from any thoughts of reward for doing one's moral duty. I am indebted to my colleague Emeritus Professor Ian Hunter for conversations on Kant.

42 John Shower, *Heaven and Hell: Or the Unchangeable State of Happiness or Misery for All Mankind in Another World* (London, 1700), pp. 17–18.

43 Richard Baxter, *The Saints' Everlasting Rest: Or, a Treatise of the Blessed State of the Saints in Their Enjoyment of God in Glory [...]* (London, 1650), p. 323.

44 Love, *Hells Terror*, p. 41.

45 Ibid., p. 43.

46 [Richard Stafford], *A Discourse of the Misery of Hell, and Happiness of Heaven* (London, 1697), p. 2.

47 John Bunyan, *A Few Sighs from Hell: Or the Groans of a Damned Soul* (London, 1658), in *The Miscellaneous Works of John Bunyan*, vol. 1, ed. T. L. Underwood and Roger Sharrock (Oxford: Clarendon, 1976), p. 300.

48 Ibid., pp. 274–5.

49 Henry More, *The Immortality of the Soul, so Farre Forth as It Is Demonstrable from the Knowledge of Nature and the Light of Reason* (London, 1659), p. 442.

50 Ibid., p. 434.

51 Thomas Goodwin, *A Discourse of the Punishment of Sin in Hell; Demonstrating the Wrath of God to Be the Immediate Cause Thereof* (London, 1680), p. 98.

52 See Philip C. Almond, *The Devil: A New Biography* (London and Ithaca, NY: I.B.Tauris and Cornell University Press, 2015), ch. 9.

53 John Brandon, Τὸ πῦρ τὸ αἰώνιον: *Or, Everlasting Fire No Fancy [...]* (London, 1678), p. 33.

54 Thomas Vincent, *Fire and Brimstone from Heaven, from Earth, from Hell [...]* (London, 1670), p. 85.

55 William Beveridge, *A Sermon Preach'd before the Queen at White-hall, October 12, 1690* (London, 1698)., p. 4.

56 See John M. Steadman, 'Milton and patristic tradition: the quality of hell-fire', *Anglia* 76 (1958), pp. 116–28. The words quoted here are *Paradise Lost* 1.61–4, in *The Works of John Milton*, vol. 2, ed. Frank A. Patterson et al. (New York, NY: Columbia University Press, 1931), p. 10.

57 Vincent, *Fire and Brimstone*, p. 103.

58 See Emma Disley, 'Degrees of glory: Protestant doctrine and the concept of rewards hereafter', *Journal of Theological Studies* 42 (1991), pp. 77–105.

59 *The Works of John Milton*, vol. 16, ed. Frank A. Patterson et al. (New York, NY: Columbia University Press, 1934), p. 71.

60 See Augustine, *The City of God* 21.9, trans. Marcus Dods, in *NPNFI*, vol. 2, pp. 460–1.
61 William Strong, *The Worm That Dyeth Not, or, Hell Torments, in the Certainty and Eternity of Them* (London, 1672), pp. 10–11.
62 Bunyan, *Few Sighs from Hell*, p. 274.
63 F. W. Farrar, *Eternal Hope* (New York, NY: E. P. Dutton, 1878), p. 66.
64 Thomas Aquinas, *Summa theologica* supplement 94.1, in Thomas Aquinas, *Summa theologica*, trans. Fathers of the English Dominican Province (New York, NY: Benziger Brothers, 1947). Available at http://www.ccel.org/ccel/aquinas/summa.html.
65 Jonathan Edwards, 'Sermon XI: the eternity of hell torments', in *The Works of Jonathan Edwards*, vol. 2, ed. Edward Hickman (Edinburgh: Banner of Truth, 1974), p. 235. Available at http://www.ccel.org/ccel/edwards/works2.
66 Pieter Spierenburg, *The Spectacle of Suffering: Executions and the Evolution of Repression* (Cambridge: Cambridge University Press, 1984), p. 185.
67 Friedrich Schleiermacher, *The Christian Faith* (Edinburgh: T. & T. Clark, 1928), p. 722 (para. 163).
68 Michael Wheeler, *Death and the Future Life in Victorian Literature and Theology* (Cambridge: Cambridge University Press, 1990), p. 188.
69 Horbery, *Enquiry*, p. 305.
70 Ibid., pp. 33–4.
71 Thomas Burnet, *A Treatise Concerning the State of Departed Souls before, and at, and after the Resurection* [*sic*] (London, 1733), p. 357.
72 Goodwin, *Discourse*, p. 79.
73 Jonathan Edwards, 'Sermon II: sinners in the hands of an angry God', in *The Works of Jonathan Edwards*, vol. 2, ed. Edward Hickman (Edinburgh: Banner of Truth, 1974), p. 27. Available at http://www.ccel.org/ccel/edwards/works2.
74 Ibid., p. 18.
75 Matthew Tindal, *Christianity as Old as the Creation* (London, 1731), p. 68.
76 Francis Blyth, *Eternal Misery the Necessary Consequence of infinite Mercy Abused: A Sermon [...]* (London, 1740), p. 26.
77 D. P. Walker, *The Decline of Hell: Seventeenth-century Discussions of Eternal Torment* (London: Routledge & Kegan Paul, 1964), p. 63.
78 William Whiston, *The Eternity of Hell Torments Considered [...]* (London, 1740), pp. 18–19.
79 William Whiston, *Sermons and Essays [...]* (London, 1709), p. 220.
80 William Whiston, *Astronomical Principles of Religion Natural and Reveal'd in Nine Parts [...]* (London, 1717), p. 156.
81 Hence the alternative name for annihilationism, namely, conditionalism.
82 Henry Constable, *The Duration and Nature of Future Punishment* (London: Kellaway, 1876), p. 211. This work ran to six editions between 1868 and 1886. For Victorian views on annihilationism, see Geoffrey Rowell, *Hell and the Victorians* (Oxford: Clarendon, 1974). I am indebted to Rowell for his discussion of the Victorian period.
83 See Walker, *Decline of Hell*, p. 59ff.; Philip C. Almond, *Heaven and Hell in Enlightenment England* (Cambridge: Cambridge University Press, 2008); and especially Richard Bauckham, 'Universalism: a historical survey', *Themelios* 4 (1978), pp. 47–54. For a list of seventeenth- and eighteenth-century universalists, see Ezra Abbott's bibliography appended to W. R. Alger, *A Critical History of the Doctrine of a Future Life* (New York, NY: W. J. Widdleton, 1878).
84 Schleiermacher, *Christian Faith*, p. 722.

85 Broad Church Anglicans attempted to steer a middle path between the extremes of Anglo-Catholic (High Church) Anglicans and evangelical (Low Church) Anglicans.
86 Farrar, *Eternal Hope*, pp. 64–5.
87 Ibid., pp. 70, 72.
88 Ibid., p. 75.
89 Ibid., p. 86 (my italics).
90 Ibid.
91 Ibid., p. 88.
92 Rowell, *Hell and the Victorians*, p. 146.
93 Ibid., p. 148.
94 Samuel Taylor Coleridge, *Aids to Reflection and the Confessions of an Inquiring Spirit* (London: George Bell, 1884), p. 102.
95 Don Cupitt, *Crisis of Moral Authority* (London: SCM Press, 1985), p. 22. On atheism, see Gavin Hyman, *A Short History of Atheism* (London: I.B.Tauris, 2010).
96 Quoted in Rowell, *Hell and the Victorians*, p. 212.
97 Thomas Hardy, *Tess of the d'Urbervilles* (London: Macmillan, 1928), ch. 14.
98 James Joyce, *A Portrait of the Artist as a Young Man* (New York, NY: B. W. Huebsch, 1916), ch. 3. Available at http://www.gutenberg.org/files/4217/4217-h/4217-h.htm#chap03.
99 Ludwig Feuerbach, *The Essence of Christianity*, trans. George Eliot [Marian Evans] (London: Kegan Paul, Trench, Trübner, 1890), p. 182.
100 Karl Marx, 'Theses on Feuerbach', in Karl Marx and Friedrich Engels, *The Marx–Engels Reader*, ed. Robert C. Tucker (New York, NY: Norton, 1978), p. 144.
101 Sigmund Freud, 'Lecture XXXV: a philosophy of life', in Sigmund Freud, *New Introductory Lectures on Psycho-analysis* (London: Hogarth Press, 1933), p. 206.
102 Ibid., p. 215.
103 Quoted in Wheeler, *Death and the Future Life*, p. 198.

7. Heavens, Sacred and Secular

1 Quoted in D. J. Enright, *The Oxford Book of Death* (Oxford: Oxford University Press,1983), p. 179.
2 Thomas Browne, *The Works of Sir Thomas Browne*, vol. 1, ed. Geoffrey Keynes (London: Faber, 1964), p. 60.
3 Richard Baxter, *The Saints' Everlasting Rest: Or, a Treatise of the Blessed State of the Saints in Their Enjoyment of God in Glory [...]* (London, 1650), p. 24.
4 Ibid., p. 86.
5 Ibid.
6 See Colleen McDannell and Bernhard Lang, *Heaven: A History* (New York, NY: Vintage, 1990), p. 173.
7 William Gearing, *A Prospect of Heaven: Or, A Treatise of the Happiness of the Saints in Glory* (London, 1673), p. 292.
8 [John Dunton], *An Essay Proving We Shall Know Our Friends in Heaven* (London, 1698), p. 29.
9 Ibid., p. 64.
10 [John Dunton (ed.)], *Athenian Gazette* (1691), vol. 3, no. 13.
11 [Dunton], *Essay*, p. 2.

12 See Peter Walmsley, 'Whigs in heaven: Elizabeth Rowe's *Friendship in Death*', *Eighteenth-century Studies* 44 (2011), pp. 315–30.
13 Ibid., p. 326.
14 Elizabeth Singer Rowe, *Friendship in Death: In Twenty Letters from the Dead to the Living [...]* (London, 1728), pp. 11–12. It is a vision of heaven which, as we will see, reappears in the mid-nineteenth century in Elizabeth Stuart Phelps's novel *The Gates Ajar*.
15 Isaac Watts, *Death and Heaven: Or the last Enemy Conquer'd, and Separate Spirits Made Perfect* (London, 1722), pp. 79–80.
16 Isaac Watts, *The World to Come: Or, Discourses on the Joys or Sorrows of Departed Souls at Death [...]* (London, 1739), p. 245.
17 Ibid., p. 322.
18 Ibid., pp. 324–5.
19 Watts, *Death and Heaven*, p. 135.
20 Watts, *World to Come*, p. 327.
21 Watts, *Death and Heaven*, p. 109.
22 Ibid., p. 143.
23 Ibid., p. 146.
24 Ibid., p. 126.
25 Ibid., p. 216.
26 Ibid., pp. 217–8.
27 Ibid., p. 145.
28 John Shower, *Death a Deliverance: Or, a Funeral Discourse, Preach'd (in Part) on the Decease of Mrs Mary Doolittle [...]* (London, 1693), p. 77.
29 Augustine, *On the Predestination of the Saints* 28, trans. Peter Holmes and Robert Ernest Wallis, in *NPNFI*, vol. 5, p. 511.
30 *Boswell's Life of Johnson*, vol. 2, ed. George Birkbeck Hill (Oxford: Clarendon, 1934–50), p. 162.
31 *The Gentleman's Magazine* 9 (1739), p. 5b. See Bernhard Lang, *Meeting in Heaven: Modernising the Christian Afterlife, 1600–2000* (Frankfurt: Peter Lang, 2011), pp. 40–1.
32 Henry More, *The Immortality of the Soul, so Farre Forth as It Is Demonstrable from the Knowledge of Nature and the Light of Reason* (London, 1659), pp. 412–13.
33 [John Dunton (ed.)], *Athenian Gazette* (1691), vol. 3, no. 23.
34 Ibid., vol. 3, no. 29.
35 More, *Immortality of the Soul*, p. 343.
36 Thomas Burnet, *A Treatise Concerning the State of Departed Souls before, and at, and after the Resurection* [*sic*] (London, 1733), p. 209.
37 Rowe, *Friendship in Death*, p. 9.
38 Gearing, *Prospect of Heaven*, p. 204.
39 McDannell and Lang, *Heaven*, p. 183.
40 Quoted in John Casey, *After Lives: A Guide to Heaven, Hell, and Purgatory* (Oxford: Oxford University Press, 2009), p. 337.
41 Immanuel Kant, *Dreams of a Spirit Seer, Illustrated by Dreams of Metaphysics* (London: S. Sonnenschein, 1900), p. 101.
42 Emanuel Swedenborg, *Heaven and Hell: The Portable New Century Edition*, trans. George F. Dole (West Chester, PA: Swedenborg Foundation, 2002), § 417. This is a translation of Swedenborg's 1758 *De coelo et eius mirabilibus, et de inferno, ex*

auditis et visis (On heaven and its wonders, and on hell, from things heard and seen). It was first translated into English in 1778. It is the most accessible source of Swedenborg's views on the afterlife. For an excellent overview see Lang, *Meeting in Heaven*, pp. 79–120.

43 Swedenborg, *Heaven and Hell*, § 535.

44 Ibid.

45 Ibid., § 427.

46 Ibid., § 457.

47 Ibid.

48 Ibid., § 75.

49 Ibid., § 236.

50 See Philip C. Almond, *Adam and Eve in Seventeenth-century Thought* (Cambridge: Cambridge University Press, 2008), pp. 26–42. Swedenborg may well have derived his apparent knowledge of the universal language from Christian Cabbala, and especially from Francis Mercurius van Helmont. See ibid., p. 130; Umberto Eco, *The Search for the Perfect Language* (Oxford: Blackwell, 1995), pp. 82–3.

51 John Engelbrecht, *The Divine Visions of John Engelbrecht [...]*, trans. Francis Okeley (Northampton, 1780), p. 62. I am indebted to Dr Leigh Penman for this reference. Engelbrecht became known among Swedenborgians as 'the German Swedenborg'.

52 Swedenborg, *Heaven and Hell*, § 184.

53 Ibid.

54 Ibid., § 185.

55 See Mark 12.25: 'Jesus said to them [...] "For when they rise from the dead, they neither marry nor are given in marriage but are like angels in heaven."'

56 Swedenborg, *Heaven and Hell*, § 367.

57 Ibid., § 383.

58 Ibid., § 547.

59 Ibid., § 550.

60 Ibid., § 586.

61 Ibid., § 578.

62 Quoted in Wouter J. Hanegraaff, *New Age Religion and Western Culture* (New York, NY: State University of New York, 1998), pp. 424–5.

63 Swedenborg, *Heaven and Hell*, § 1.

64 See Hanegraaff, *New Age Religion*, p. 429, where Hanegraaff argues that Swedenborg marks the 'creation' in Western thought of 'occultism' as an adaptation of 'esotericism' to a disenchanted world.

65 The only people about whom Swedenborg is uncertain about their entering heaven are 'papists'. He is strongly anti-Catholic.

66 *The Examiner*, 7 August 1808, quoted in Robert Rix, *William Blake and the Cultures of Radical Christianity* (Aldershot: Ashgate, 2007), p. 100. For Blake's reception of Swedenborg, see especially ch. 3.

67 Quoted in Michael Wheeler, *Death and the Future Life in Victorian Literature and Theology* (Cambridge: Cambridge University Press, 1990), p. 151.

68 Reginald Heber, 'Holy, holy, holy', in *The New English Hymnal* (Norwich: Canterbury Press, 1986).

69 Quoted in Wheeler, *Death and the Future Life*, p. 162.

70 Quoted in Rix, *William Blake*, p. 137.

71 See Robert W. Delp, 'Andrew Jackson Davis: prophet of American spiritualism', *Journal of American History* 54 (1967), pp. 43–56.
72 Selling 80,000 copies in the United States and over 100,000 in England in 55 editions, it was beaten only by Harriet Beecher Stowe's *Uncle Tom's Cabin*.
73 Elizabeth Stuart Phelps, *The Gates Ajar* (Boston, MA: Fields, Osgood, 1868), p. 170.
74 Ibid., p. 97.
75 Ibid., p. 116.
76 Ibid., p. 201.
77 Ibid., p. 171.
78 Ibid., pp. 172–3.
79 See ibid., pp. 169–70.
80 Ibid., p. 70. See also p. 155.
81 Quoted in Elizabeth Stuart Phelps, *The Gates Ajar*, ed. Helen Sootin Smith (Cambridge, MA: Belknap Press of Harvard University Press, 1964), p. xxii.
82 Phelps, *Gates Ajar* [1869], p. 81.
83 Ibid., p. 140.
84 Ibid., p. 181.
85 François-René Blot, *In Heaven We Know Our Own: Or, Solace for the Suffering* (New York, NY: Benziger Brothers, n.d), p. 109. I have drawn upon the seventh edition published in the 1890s. The first English edition was in 1863.
86 Ibid., p. 146.
87 Phelps, *Gates Ajar* [1869], p. 188.
88 See Peter Harrison, 'Animal souls, metempsychosis, and theodicy', *Journal of the History of Philosophy* 31 (1993), pp. 519–44.
89 J. G. Wood, *Man and Beast: Here and Hereafter* (London: Gibbings, 1903), p. 484. See also the German Darwinist Ernst Haeckel's *The Riddle of the Universe* (London: Watts, 1929), p. 164. That animals will ultimately be 'saved' has been reinforced in 2015 in the papal encyclical *Laudato si'* (Praise be to you): 'At the end, we will find ourselves face to face with the infinite beauty of God (cf. 1 Cor. 13.12), and be able to read with admiration and happiness the mystery of the universe, which with us will share in unending plenitude. Even now we are journeying towards the sabbath of eternity, the new Jerusalem, towards our common home in heaven. Jesus says: "I make all things new" (Rev. 21:5). Eternal life will be a shared experience of awe, in which each creature, resplendently transfigured, will take its rightful place and have something to give those poor men and women who will have been liberated once and for all' (243). If Pope Francis does not go so far here as to endorse animals in heaven immediately after their deaths, he does nonetheless suggest that, at the end of history, there will be a restoration to life of all creatures: this is one aspect of the tradition of Eden restored, a place where the 'wolf and the lamb shall feed together, the lion shall eat straw like the ox' (Isa. 65.25). This is usually misquoted as 'The lion will lie down with the lamb', to which Woody Allen (not quite up on his 'end of history' eschatology) added: 'But the lamb won't get much sleep.'
90 Quoted in R. Laurence Moore, 'Spiritualism and science: reflections on the first decade of the spirit rappings', *American Quarterly* 24 (1972), p. 483. See also R. Laurence Moore, 'Spiritualism', in Edwin S. Gaustad (ed.), *The Rise of Adventism: Religion and Society in Mid-nineteenth-century America* (New York, NY: Harper & Row, 1974), pp. 79–103. I am particularly indebted to Moore.

91 See E. E. Lewis, *A Report of the Mysterious Noises, Heard in the House of Mr John D. Fox, in Hydesville, Arcadia, Wayne County [...]* (Canandaigua, NY: E. E. Lewis, 1848).
92 See Frank Podmore, *Modern Spiritualism: A History and a Criticism*, vol. 1 (London: Methuen, 1902), p. 183.
93 Quoted in Hanegraaff, *New Age Religion*, p. 437.
94 See Alex Owen, *The Darkened Room: Women, Power, and Spiritualism in Late Nineteenth Century England* (London: Virago, 1989).
95 Quoted in Moore, 'Spiritualism', p. 93.
96 Ibid., pp. 92–3.
97 Ibid., p. 85.
98 Quoted in Katherine H. Porter, *Through a Glass Darkly: Spiritualism in the Browning Circle* (Lawrence, KS: University of Kansas Press, 1958), p. 46.
99 Ibid., p. 49. Robert Browning's poem 'Mr Sludge the medium' was based on D. D. Home.
100 See Peter Harrison, *The Territories of Science and Religion* (Chicago, IL: University of Chicago Press, 2015) and Richard Noakes, 'The sciences of spiritualism in Victorian Britain: possibilities and problems', in Tatiana Kontou and Sarah Willburn (eds), *The Ashgate Research Companion to Nineteenth-century Spiritualism and the Occult* (Farnham: Ashgate, 2012), pp. 25–54.
101 Anon., 'Mr Baden-Powell's new work', *British Spiritual Telegraph* 4 (1859), p. 138.
102 J. H. Powell, *Spiritualism; Its Facts and Phases* (London: F. Pitman, 1864), p. 55.
103 'Objects of the society', *Proceedings of the Society for Psychical Research* 1 (1882), p. 4.
104 *Life and Letters of Thomas Henry Huxley*, vol. 2, ed. Leonard Huxley (London: Macmillan, 1908), p. 144. An account of a seance that Huxley attended follows on pp. 144–8.
105 Ibid.
106 William Kalush and Larry Sloman, *The Secret Life of Harry Houdini: The Making of America's First Superhero* (New York, NY: Atria, 2006), p. 488.
107 Quoted in McDannell and Lang, *Heaven*, p. 325.
108 *The Autobiography of Charles Darwin 1809–1882*, ed. Nora Barlow (London: Collins, 1958), p. 91.
109 Haeckel, *Riddle of the Universe*, p. 172. Haeckel would himself distinguish his 'monism' from 'materialism'. This distinction, however, does not impact on his views on *personal* immortality. See also p. 166 for various 'proofs' of the immortality of the soul described as pure myth, baseless dogma, false anthropism [*sic*], pious wish, error and spiritualistic fantasy.
110 Ibid., p. 170.
111 Jürgen Moltmann, 'Resurrection as hope', *Harvard Theological Review* 61 (1968), p. 129. His theology of hope was intended to offer a modern rethink of personal and cosmic eschatology.
112 Rosemary Radford Ruether, *Sexism and God-talk: Toward a Feminist Theology* (Boston, MA: Beacon Press, 1983), p. 258.
113 Karl Rahner, *Theological Investigations*, vol. 4: *More Recent Writings* (London: Darton, Longman & Todd, 1974), p. 347.
114 Ibid., p. 348.
115 Ibid., pp. 353–4.

116 'The builder's creed', Hubert L. Eaton [website]. Available at http://huberteaton.com/the-builders-creed.html.
117 Casey, *After Lives*, p. 389.
118 Evelyn Waugh, *The Loved One: An Anglo-American Tragedy* (Boston, MA: Little, Brown, 1948), p. 39.
119 Aldous Huxley, *The Perennial Philosophy* (London: Chatto & Windus, 1947), p. 8.
120 Huxley saw his perennial philosophy as the same as that which the early modern philosopher Agostino Steuco (1497–1548) had identified as the *perenni philosophia* and which the philosopher Gottfried Leibniz (1646–1716) later adapted to his philosophy of harmony. See Charles B. Schmitt, 'Perrenial [*sic*] philosophy from Agostino Steuco to Leibniz', *Journal of the History of Ideas* 27 (1966), pp. 505–32. The synthesis of Western and Eastern ideas that makes up Huxley's perennial philosophy can only be traced back to the late nineteenth-century Theosophical Society of Helena Blavatsky (1831–91), where it was labelled the 'Ancient Wisdom'.
121 Huxley, *Perennial Philosophy*, pp. 231–2. Perennial philosophy generally assumes that mystical experience is everywhere the same. For a critique of this view, see Steven T. Katz, *Mysticism and Language* (New York, NY: Oxford University Press, 1992).
122 H. P. Blavatsky, *Isis Unveiled: A Master Key to the Mysteries of Ancient and Modern Science and Theology*, vol. 1: *Science* (Pasadena, CA: Theosophical University Press, 1976), p. 9.
123 Anon., *The Wisdom of Ramala*, pp. 90–1, quoted in Hanegraaff, *New Age Religion*, p. 287. These teachings are given by a group of 'Masters on the Spiritual Planes' using the collective name of Ramala. Their teachings are 'channelled' by a husband-and-wife team, David and Ann Jevons.
124 Arthur Conan Doyle, *The Wanderings of a Spiritualist* (New York, NY: George H. Doran, 1921), p. 64.
125 Arthur Conan Doyle, *Memories and Adventures* (Boston, MA: Little, Brown, 1924), ch. 9. Available at http://gutenberg.net.au/ebooks14/1400681h.html#ch-09.
126 Doyle, *Wanderings*, p. 72.
127 Doyle, *Memories and Adventures*, ch. 32.
128 Quoted in Paul Smith, 'The Cottingley fairies: the end of a legend', in Peter Narváez (ed.), *The Good People: New Fairylore Essays* (Lexington, KY: University Press of Kentucky, 1997), p. 382.
129 Arthur Conan Doyle, 'Fairies photographed', *Strand Magazine* (December 1920), p. 468. See also Arthur Conan Doyle, *The Coming of the Fairies* (New York, NY: George H. Doran, 1922).
130 Max Weber, 'Science as a vocation' (1918) [published as 'Wissenschaft als Beruf', in Max Weber, *Gesammelte Aufsaetze zur Wissenschaftslehre* (Tübingen: J. C. B. Mohr, 1922), pp. 524–55]. Available at www.wisdom.weizmann.ac.il/~oded/X/WeberScienceVocation.pdf.
131 Michael Saler, 'Modernity and enchantment: a historical review', *American Historical Review* 111 (2006), p. 695. I am grateful to Saler for his persuasive discussion of this issue.
132 Ursula Le Guin, *The Earthsea Quartet* (London: Penguin, 1993), p. 457.
133 Ibid., p. 456.
134 Cormac McCarthy, *The Road* (London: Picador, 2007), p. 181. The Muslim confession of faith is: 'There is no God but God and Muhammad is his prophet.'
135 Ibid., pp. 306–7.

136 Ibid., p. 306.

137 Marilyn Ferguson, *The Aquarian Conspiracy: Personal and Social Transformation in the 1980s* (Los Angeles, CA: J. P. Tarcher, 1980), p. 70.

138 Pierre Teilhard de Chardin, *The Phenomenon of Man* (London: Harper & Row, 1965), p. 221.

139 Ibid., p. 130.

140 Ibid., pp. 261–2.

141 Hal Lindsey, *The Late Great Planet Earth* (Grand Rapids, MI: Zondervan, 1970), p. 177.

142 Paul Boyer, *When Time Shall Be No More: Prophecy Belief in Modern American Culture* (Cambridge, MA: Harvard University Press, 1992), pp. 317–18.

143 Quoted in Ian Hesketh, 'The story of big history', *History of the Present* 4 (2014), p. 171. I am indebted to my colleague Ian Hesketh for this discussion.

144 David Christian, *Maps of Time: An Introduction to Big History* (Berkeley, CA: University of California Press, 2011), p. 3.

145 Ibid., p. 2.

146 Ibid., p. 3.

Epilogue

1 *Bede's Ecclesiastical History of England: A Revised Translation with Introduction, Life, and Notes*, ed. and trans. A. M. Sellar (London: George Bell, 1907), 2.13.

Bibliography

Abelard, Peter, *Abelard's Christian Theology*, ed. and trans. J. Ramsay McCallum (Oxford: Blackwell, 1948).

—— *Commentary on the Epistle to the Romans*, trans. Steven Cartwright (Washington DC: Catholic University of America Press, 2012).

Alger, W. R., *A Critical History of the Doctrine of a Future Life* (New York, NY: W. J. Widdleton, 1878).

Allen, Don Cameron, *Doubt's Boundless Sea* (Baltimore, MD: Johns Hopkins Press, 1964).

Almond, Philip C., *The British Discovery of Buddhism* (Cambridge: Cambridge University Press, 1988).

—— *Adam and Eve in Seventeenth-century Thought* (Cambridge: Cambridge University Press, 2008).

—— *Heaven and Hell in Enlightenment England* (Cambridge: Cambridge University Press, 2008).

—— *The Devil: A New Biography* (London and Ithaca, NY: I.B.Tauris and Cornell University Press, 2015).

Anon., 'Mr Baden-Powell's new work', *British Spiritual Telegraph* 4 (1859), pp. 137–8.

Anselm, *The Virgin Conception and Original Sin*, in *Anselm of Canterbury*, vol. 3, ed. and trans. Jasper Hopkins and Herbert Richardson (Toronto and New York, NY: Edwin Mellen Press, 1976).

Aquinas, Thomas, *Compendium of Theology*, trans. Cyril Vollert (St Louis, MO, and London: Herder, 1947).

—— *Summa theologica*, trans. Fathers of the English Dominican Province (New York, NY: Benziger Brothers, 1947). Available at http://www.ccel.org/ccel/aquinas/summa.html.

—— *On the Power of God*, trans. English Dominican Fathers (Westminster, MD: Newman Press, 1952). Available at http://dhspriory.org/thomas/QDdePotentia.htm.

—— *The Disputed Question on Truth*, vol. 2, trans. James V. McGlynn (Chicago, IL: Henry Regnery, 1953). Available at http://dhspriory.org/thomas/QDdeVer.htm.

—— *Summa contra Gentiles*, ed. Joseph Kenny (New York, NY: Hanover House, 1955–7). Available at http://dhspriory.org/thomas/ContraGentiles4.htm.

—— *On Evil*, trans. Richard Regan, ed. Brian Davies (Oxford: Oxford University Press, 2003).

—— *Compendium of Theology*, trans. Richard J. Regan (Oxford: Oxford University Press, 2009).

Argyle, A. W., 'The Christian doctrine of the origin of the soul', *Scottish Journal of Theology* 18 (1965), pp. 273–93.

[Asgill, John], *An argument proving that according to the covenant of eternal life revealed in the Scriptures, man may be translated from hence into that eternal life without passing through death, although the humane nature of Christ himself could not be thus translated till he had passed through death* (London, 1700).

Atwell, R. R., 'From Augustine to Gregory the Great: an evaluation of the emergence of the doctrine of Purgatory', *Journal of Ecclesiastical History* 38 (1987), pp. 173–86.

Augustine, *The Enchiridion*, trans. J. F. Shaw, in Philip Schaff (ed.), *Nicene and Post-Nicene Fathers: First Series*, vol. 3 (Buffalo, NY: Christian Literature, 1887). Available at http://www.newadvent.org/fathers/1302.htm.

—— *The Letters of St Augustine*, ed. W. J. Sparrow-Simpson (London and New York, NY: SPCK and Macmillan, 1919).

—— *Selected Writings*, ed. and trans. Mary T. Clark (Mahwah, NJ: Paulist Press, 1984).

—— *On Free Choice of the Will*, trans. Thomas Williams (Indianapolis, IN: Hackett, 1993).

Ball, Brian W., *The Soul Sleepers: Christian Mortalism from Wycliffe to Priestley* (Cambridge: James Clarke, 2008).

Barth, Karl, *Dogmatics in Outline* (New York, NY: Philosophical Library, 1949).

Bartsch, Hans Werner (ed.), *Kerygma and Myth: A Theological Debate* (New York, NY, and Evanston, IL: Harper & Row, 1961).

Bauckham, Richard, 'Universalism: a historical survey', *Themelios* 4 (1978), pp. 47–54.

Baun, Jane, 'The fate of babies dying before baptism in Byzantium', in Diana Wood (ed.), *The Church and Childhood* (Oxford: Blackwell, 1994), pp. 115–25.

Baxter, Richard, *The Saints' Everlasting Rest: Or, a Treatise of the Blessed State of the Saints in Their Enjoyment of God in Glory [...]* (London, 1650).

Beatrice, Pier Franco, *The Transmission of Sin: Augustine and the Pre-Augustinian Sources*, trans. Adam Kamesar (Oxford: Oxford University Press, 2013).

Bede, *Bede's Ecclesiastical History of England: A Revised Translation with Introduction, Life, and Notes*, ed. and trans. A. M. Sellar (London: George Bell, 1907).

Benedict XII, *Benedictus Deus* (1336). Available at http://www.papalencyclicals.net/Ben12/B12bdeus.html.

Bernstein, Alan E., 'Esoteric theology: William of Auvergne on the fires of hell and Purgatory', *Speculum* 57 (1982), pp. 509–31.

—— *The Formation of Hell: Death and Retribution in the Ancient and Early Christian Worlds* (Ithaca, NY, and London: Cornell University Press, 1993).

Bettenson, Henry, and Chris Maunder (eds), *Documents of the Christian Church* (Oxford: Oxford University Press, 1999).

Beveridge, William, *A Sermon Preach'd before the Queen at White-hall, October 12, 1690* (London, 1698).

Blavatsky, H. P., *Isis Unveiled: A Master Key to the Mysteries of Ancient and Modern Science and Theology*, vol. 1: *Science* (Pasadena, CA: Theosophical University Press, 1976).

Blot, François-René, *In Heaven We Know Our Own: Or, Solace for the Suffering* (New York, NY: Benziger Brothers, n.d).

Blunt, Henry, *A Voyage into the Levant [...]* (London, 1664).

Blyth, Francis, *Eternal Misery the Necessary Consequence of infinite Mercy Abused: A Sermon [...]* (London, 1740).

Boniface, St, *The Letters of Saint Boniface*, trans. Ephraim Emerton (New York, NY: Norton, 1976).

Boswell, James, *Boswell's Life of Johnson*, ed. George Birkbeck Hill, 6 vols (Oxford: Clarendon, 1934–50).

Boyer, Paul, *When Time Shall Be No More: Prophecy Belief in Modern American Culture* (Cambridge, MA: Harvard University Press, 1992).

Boyle, Robert, *The Works of the Honourable Robert Boyle*, ed. Thomas Birch, 6 vols (2nd edn, London, 1772).

Brandon, John, *Tὸ πῦρ τὸ αἰώνιον: Or, Everlasting Fire No Fancy* [...] (London, 1678).

Brown, Peter, *The Ransom of the Soul: Afterlife and Wealth in Early Western Christianity* (Cambridge, MA: Harvard University Press, 2015).

Browne, Thomas, *The Works of Sir Thomas Browne*, ed. Geoffrey Keynes, 4 vols (London: Faber, 1964).

'The builder's creed', Hubert L. Eaton [website]. Available at http://huberteaton.com/the-builders-creed.html.

Bullinger, Heinrich, *An Holsome Antidotus or Counter-poysen, agaynst the Pestylent Heresye and Secte of the Anabaptistes* (London, 1548).

Bultmann, Rudolf, *Jesus Christ and Mythology* (New York, NY: Charles Scribner's Sons, 1958).

Bunyan, John, *A Few Sighs from Hell: Or the Groans of a Damned Soul* (London, 1658), in *The Miscellaneous Works of John Bunyan*, vol. 1, ed. T. L. Underwood and Roger Sharrock (Oxford: Clarendon, 1976).

Burkert, Walter, *Greek Religion: Archaic and Classical*, trans. John Raffan
(Oxford: Blackwell, 1985).

Burnet, Thomas, *A Treatise Concerning the State of Departed Souls before, and at, and after the Resurection* [*sic*] (London, 1733).

Burns, Norman T., *Christian Mortalism from Tyndale to Milton* (Cambridge, MA: Harvard University Press, 1972).

Burton, Robert, *The Anatomy of Melancholy*, ed. Thomas C. Faulkner, Nicholas K. Kiessling, Rhonda L. Blair, 6 vols (Oxford: Clarendon, 1989–2001).

Bynum, Caroline Walker, *Fragmentation and Redemption: Essays on Gender and the Human Body in Medieval Religion* (New York, NY: Zone, 1992).

—— *The Resurrection of the Body in Western Christianity, 200–1336* (New York, NY: Columbia University Press, 1995).

Calvin, John, *Tracts Relating to the Reformation*, trans. Henry Beveridge, 3 vols (Edinburgh: Calvin Translation Society, 1844–51).

——*Institutes of the Christian Religion*, ed. John T. McNeill (Louisville, KY, and London: Westminster John Knox Press, 2006).

Campbell, Archibald, *The Doctrines of a Middle State between Death and the Resurrection [...]* (London, 1721).

Carnley, Peter, *The Structure of Resurrection Belief* (Oxford: Clarendon, 1987).

Casey, John, *After Lives: A Guide to Heaven, Hell, and Purgatory* (Oxford: Oxford University Press, 2009).

Cassirer, Ernst, P. O. Kristeller and J. H. Randall (eds), *The Renaissance Philosophy of Man* (Chicago, IL: University of Chicago Press, 1948).

Charlesworth, James H. (ed.), *The Old Testament Pseudepigrapha*, vol. 1: *Apocalyptic Literature and Testaments* (New York, NY: Doubleday, 1983).

Christian, David, *Maps of Time: An Introduction to Big History* (Berkeley, CA: University of California Press, 2011).

Cohn, Norman, *The Pursuit of the Millennium: Revolutionary Millenarians and Mystical Anarchists of the Middle Ages* (London: Pimlico, 1993).

Coleridge, Samuel Taylor, *Aids to Reflection and the Confessions of an Inquiring Spirit* (London: George Bell, 1884).
The Confession of Faith [...] First Agreed upon by the Assembly of Divines at Westminster (Glasgow, 1669).
Constable, Henry, *The Duration and Nature of Future Punishment* (London: Kellaway, 1876).
Coppin, Richard, *Divine Teachings* (London, 1653).
Coward, William, *Second Thoughts Concerning Human Soul [...]* (London, 1702).
Crouzel, Henri, 'L'Hades et la Gehenne selon Origene', *Gregorianum* 59 (1978), pp. 291–329.
Cullman, Oscar, *Immortality of the Soul or Resurrection of the Dead?* (New York, NY: Macmillan, 1958).
Cupitt, Don, *Crisis of Moral Authority* (London: SCM Press, 1985).
Cyprian, *An Address to Demetrianus*, trans. Robert Ernest Wallis, in Alexander Roberts, James Donaldson and A. Cleveland Coxe (eds), *Ante-Nicene Fathers*, vol. 5 (Buffalo, NY: Christian Literature, 1886). Available at http://www.newadvent.org/fathers/050705.htm.
Daley, Brian E., *The Hope of the Early Church* (Grand Rapids, MI: Baker Academic, 2010).
Dalton, William Joseph, *Christ's Proclamation to the Spirits: A Study of I Peter 3:18–4.6* (Rome: Pontificio Istituto Biblico, 1989).
Dante, *Inferno*, ed. and trans. Robin Kirkpatrick (London: Penguin, 2006).
—— *Purgatorio*, ed. and trans. Robin Kirkpatrick (London: Penguin, 2007).
—— *The Divine Comedy*, trans. A. S. Kline (n.p.: Poetry in Translation, 2014). Available at http://www.poetryintranslation.com/PITBR/Italian/Danthome.htm.
Darwin, Charles, *The Autobiography of Charles Darwin 1809–1882*, ed. Nora Barlow (London: Collins, 1958).
Defoe, Daniel, *An Enquiry into the Case of Mr Asgil's General Translation* (London, 1704).
Delp, Robert W., 'Andrew Jackson Davis: prophet of American spiritualism', *Journal of American History* 54 (1967), pp. 43–56.
Denison, Stephen, *A Compendious Catechisme [...]* (London, 1621).
—— *The Doctrine of Both the Sacraments: To Witte, Baptisme, and the Supper of the Lord [...]* (London, 1621).
Disley, Emma, 'Degrees of glory: Protestant doctrine and the concept of rewards hereafter', *Journal of Theological Studies* 42 (1991), pp. 77–105.
Dixon, Leif, *Practical Predestinarians in England, c.1590–1640* (Farnham: Ashgate, 2014).
Dodwell, Henry, *An Epistolary Discourse Proving [...] That the Soul is a Principle Naturally Mortal* (London, 1706).
—— *A Preliminary Defence of the Epistolary Discourse, Concerning the Distinction between Soul and Spirit* (London, 1707).
Douie, D., 'John XXII and the Beatific Vision', *Dominican Studies* 3 (1950), pp. 157–74.
Doyle, Arthur Conan, 'Fairies photographed', *Strand Magazine* (December 1920), pp. 463–8.
—— *The Wanderings of a Spiritualist* (New York, NY: George H. Doran, 1921).
—— *The Coming of the Fairies* (New York, NY: George H. Doran, 1922).
—— *Memories and Adventures* (Boston, MA: Little, Brown, 1924). Available at http://gutenberg.net.au/ebooks14/1400681h.html#ch-09.
Drexelius, Hieremy, *A Pleasant and Profitable Treatise of Hell* (n.p., 1668).
[Dunton, John], *An Essay Proving We Shall Know Our Friends in Heaven* (London, 1698).

Dyer, George J., *Limbo: Unsettled Questions* (New York, NY: Sheed & Ward, 1964).

Eco, Umberto, *The Search for the Perfect Language* (Oxford: Blackwell, 1995).

Edwards, Jonathan, 'Sermon II: sinners in the hands of an angry God', in *The Works of Jonathan Edwards*, vol. 2, ed. Edward Hickman (Edinburgh: Banner of Truth, 1974). Available at http://www.ccel.org/ccel/edwards/works2.

——'Sermon XI: the eternity of hell torments', in *The Works of Jonathan Edwards*, vol. 2, ed. Edward Hickman (Edinburgh: Banner of Truth, 1974). Available at http://www.ccel.org/ccel/edwards/works2.

Elliott, J. K. (ed.), *The Apocryphal New Testament: A Collection of Apocryphal Christian Literature in an English Translation* (Oxford: Clarendon, 1993).

Engelbrecht, John, *The Divine Visions of John Engelbrecht [...]*, trans. Francis Okeley (Northampton, 1780).

Enright, D. J., *The Oxford Book of Death* (Oxford: Oxford University Press,1983).

Farrar, F. W., *Eternal Hope* (New York, NY: E. P. Dutton, 1878).

Ferguson, Marilyn, *The Aquarian Conspiracy: Personal and Social Transformation in the 1980s* (Los Angeles, CA: J. P. Tarcher, 1980).

Feuerbach, Ludwig, *The Essence of Christianity*, trans. George Eliot [Marian Evans] (London: Kegan Paul, Trench, Trübner, 1890).

Fitzgerald, Alan D. (ed.), *Augustine through the Ages: An Encyclopedia* (Grand Rapids, MI: Eerdmans, 1999).

Freud, Sigmund, 'Lecture XXXV: a philosophy of life', in Sigmund Freud, *New Introductory Lectures on Psycho-analysis* (London: Hogarth Press, 1933).

Froom, Le Roy Edwin, *The Conditionalist Faith of Our Fathers* (Washington DC: Review & Herald, 1965–6).

Gearing, William, *A Prospect of Heaven: Or, A Treatise of the Happiness of the Saints in Glory* (London, 1673).

Goodwin, Thomas, *A Discourse of the Punishment of Sin in Hell; Demonstrating the Wrath of God to Be the Immediate Cause Thereof* (London, 1680).

Gowland, Angus, 'The problem of early modern melancholy', *Past and Present* 191 (2006), pp. 77–120.

Gregory of Nyssa, *On Infants' Early Deaths*, trans. William Moore and Henry Austin Wilson, in Philip Schaff and Henry Wace (eds), *Nicene and Post-Nicene Fathers: Second Series*, vol. 5 (Buffalo, NY: Christian Literature, 1893).

Gregory the Great, *Morals on the Book of Job by St Gregory the Great, Translated with Notes and Indices*, trans. James Bliss, 3 vols (Oxford and London: John Henry Parker and J. G. F. and J. Rivington, 1844).

—— *The Dialogues of Saint Gregory, Surnamed the Great: Pope of Rome and the First of That Name*, ed. Edmund G. Gardner (London: Philip Lee Warner, 1911).

Haeckel, Ernst, *The Riddle of the Universe* (London: Watts, 1929).

[Hallywell, Henry], *A Private Letter of Satisfaction to a Friend* (n.p., 1667).

Hanegraaff, Wouter J., *New Age Religion and Western Culture* (New York, NY: State University of New York, 1998).

Hardy, Thomas, *Tess of the d'Urbervilles* (London: Macmillan, 1928).

Harrison, Peter, 'Animal souls, metempsychosis, and theodicy', *Journal of the History of Philosophy* 31 (1993), pp. 519–44.

—— *The Territories of Science and Religion* (Chicago, IL: University of Chicago Press, 2015).

Hartshorne, Charles, *A Natural Theology for Our Time* (LaSalle, IL: Open Court, 1967).

Hennessey, Lawrence, 'The place of saints and sinners after death', in Charles Kannengiesser and William L. Petersen (eds), *Origen of Alexandria: His World and his Legacy* (Notre Dame, IN: University of Notre Dame Press, 1988), pp. 295–312.
Herbert, Thomas, *Some Yeares Travels into Divers Parts of Africa and Asia the Great* (London, 1665).
Hesiod, *The Homeric Hymns, and Homerica*, trans. Hugh G. Evelyn-White (London: Heinemann, 1914).
Hesketh, Ian, 'The story of big history', *History of the Present* 4 (2014), pp. 171–202.
Hill, Christopher, *The World Turned Upside Down* (Harmondsworth: Penguin, 1975).
Hobbes, Thomas, *Leviathan* (London: Dent, 1973).
Hody, Humphrey, *The Resurrection of the (Same) Body Asserted* (London, 1694).
Homer, *The Odyssey*, trans. A. T. Murray (Cambridge, MA, and London: Harvard University Press and Heinemann, 1919).
——*The Iliad*, trans. A. T. Murray (Cambridge, MA, and London: Harvard University Press and Heinemann, 1924).
Horbery, Matthew, *An Enquiry into the Scripture-doctrine Concerning the Duration of Future Punishments [...]* (London, 1744).
Hughes, Ann, *Gangraena and the Struggle for the English Revolution* (New York, NY: Oxford University Press, 2004).
Huxley, Aldous, *The Perennial Philosophy* (London: Chatto & Windus, 1947).
Huxley, Thomas Henry, *Life and Letters of Thomas Henry Huxley*, ed. Leonard Huxley, 2 vols (London: Macmillan, 1908).
Hyman, Gavin, *A Short History of Atheism* (London: I.B.Tauris, 2010).
Iannucci, Amilcare A., 'Dante's limbo: at the margins of orthodoxy', in James Miller (ed.), *Dante and the Unorthodox: The Aesthetics of Transgression* (Waterloo, Ontario: Wilfrid Laurier University Press, 2005), pp. 63–82.
International Theological Commission, 'The hope of salvation for infants who die without being baptised' (2007). Available at http://www.vatican.va/roman_curia/congregations/cfaith/cti_documents/rc_con_cfaith_doc_20070419_un-baptised-infants_en.html.
James, M. R. (ed. and trans.), *The Apocryphal New Testament* (Oxford: Clarendon, 1953).
Jerome, St, *Commentary on Ecclesiastes*, ed. and trans. Richard J. Goodrich and David J. D. Miller (New York, NY, and Mahwah, NJ: Newman Press, 2012).
Johnstone, P. De Lacy, *Muhammad and His Power* (Edinburgh: T. & T. Clark, 1901).
Joyce, James, *A Portrait of the Artist as a Young Man* (New York, NY: B. W. Huebsch, 1916). Available at http://www.gutenberg.org/files/4217/4217-h/4217-h.htm#chap03.
Kalush, William, and Larry Sloman, *The Secret Life of Harry Houdini: The Making of America's First Superhero* (New York, NY: Atria, 2006).
Kant, Immanuel, *Dreams of a Spirit Seer, Illustrated by Dreams of Metaphysics* (London: S. Sonnenschein, 1900).
——*Critique of Practical Reason*, trans. Lewis White Beck (Indianapolis, IN: Bobbs–Merrill Co., 1956).
——*On History*, trans. Lewis White Beck (Indianapolis, IN: Bobbs–Merrill Co., 1957).
Katz, Steven T., *Mysticism and Language* (New York, NY: Oxford University Press, 1992).
Kelly, J. N. D., *Early Christian Creeds* (London: Longman, 1972).
Ketley, Joseph (ed.), *The Two Liturgies, AD 1549, and AD 1552* (Cambridge: Cambridge University Press, 1844).

Kontou, Tatiana, and Sarah Willburn (eds), *The Ashgate Research Companion to Nineteenth-century Spiritualism and the Occult* (Farnham: Ashgate, 2012).

Kosior, Wojciech, 'The underworld or its ruler? Some remarks on the concept of Sheol in the Hebrew Bible', *Polish Journal of Biblical Research* 13 (2014), pp. 29–40.

Kraus, Wolfgang, and Martin Kraus, 'On eschatology in Paul's First Epistle to the Corinthians', in Jan G. van der Watt, *Eschatology of the New Testament and Some Related Documents* (Tübingen: Mohr Siebeck, 2011), pp. 197–224.

Lake, Peter, *The Boxmaker's Revenge: 'Orthodoxy', 'Heterodoxy' and the Politics of the Parish in Early Stuart London* (Stanford, CA: Stanford University Press, 2001).

Lang, Bernhard, *Meeting in Heaven: Modernising the Christian Afterlife, 1600–2000* (Frankfurt: Peter Lang, 2011).

Le Goff, Jacques, *The Birth of Purgatory* (Chicago, IL: University of Chicago Press, 1981).

Le Guin, Ursula, *The Earthsea Quartet* (London: Penguin, 1993).

Lea, Henry Charles, *A History of Auricular Confession and Indulgences in the Latin Church*, 3 vols (Philadelphia, PA: Lea Brothers, 1896).

Leibniz, G. W., *Theodicy: Essays on the Goodness of God, the Freedom of Man and the Origin of Evil*, trans. E. M. Huggard (London: Routledge & Kegan Paul, 1951).

Lewis E. E., *A Report of the Mysterious Noises, Heard in the House of Mr John D. Fox, in Hydesville, Arcadia, Wayne County [...]* (Canandaigua, NY: E. E. Lewis, 1848).

Lindberg, Carter (ed.), *The European Reformations Sourcebook* (Oxford: Blackwell, 2000).

Lindsey, Hal, *The Late Great Planet Earth* (Grand Rapids, MI: Zondervan, 1970).

Locke, John, *An Essay Concerning Humane Understanding* (London, 1690).

—— *Writings on Religion*, ed. Victor Nuovo (Oxford: Clarendon, 2002).

Lossky, Vladimir, *The Mystical Theology of the Eastern Church* (Crestwood, NY: St Vladimir's Seminary Press, 1976).

Louth, Andrew, *The Origins of the Christian Mystical Tradition: From Plato to Denys* (Oxford: Oxford University Press, 2007).

Love, Christopher, *Hells Terror: Or, A Treatise of the Torments of the Damned, as a Preservative against Security* (London, 1653).

Lupton, William, *The Eternity of Future Punishment Proved and Vindicated* (Oxford, 1708).

[Luther, Martin], *An Exposition of Salomons Booke, Called Ecclesiastes or the Preacher* (London, 1573).

Luther, Martin, *Works of Martin Luther with Introduction and Notes*, vol. 1, ed. and trans. Adolph Spaeth (Philadelphia, PA: A. J. Holman, 1915).

—— *A Compend of Luther's Theology*, ed. Hugh T. Kerr (Philadelphia, PA: Westminster Press, 1943).

—— *Luther's Works*, vol. 4: *Lectures on Genesis Chapters 21–25*, ed. Jaroslav Pelikan and Walter A. Hansen (St Louis, MO: Concordia Publishing House, 1964).

McCarthy, Cormac, *The Road* (London: Picador, 2007)

MacCulloch, J. A., *The Harrowing of Hell: A Comparative Study of an Early Christian Doctrine* (Edinburgh: T. & T. Clark, 1930).

McDannell, Colleen, and Bernhard Lang, *Heaven: A History* (New York, NY: Vintage, 1990).

McGinn, Bernard, John J. Collins and Stephen J. Stein (eds), *The Encyclopedia of Apocalypticism* (New York, NY, and London: Continuum, 1998).

McGrath, Alister E., *Reformation Thought: An Introduction* (Oxford: Blackwell, 1993).

—— *Luther's Theology of the Cross* (Chichester: Wiley-Blackwell, 2011).

McLaughlin, Megan, *Consorting with Saints: Prayers for the Dead in Early Medieval France* (Ithaca, NY: Cornell University Press, 1994).

Martens, Peter, 'Origen's doctrine of pre-existence and the opening chapters of Genesis', *Zeitschrift für Antikes Christentum* 16 (2013), pp. 516–49.

Marx, Karl, and Friedrich Engels, *The Marx–Engels Reader*, ed. Robert C. Tucker (New York, NY: Norton, 1978).

'Medieval sourcebook: twelfth ecumenical council: Lateran IV 1215', in H. J. Schroeder (ed.), *Disciplinary Decrees of the General Councils: Text, Translation and Commentary* (St Louis, MO: B. Herder, 1937). pp. 236–96. Available at http://www.fordham.edu/halsall/basis/lateran4.asp.

Milikowsky, Chaim, 'Which Gehenna? Retribution and eschatology in the synoptic Gospels and in early Jewish texts', *New Testament Studies* 34 (1988), pp. 238–49.

Milton, John, *The Works of John Milton*, ed. Frank A. Patterson et al., 18 vols (New York, NY: Columbia University Press, 1931–8).

Moltmann, Jürgen, 'Resurrection as hope', *Harvard Theological Review* 61 (1968), pp. 129–47.

Moore, R. Laurence, 'Spiritualism and science: reflections on the first decade of the spirit rappings', *American Quarterly* 24 (1972), pp. 474–500.

——'Spiritualism', in Edwin S. Gaustad (ed.), *The Rise of Adventism: Religion and Society in Mid-nineteenth-century America* (New York, NY: Harper & Row, 1974), pp. 79–103.

More, Henry, *The Immortality of the Soul, so Farre Forth as It Is Demonstrable from the Knowledge of Nature and the Light of Reason* (London, 1659).

——*A Modest Inquiry into the Mystery of Iniquity [...]* (London, 1664).

More, Thomas, *The Yale Edition of the Complete Works of St Thomas More*, vol. 6: *A Dialogue Concerning Heresies*, eds. Thomas M. C. Lawler, Richard C. Marius and Germain Marc'hadour (New Haven, CT: Yale University Press, 1981).

Muggleton, Lodowick, *The Acts of the Witnesses of the Spirit* (London, 1699).

Nauta, Lodi, 'The pre-existence of the soul in medieval Europe', *Recherches de théologie ancienne et medievale* 63 (1996), pp. 93–135.

The New English Hymnal (Norwich: Canterbury Press, 1986).

Nickelsburg, George W. E., *1 Enoch 1: A Commentary on the Book of Enoch Chapters 1–36; 81–108* (Minneapolis, MN: Fortress Press, 2001).

Noakes, Richard, 'The sciences of spiritualism in Victorian Britain: possibilities and problems', in Tatiana Kontou and Sarah Willburn (eds), *The Ashgate Research Companion to Nineteenth-century Spiritualism and the Occult* (Farnham: Ashgate, 2012).

'Objects of the society', *Proceedings of the Society for Psychical Research* 1 (1882), pp. 3–6.

O'Ceallaigh, G. C., 'Dating the commentaries of Nicodemus', *Harvard Theological Review* 56 (1963), pp. 21–58.

Origen, *On First Principles*, trans. G. W. Butterworth (Gloucester, MA: Peter Smith, 1973).

O[verton], R[ichard], *Man Wholly Mortal [...]* (London, 1655).

Owen, Alex, *The Darkened Room: Women, Power, and Spiritualism in Late Nineteenth Century England* (London: Virago, 1989).

Pelagius, *Pelagius's Commentary on St Paul's Epistle to the Romans*, trans. Theodore de Bruyn (Oxford: Clarendon, 1993).

Phelps, Elizabeth Stuart, *The Gates Ajar* (Boston, MA: Fields, Osgood, 1869).

—— *The Gates Ajar*, ed. Helen Sootin Smith (Cambridge, MA: Belknap Press of Harvard University Press, 1964).
Plato, *The Collected Dialogues of Plato, Including the Letters*, ed. Edith Hamilton and Huntington Cairns (Princeton, NJ: Princeton University Press, 1961).
Pocock, J. G. A., 'Time, history and eschatology in the thought of Thomas Hobbes', in J. H. Elliott and H. G. Koenigsberger (eds), *The Diversity of History* (Ithaca, NY: Cornell University Press, 1949), pp. 149–98.
Podmore, Frank, *Modern Spiritualism: A History and a Criticism*, 2 vols (London: Methuen, 1902).
Porter, Katherine H., *Through a Glass Darkly: Spiritualism in the Browning Circle* (Lawrence, KS: University of Kansas Press, 1958).
Powell, J. H., *Spiritualism; Its Facts and Phases* (London: F. Pitman, 1864).
Priestley, Joseph, *An History of the Corruptions of Christianity*, 2 vols (Birmingham: J. Johnson, 1882).
Quistorp, H., *Calvin's Doctrine of the Last Things* (Eugene, OR: Wipf & Stock, 2009).
Rahner, Karl, *Theological Investigations*, vol. 4: *More Recent Writings* (London: Darton, Longman & Todd, 1974).
——'Experiences of a Catholic theologian', *Theological Studies* 61 (2000), pp. 3–15.
Rankin, David, *Athenagoras: Philosopher and Theologian* (Farnham: Ashgate, 2009).
Rauschenbusch, Walter, *Christianity and the Social Crisis* (London: Macmillan, 1907).
Reeve, John, and Lodowick Muggleton, *Joyful News from Heaven* (London, 1658).
Rex, Richard, 'Thomas More and the heretics: statesman or fanatic?', in George M. Logan (ed.), *The Cambridge Companion to Thomas More* (Cambridge: Cambridge University Press, 2011), pp. 93–115.
Ricciardo, Salvatore, 'Robert Boyle on God's "experiments": resurrection, immortality and mechanical philosophy', *Intellectual History Review* 24 (2014), pp. 1–17.
Rix, Robert, *William Blake and the Cultures of Radical Christianity* (Aldershot: Ashgate, 2007).
Ross, Alexander, *The Philosophicall Touch-stone [...]* (London, 1645).
Rowe, Elizabeth Singer, *Friendship in Death: In Twenty Letters from the Dead to the Living [...]* (London, 1728).
Rowell, Geoffrey, *Hell and the Victorians* (Oxford: Clarendon, 1974).
Ruether, Rosemary Radford, *Sexism and God-talk: Toward a Feminist Theology* (Boston, MA: Beacon Press, 1983).
Saler, Michael, 'Modernity and enchantment: a historical review', *American Historical Review* 111 (2006), pp. 692–716.
Salmon, Joseph, *Heights in Depths* (London, 1651).
Schaff, Philip (ed.), *The Creeds of Christendom*, 3 vols (New York, NY: Harper, 1919).
Shaffern, Robert W., 'Learned discussions of indulgences for the dead in the Middle Ages', *Church History* 61 (1992), pp. 367–81.
——'The medieval theology of indulgences', in Robert N. Swanson (ed.), *Promissory Notes on the Treasury of Merits in Late Medieval Europe* (Leiden: Brill, 2006), pp. 11–36.
Schleiermacher, Friedrich, *The Christian Faith* (Edinburgh: T. & T. Clark, 1928).
Schmitt, Charles B., 'Perrenial [*sic*] philosophy from Agostino Steuco to Leibniz', *Journal of the History of Ideas* 27 (1966), pp. 505–32.
Schwab, Raymond, *The Oriental Renaissance: Europe's Rediscovery of India and the East* (New York, NY: Columbia University Press, 1984).

Shower, John, *Death a Deliverance: Or, a Funeral Discourse, Preach'd (in Part) on the Decease of Mrs Mary Doolittle [...]* (London, 1693).
——*Heaven and Hell: Or the Unchangeable State of Happiness or Misery for All Mankind in Another World* (London, 1700).
Smith, Nigel (ed.), *A Collection of Ranter Writings from the Seventeenth Century* (London: Junction, 1993).
Smith, Paul, 'The Cottingley fairies: the end of a legend', in Peter Narváez (ed.), *The Good People: New Fairylore Essays* (Lexington, KY: University Press of Kentucky, 1997), pp. 371–405.
Spierenburg, Pieter, *The Spectacle of Suffering: Executions and the Evolution of Repression* (Cambridge: Cambridge University Press, 1984).
[Stafford, Richard], *A Discourse of the Misery of Hell, and Happiness of Heaven* (London, 1697).
Steadman, John M., 'Milton and patristic tradition: the quality of hell-fire', *Anglia* 76 (1958), pp. 116–28.
[Stegmann, Joachim], *Brevis disquisitio: Or, a Brief Enquiry Touching a Better Way [...] to Refute Papists, and Reduce Protestants to Certainty and Unity in Religion* (London, 1653).
Strong, William, *The Worm That Dyeth Not, or, Hell Torments, in the Certainty and Eternity of Them* (London, 1672).
Studer, Basil, 'Der Abstieg Christi in die Unterwelt bei Augustinus von Hippo', in I. Scicolone (ed.), *Psallendum: miscellanea di studi in onore del Prof. Jordi Pinelli i Pons, OSB* (Rome: Pontificio Ateneo Sant'Anselmo, 1992), pp. 267–74.
Swedenborg, Emanuel, *Heaven and Hell: The Portable New Century Edition*, trans. George F. Dole (West Chester, PA: Swedenborg Foundation, 2002).
Swinden, Tobias, *An Enquiry into the Nature and Place of Hell* (London, 1727).
Teilhard de Chardin, Pierre, *The Phenomenon of Man* (London: Harper & Row, 1965).
Teske, R. J., 'Saint Augustine on the incorporeality of the soul', *Modern Schoolman* 60 (1983), pp. 220–35.
Tindal, Matthew, *Christianity as Old as the Creation* (London, 1731).
Tindale, Willyam [*sic*], *The New Testament Diligently Corrected and Compared with the Greek* (Antwerp, 1534).
Trumbower, Jeffrey A., *Rescue for the Dead: The Posthumous Salvation of Non-Christians in Early Christianity* (Oxford: Oxford University Press, 2001).
Turner, John, *Justice Done to Human Souls [...]* (London 1706).
Turner, Ralph V., 'Descendit ad inferos: medieval views on Christ's descent into hell and the salvation of the ancient just', *Journal of the History of Ideas* 27 (1966), pp. 173–94.
Tyndale, William, *An Answer to Sir Thomas More's Dialogue*, ed. Henry Walter (Cambridge: Cambridge University Press, 1850).
Vincent, Thomas, *Fire and Brimstone from Heaven, from Earth, from Hell [...]* (London, 1670).
Walker, D. P., *The Decline of Hell: Seventeenth-century Discussions of Eternal Torment* (London: Routledge & Kegan Paul, 1964).
——'Eternity and the afterlife', *Journal of the Warburg and Courtauld Institutes* 27 (1964), pp. 241–50.
Walmsley, Peter, 'Whigs in heaven: Elizabeth Rowe's *Friendship in Death*', *Eighteenth-century Studies* 44 (2011), pp. 315–30.

W[arren], E[dward], *No Praeexistence: Or a Brief Dissertation against the Hypothesis of Humane Souls, Living in a State Antecedaneous to This* (London, 1667).

Watts, Isaac, *Death and Heaven: Or the last Enemy Conquer'd, and Separate Spirits Made Perfect* (London, 1722).

—— *The World to Come: Or, Discourses on the Joys or Sorrows of Departed Souls at Death [...]* (London, 1739).

Waugh, Evelyn, *The Loved One: An Anglo-American Tragedy* (Boston, MA: Little, Brown, 1948).

Weber, Max, 'Science as a vocation' (1918) [published as 'Wissenschaft als Beruf', in Max Weber, *Gesammelte Aufsaetze zur Wissenschaftslehre* (Tübingen: J. C. B. Mohr, 1922), pp. 524–55]. Available at www.wisdom.weizmann.ac.il/~oded/X/WeberScienceVocation.pdf.

—— *The Protestant Ethic and the Spirit of Capitalism*, trans. Talcott Parsons (New York, NY, and London: Charles Scribner's Sons and George Allen & Unwin, 1950).

Wheeler, Michael, *Death and the Future Life in Victorian Literature and Theology* (Cambridge: Cambridge University Press, 1990).

Whiston, William, *Sermons and Essays [...]* (London, 1709).

—— *Astronomical Principles of Religion Natural and Reveal'd in Nine Parts [...]* (London, 1717).

—— *The Eternity of Hell Torments Considered [...]* (London, 1740).

Williams, George Hunston, *The Radical Reformation* (Philadelphia, PA: Westminster Press, 1962).

Wood, J. G., *Man and Beast: Here and Hereafter* (London: Gibbings, 1903).

Yates, John, *Gods Arraignment of Hypocrites* (London, 1615).

Index

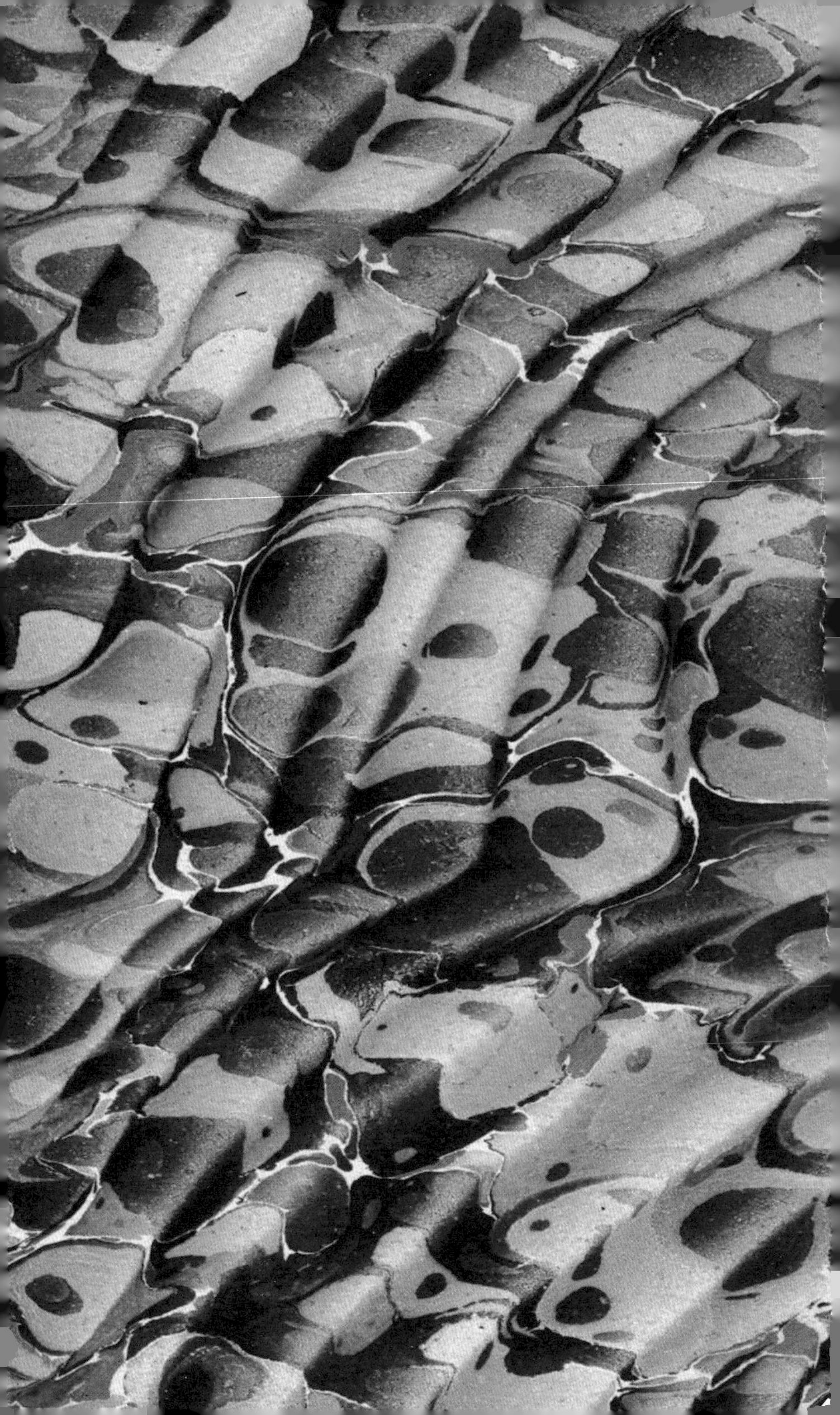